C0-ATG-899

ELECTRO-CHEMICAL SCIENCE

ELECTRO-CHEMICAL SCIENCE

J. O'M. BOCKRIS
University of Pennsylvania, Philadelphia
and
D. M. DRAŽIĆ
University of Belgrade, Yugoslavia

TAYLOR & FRANCIS LTD
LONDON
BARNES & NOBLE BOOKS
NEW YORK
1972

First published 1972 by Taylor & Francis Ltd London and Harper & Row Publishers, Inc./ Barnes & Noble Import Division, New York

Taylor & Francis ISBN 0 85066 051 3
Barnes & Noble Books ISBN 06 4905365

Printed and bound in Great Britain by Taylor & Francis Ltd 10–14 Macklin Street, London WC2B 5NF

Preface

This book tries to explain, in a fairly simple and largely qualitative way, the most important ideas of Electrochemical Science. We have tried to help the reader to appreciate, and perhaps to play his part in furthering, the great future that lies before electrochemistry. Electrochemical Science is not a specialised discipline. On the contrary, it is an interdisciplinary area which studies the behaviour of electrified interfaces wherever they arise—in chemistry, materials science, energetics, biology, engineering, and so on.

We believe that in the teaching of the Sciences a disproportionate amount of attention has been given to the properties of matter in bulk, when really surface properties—and in particular the properties of electrically charged interfaces—often determine the behaviour that is observed. We hope that this book will.

J. O'M. BOCKRIS

Contents

CHAPTER 1

the electrochemical future

Electrochemical Science

LET us start by considering the electrolysis of water in the familiar school apparatus of fig. 1. The water contains H^+ and OH^- ions; these are attracted electrically to the metal electrodes which are connected to an external power supply. *Transfer of electric charge* takes place at the solution/metal interfaces. The cathode gives electrons to the protons in solution; the protons then become hydrogen atoms and combine to form hydrogen molecules and hydrogen gas. At the anode OH^- ions give up their electrons to become OH radicals, and these combine to give oxygen molecules and water.† So while an

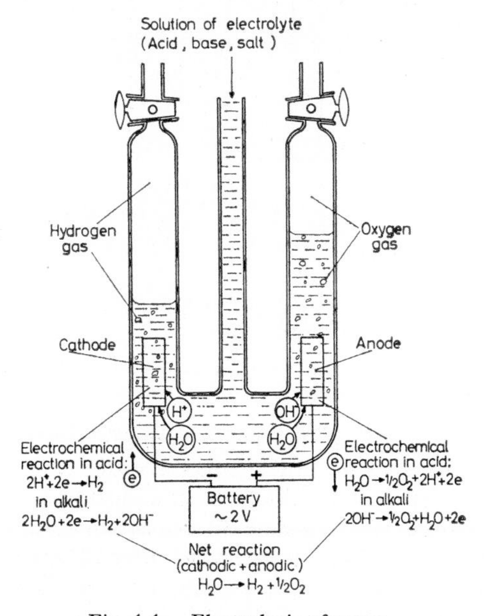

Fig. 1.1. Electrolysis of water.

† In reality, the picture is a little more complicated. Besides the reaction mentioned above, *in alkaline solutions* containing very small amounts of H^+ ions, H_2 evolves predominantly by reaction of H_2O molecules with electrons on the *cathode*, as shown in fig. 1.1. *In acid solutions*, where OH^- ion concentration is very low, the reactants at the *anode* are predominantly H_2O molecules, reacting according to the equation:

$$2H_2O \rightarrow O_2 + 4H^+ + 4e.$$

electric current is passing, water is being decomposed into hydrogen and oxygen.

It is not too far a cry from this school laboratory experiment to electrochemical provision of the auxiliary power on space flights and journeys to the moon. For the process used is *just the reverse* of that in electrolysis. Thus, in fig. 1.1, the electrons are ejected from the cathode by the outside source and force the protons and hydroxyl ions to give up their charges and form hydrogen and oxygen. In the fuel cells of the astronauts, the reverse happens. Hydrogen and oxygen are forced across electrode surfaces, and they *spontaneously* undergo charge transfer with the electrodes, as shown in fig. 1.2. Hence, they produce electrical energy and water. The astronauts use the electrical

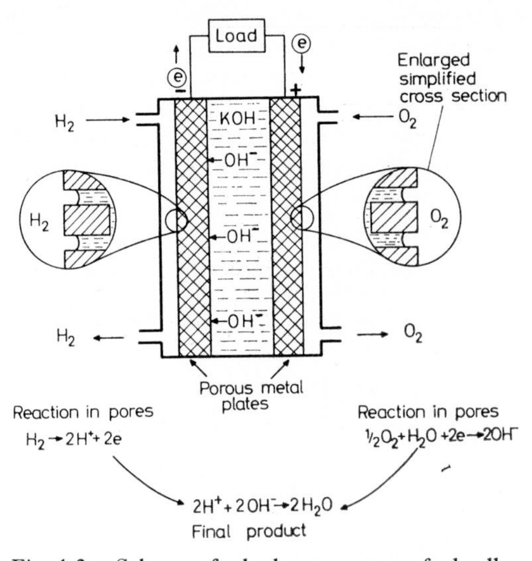

Fig. 1.2. Scheme of a hydrogen–oxygen fuel cell.

energy for the operation of the radio communications, lighting, and heating of the space capsule, and drink the water which evaporates out of the fuel cells, a by-product of electrochemical power conversion.

Two more examples will illustrate the importance and wide occurrence of electrochemical processes in everyday life. Consider the stability of metals. The thermodynamic energy balance for the reaction of metals with oxygen and water in the atmosphere shows that, except for the noble metals, all metals tend to form oxides which often flake off the metal surface. But the moisture films (often invisible) which are usually present on metal surfaces exposed to the atmosphere, make the process of decay an electrochemical one (fig. 1.3).

Some atoms in the surface of the metal tend to give up an electron, perhaps two, to the metal and become ions in the water of the moisture layer. They 'like it better that way', for they are in a lower energy state when in solution than when they are in the lattice of the solid metal. The electrons produced by this first step in corrosion have to go somewhere, otherwise the metal would build up a huge excess negative charge. What these electrons do is to move out from the metal across a distance of a few ångströms† and attach themselves to protons (H^+ ions) giving hydrogen *atoms* which then combine with each other form molecular hydrogen. The process repeats itself on various parts of the surface. The net result is that the metal dissolves away as ions and hydrogen is evolved. The rate of the process concerned is one which is controlled (and this we shall show in detail in Chapter 3) by a difference of electrical potential across the metal–solution interface. The permanence and *stability of materials is very definitely a matter involving electrochemistry.*

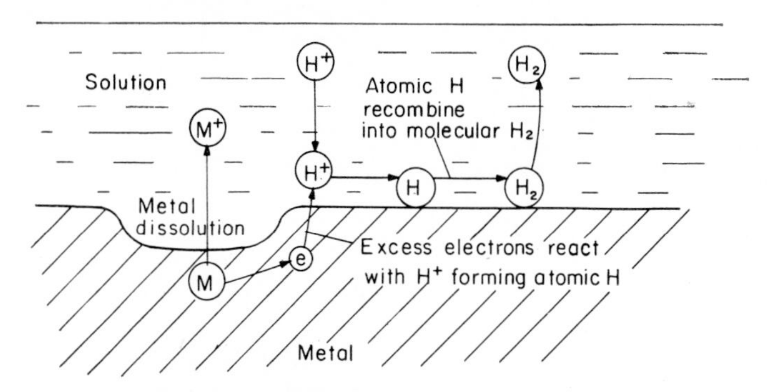

Fig. 1.3. In corrosion, the metal dissolves electrochemically leaving behind electrons. If these electrons can be taken up by some other electrochemical reaction (e.g., hydrogen evolution) the metal continues to dissolve.

Another example concerns the artificial heart and the possibility of putting foreign materials inside the human body and having them remain stable for many years. What usually happens when one tries to do this is that the blood with which they come into contact clots and forms thrombous deposits which, when plucked away into the rest of the blood stream, may cause sudden death by blocking an important path of blood to the heart. The fact that these foreign materials cause this clotting is the principal difficulty in progress towards making permanent prosthetic devices, i.e., spare parts for humans.

A little while ago Philip Sawyer and Supramaniam Srinivasan discovered that whether the blood clotted or not depended upon the electrical potential difference across the boundary between the inserted

† Throughout the book we have used SI units. In addition, the litre (dm^3) has been used in defining the concentration of solutions and the ångström ($1\ \text{Å} = 10^{-10}\ \text{m} = 0{\cdot}1\ \text{nm}$) for small distances when dealing with dimensions of atoms.

material and the blood.† To be sure, this is one of ten or so factors which may affect the clotting of blood, but at the moment it looks as though it may be the most important one. At least, in a quite remarkable way, it is possible to switch on and switch off the clotting of blood in contact with metals. The essential result of the Sawyer and Srinivasan experiments is shown in fig. 1.4.

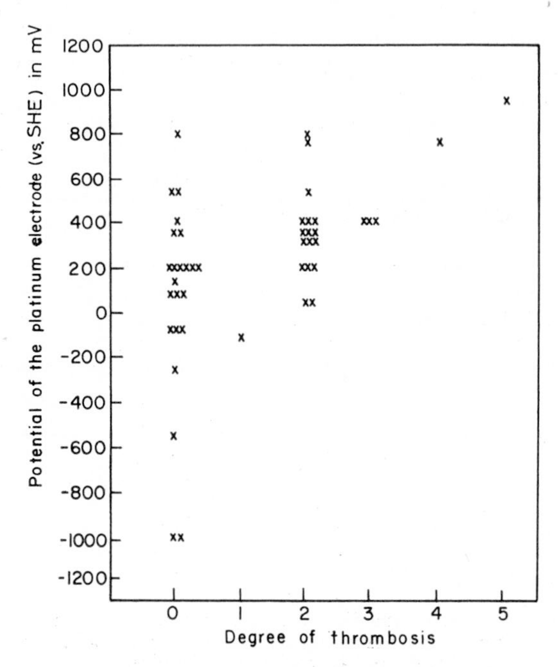

Fig. 1.4. Relative degree of thrombus formation on platinum wire electrode inserted into canine carotid and femoral arteries as a function of electrode potential. Each × represents the result of one experiment. Only when the electrode potential is positive does clotting occur.

These examples, all involve one common factor. We have discussed the production of hydrogen and oxygen in the first example; power conversion in the second; the destruction of materials in the third; and the stability of blood in the fourth. All of these involve an *electrical potential difference across the interface between two phases*, one phase usually being solid, and the other phase usually being a solution. Electrochemistry, therefore, could be defined as *the study of the effects*

† Blood can be considered as a colloidal solution in which the larger colloidal particles erythrocytes, leukocytes and platelets (thrombocytes) are suspended in blood plasma. Blood plasma itself is a colloidal solution composed of about 90% water and 10% solutes, mostly in colloidal form, 7% of the solutes are proteins, 0·9% inorganic salts, mostly sodium chloride, and the rest are numerous organic substances like carbohydrates, amino-acids, urea, lactic acid, etc.

occurring at the interface between an electronically conducting phase (usually a metal) and an *ionically conducting phase* (usually a solution in water).

Electrochemical Science Has a Very Curious History

One of the first recorded electrochemical events is the experiment of Luigi Galvani in 1791. 'I had dissected a frog,' wrote Galvani, 'and had placed it upon a table on which there was an electric machine, whilst I set about doing other things. The frog was entirely separated from the machine, and indeed was no small distance away from it. While one of those who were assisting me touched lightly and by chance

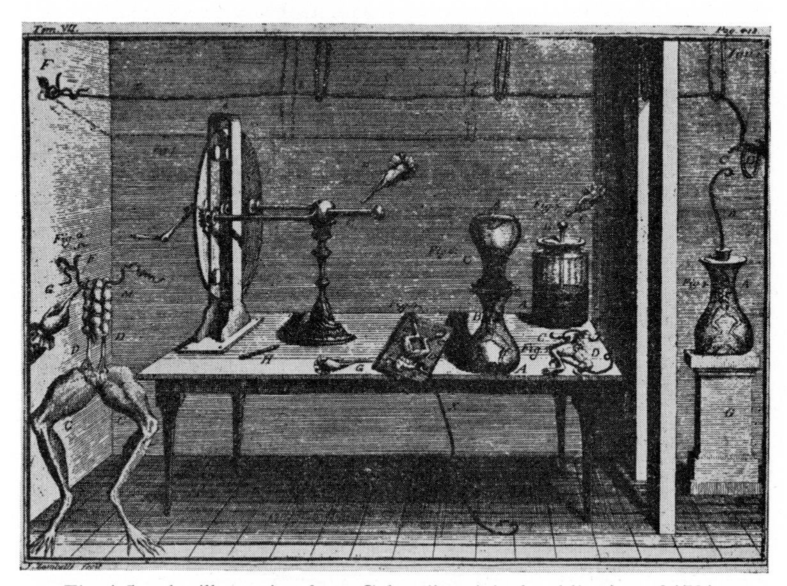

Fig. 1.5. An illustration from Galvani's original publication of 1791.

the point of his scalpel to the internal crural nerves of the frog, suddenly all the muscles of its limbs were seen to be so contracted that they seemed to have fallen into tonic convulsions. . . .' It was concluded that there is 'a profound connection' between biological and electrochemical events (cf. fig. 1.5).

Michael Faraday produced in 1834 his laws of electrolysis, according to which the passage of a definite quantity of electric charge deposits a definite mass of a given material.

A third great discovery was that of the fuel cell by Sir William Grove in 1839 (cf. fig. 1.2).

In 1905, Julius Tafel discovered the relation between the current density i (unit, A m^{-2}) and the difference η between the potential of the electrode at this current density and its potential when no current was passing. It is

$$\eta = a + b \log i, \tag{1.1}$$

where a and b are constants.

This equation can be rewritten

$$i = A \exp (B\eta/RT) \tag{1.2}$$

where A and B are also constants. This is an important relation, for it tells us how much one has to change the potential of an electrode from its equilibrium no-current value in order to get a given current-density.†

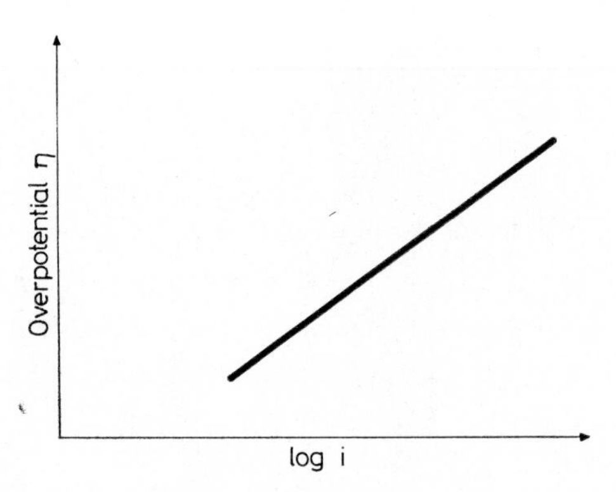

Fig. 1.6. Graphical representation of Tafel's equation.

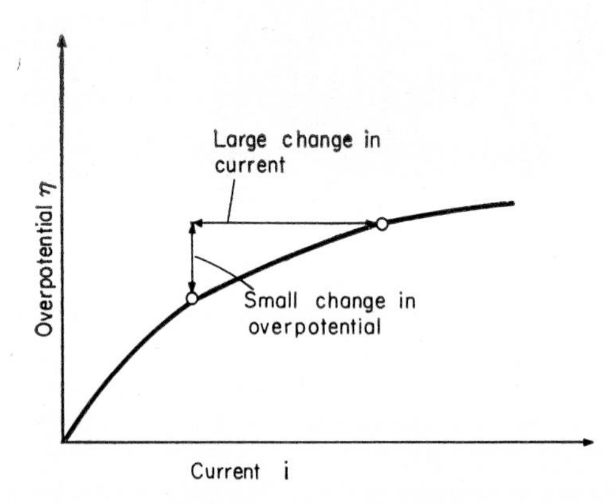

Fig. 1.7. Graphical representation of the relation between current i, and overpotential η. A *small* change in η causes a big change in current, i.e. in reaction rate.

† Current density is the electrochemical equivalent of rate per unit area. Thus, current in amps is coulombs per second. By Faraday's Laws, 96 500 coulombs passed from an electrode into ions in solution produce one mole of material. Hence, current per unit area per second is equivalent to moles per unit area per second.

While electrochemistry *per se* was making its tentative beginning, another aspect of electrochemical science, which was later to become important, was struggling to be born. Sir William Grove had produced his fuel cell in 1839, just after Faraday had discovered his laws. Wilhelm Ostwald realized the importance of the idea of electrochemical energy conversion, and even talked about pollution and smoke-laden cities in 1894. Jacques published an audacious article in *Harper's Magazine* in 1897 which contained a detailed design for powering a ship using a fuel cell, with calculations of how much energy was needed to cross the Atlantic, quite correctly pointing out that the amount of fuel needed would be much less than that consumed in a conventional coal-burning ship.

Why did things go no further then? There are doubtless many reasons, but we need cite only one—the dominance of thermodynamics. The evolution of thermodynamics was one of the greatest triumphs of the nineteenth century. And the thermodynamics of Gibbs and van't Hoff and Ostwald and Nernst was the basis of much of the physical chemistry taught at universities during the first 40 or 50 years of the twentieth century. Unfortunately for electrochemical science, Nernst's celebrated treatment of the electrochemical cell considered only the special and unusual conditions in which the reactions at its electrodes are at equilibrium. He supposed that the reactions at the electrodes were occurring so slowly that the whole ensemble could be said to be virtually 'at chemical equilibrium'. The equation of Nernst—which we shall show later arises from the quantum mechanical equations for the backward and forward rates of electron transfer reactions—is given by:

$$V = V_0 + \frac{RT}{nF} \ln \frac{c_2}{c_1} \tag{1.3}$$

where V is the equilibrium voltage, F is the Faraday constant, R is the gas constant, T the absolute temperature in K, c_1 and c_2 are the concentrations of ions in the solution (fig. 1.8), n is the number of moles of electrons involved in the overall reaction, and V_0 a constant, characteristic for the system.

Nernst's equation became well-known about 1900. In the succeeding years, when people tried to interpret electrochemical cells, they looked to the Nernst equation, which is strictly applicable only to equilibrium thermodynamic situations. Of course, they failed, because the situation at metal–solution interfaces *across which current passes* is not the one which Nernst had assumed.

But why did all this happen? This question has some sociological importance, for it was Nernst's approach which in the 1890's helped the swing towards the internal combustion engine (rather than the fuel cell) as a means of converting the energy associated with the combustion of fuels, like coal and oil, to useful energy, and so contributed to the resulting polluted atmosphere. Why did scientists and engineers make this mistake at that time?

The answer lies in the spirit of the time, and in the unfortunate separation of chemistry from physics. It was easier for chemists and engineers to go along the thermodynamic route, and treat an *irreversible* process as if it were reversible. A proper kinetic treatment *in solution* was thought to be extremely difficult.

However, there were people who doubted the assumption that electron-transfer across an interface went so quickly that it did not 'hold anything up', and so did not disturb equilibrium.

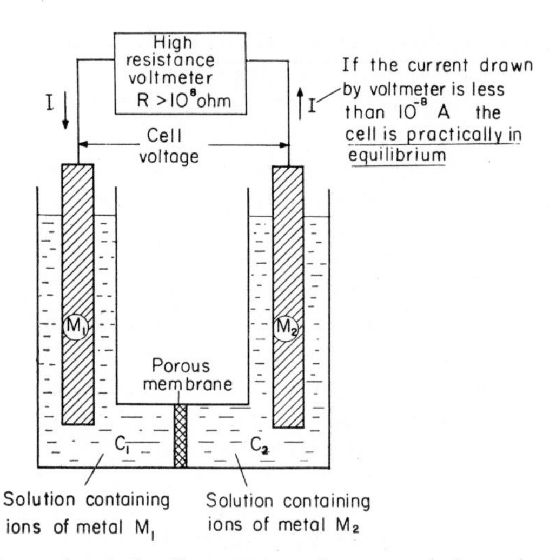

Fig. 1.8. An electrochemical cell consisting of two metal electrodes in contact with solutions containing the corresponding ions.

Nernst pushed the matter aside, pointing out that there were well-known 'redox systems' in which the only thing occurring was the transfer of electrons across an interface (for example, the reaction $Fe^{3+} + e \rightleftarrows Fe^{2+}$, an example which, since it involves hydrated species is in fact quite complex). Nernst's equation applies well to such systems, since here the electron transfer step is very rapid, hence does not act as a barrier, and could be thought of as thermodynamically reversible. It must have seemed that this was a result which could be generalized.

It was conceded that the *transport* of materials to the interface might well not be a reversible process, and by accounting for non-equilibrium diffusion and convection—done in an elementary way at the beginning of the century—chemists were able to follow Nernst with a better conscience!

By 1910, electrochemical science was stagnating. When the Nernst equation could be applied, everyone was happy. But this was seldom so, and people grew worried, stirred up the solutions (cf. the diffusion equations) in different ways to promote convection, and generally became more puzzled. None of this helped.

This lack of progress, which lasted for nearly fifty years, was less marked in Russia, where scientists dealt with electrochemistry in a less Nernst-influenced way, and where, from the early 1930's, there existed a vigorous school of electrochemistry under the great Russian Academician, Frumkin.

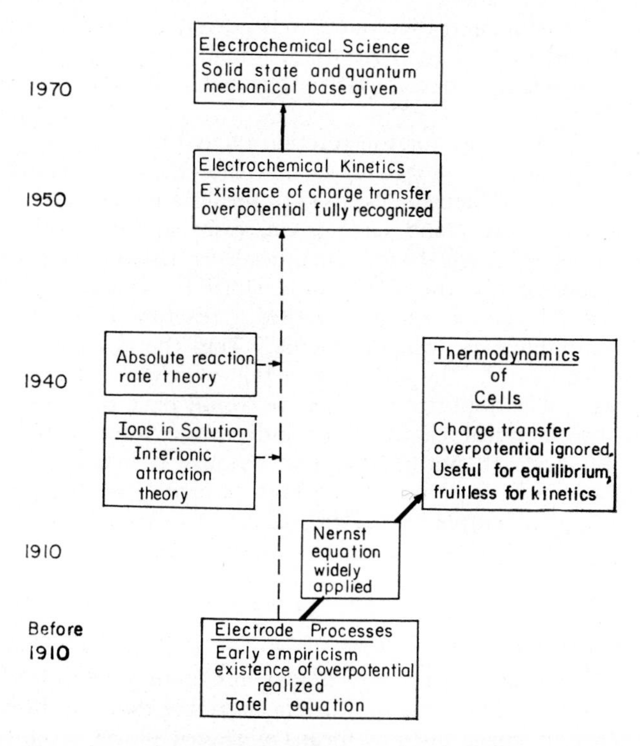

Fig. 1.9. How thermodynamics isolated electrochemistry from solid state physics and quantum mechanics until the 1960's.

As a result of Nernst's influence, electrochemical science *in practice* is half a century behind the progress it might possibly otherwise have made. The assumption that the transfer of electrons between phases takes place in a manner which is amenable to thermodynamics, rather than to kinetics, did make a great difference. Most people did not begin to think kinetically in electrochemistry until after 1950 (fig. 1.9).

The manner of thinking of the people who remained preoccupied with traditional electrochemistry after 1950 (and there were very many) became limited by the thermodynamic type of reasoning. No better example of this can be given than the use, by thermodynamically-oriented metallurgists and engineers, of thermodynamic rules to find out whether a system corrodes or not. Being confronted by, say, solid iron sheet in contact with a conducting solution, the question they asked was: 'If iron corrodes, it is equivalent to the reaction

$$Fe + 2H^+ \rightarrow Fe^{2+} + H_2.$$

Is the free energy change for this reaction negative, so that (thermodynamically) the reaction will go?' If the Nernst equation answers yes, then there is danger, the system may corrode. Efforts along these lines are bound to lead to frustration, for although statements based upon this method are never *wrong*, they tell only part of the whole story.

Thus, the free energy for the reaction of hydrocarbons with oxygen at room temperature is negative, so that the reaction *should* go. We do not, however, see benzene exposed to the air spontaneously bursting into flame. Hydrogen and oxygen can exist stably together for an indefinite time, although thermodynamics says that they *ought* to combine. Of course, the thermodynamic story is always correct. But thermodynamics cannot tell us whether a reaction *will actually* take place at a speed which will interest us. Had the science of *chemical kinetics* been guided by the same star as that which led electrochemistry for fifty years, it is doubtful whether we would have the production of ammonia by chemical catalysis, or indeed the internal combustion engine. (It is worth noting that just because it helps the *rate*, the ammonia synthesis is performed at high temperature, in spite of the fact that at higher temperatures, the negative free energy is less than at lower ones. It is the *rate* which is important, and this is higher at higher temperatures.)

Electrochemistry in All Directions

In 'the Electrochemistry of everyday life', one encounters battery power for starting one's car or working portable radios. Pictures are transmitted from space ships by means of electric power produced from fuel cells. Aluminium, very much a metal of everyday life, is extracted from its ore, Al_2O_3, by electrodeposition. An increasingly economic way of obtaining drinking water from brackish water is by a process known as electrodialysis. Clothing is often made of nylon, a substance produced by an electrochemical process.

Corrosion inhibitors control and slow down the rusting in the cooling system in one's car. Lastly, the movement of one's muscles, the transfer of messages from one's brain to the muscles, and doubtless many other biological processes, involve electrochemical mechanisms.

This electrochemistry of present-day life may encourage us to look forward to the electrochemistry of the near future. This will involve the use of fuel cells to produce energy from chemical compounds, with a great reduction in the amount of undesirable pollutants put into the atmosphere. It will also lead to a variety of electrically driven processes which will change the smoke-affected carbon dioxide-threatened fossil-fuel-driven world to one in which man may have a healthy future for an indefinitely long time. Nuclear science will provide abundant electrical energy in the future, and electrochemical science will be its necessary partner. The present world-wide pollution is partly the result of a century of burning coal and oil to get energy and of discarding into the atmosphere the products of the combustion. Electrochemical science is the link between nuclear electricity and *clean* technology.

The Growing Reaction Against Pollution

The way the modern world is energized, essentially, is that coal and/or oil are burned with air. The reaction between hydrocarbons in oil and oxygen in the air gives carbon dioxide and heat. This heat expands the gases surrounding the region in which the reaction has

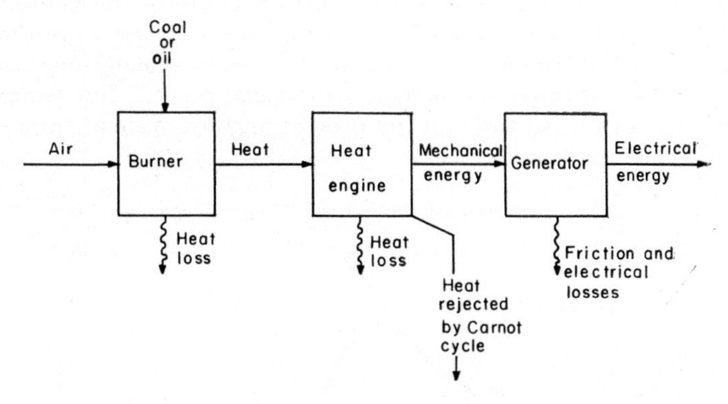

Fig. 1.10. Stages involved in electrical energy production by fuel burning, showing the energy losses.

taken place and the expansion moves something (for example, the piston in the cylinder of an internal combustion engine) so that mechanical energy is produced. If electrical energy is needed, it is produced from this mechanical energy in an electromagnetic generator (fig. 1.10).

Only very recently has it been widely realized that the continuation of human life on earth can be quite limited (a few generations at most) if we continue to get our energy in this way. There are three ecological problems connected with this type of energy conversion:

(1) The hydrocarbon-burning (energy producing) reaction is always accompanied by *side* reactions which are deleterious to the environment —for example, the production of the carcinogenic benzpyrene. Much research is being carried out by the oil refiners and by the motor manufacturers to try to reduce the pollutants from side reactions, which have caused such a general outcry (fig. 1.11). Improvements in engine

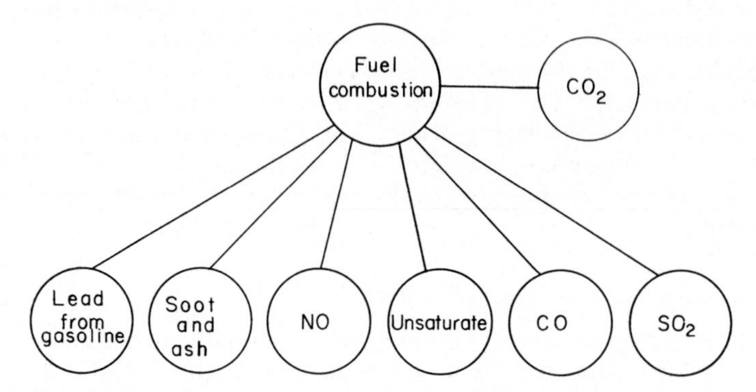

Fig. 1.11. Products obtained by combustion of fuel.

design such as the injection of increased oxygen into the combustion process to encourage complete combustion into CO_2 and suppress the side reactions, can reduce the amount of smog-producing unsaturated hydrocarbons and other products from exhaust pipes. But we cannot continue to burn fossil fuels on the present gigantic scale for more than some 15–25 years (see fig. 1.12).

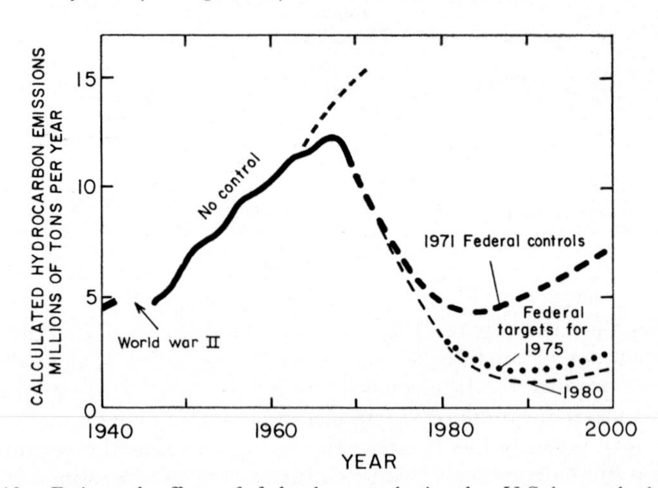

Fig. 1.12. Estimated effect of federal controls in the U.S.A. on hydrocarbon emissions from passenger vehicles. A rising trend is expected after 1985 because of the increasing numbers of cars.

It is unrealistic to assume that pollutants will be cleaned up to an extent better than 90%. This only gives us until the year 1985—the middle age of many of the readers of this book—until the expected increase in the number of cars throughout the world overcomes the most optimistically forecast decrease in the exhaust pollutant per vehicle.

(2) But, however effectively research and improved engineering may remove smog-producing unsaturates from automobile exhausts, it is impossible to stop the carbon dioxide producing reaction which is the source of nearly all our present energy. This carbon dioxide distributed in the atmosphere will tend to give a 'greenhouse effect'—for the gas behaves like the glass of a greenhouse. Carbon dioxide transmits direct solar radiation well, but the re-radiation from the heated earth is mainly in the far infra red region of the spectrum where carbon dioxide absorbs strongly. The energy thus trapped by the CO_2

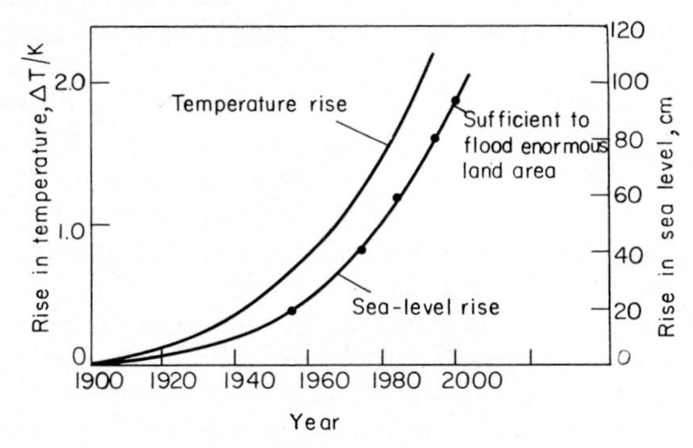

Fig. 1.13. Temperature and sea-level rise due to accumulation of carbon dioxide in the atmosphere.

molecules helps to raise the temperature of the atmosphere. The temperature of the earth's surface results from a balance between the incoming radiant heat of the sun, the heat from the weak radioactivity of materials inside the earth, and the amount of heat *reflected* from the earth, which is mostly returned to space, but some of which is absorbed in the CO_2. If this CO_2 grows more than the equilibrium quantity corresponding to the balance of Nature (fig. 1.13), the earth will heat up. As the earth heats up, polar ice melts and the seas rise. It is possible to make a calculation of this; and if one neglects feedbacks (for example, that there is an increasing amount of solid matter suspended in the atmosphere, and this may decrease the solar heat reaching us), one comes to the conclusion that there will be a rise of up to about one metre in the level of the sea throughout the world by the year 2000, succeeded by an increasing rate or rise which has been put as high as 30 cm per year.

These predictions of the decade in which our excessive production of carbon dioxide from the burning of fossil fuels to get power will lead to a disastrous rise of sea level resemble in one respect the prediction of Malthus, which was that more food would cause people to multiply at a rate which would lead to disastrous overcrowding of this planet. The date at which disaster comes is later than the prophet at first predicts, but the prediction remains sound. The climatic change to be expected from continued CO_2 injection into the atmosphere is the most cogent reason for abandoning the burning of fossil fuels to obtain energy.

For the last fifty years or so, carbon dioxide produced by man in home and factory has exceeded the natural balance between photosynthesis (which removes carbon dioxide) and the production of carbon dioxide in metabolism. The sea could easily absorb the excess carbon dioxide, but this gas is only *in equilibrium* with the sea for the first 10–100 metres of sea depth. Thereafter, it no longer circulates freely, but diffuses downwards slowly. To absorb the excess carbon dioxide in this way would take thousands of years.

(3) There is a considerable problem over the sulphur dioxide evolved in the burning of fossil fuels. It is easy to convert the SO_2 to SO_3 and sulphuric acid, but this would only mean that *sulphuric acid* became the pollutant, for the amounts which would be produced if we were to extract all the sulphur dioxide would far exceed the amounts for which any possible use could be found.

It is obvious, and even accepted by executives of oil companies, that future sources of energy will largely be atomic (also probably solar, and possibly geothermal—using the heat of the earth at depths of the order of 1–10 miles). How will this energy be distributed? It will be available to us at the converter sites in the form of electrical energy. The provision of cheap electrical energy from atomic energy has profound consequences for the development of electrochemical science. This is not only so for the replacement of the internal combustion engine in cars by batteries or fuel cells, and electric motors. It will not be feasible in the future to eject pollutants of any kind into the atmosphere, the rivers, or the sea. So the only way of managing will be to convert present *chemical* processes—most of which produce pollutants at present ejected into the air or water—to electrochemical ones (which do not exude pollutants). Thus, the present process for the production of copper is to take the copper ore in the form of its sulphide and to force a stream of oxygen through it at high temperature so that copper is produced and sulphur dioxide is evolved into the atmosphere. The surrounding countryside becomes blighted, and the atmosphere has an increasing content of sulphur dioxide. The corresponding electrochemical process would involve the direct solution of the copper sulphide ore and the electrolytic deposition of copper, with the evolution of oxygen (or the deposition of sulphur) as a by-product.

The Electrochemistry of Cleaner Environments

Let us first start off with the problem of atomic wastes. It is no use preaching that man has an indefinitely long future on this planet by changing from a coal and oil-burning society to one driven by electricity produced from atomic energy, stored electrochemically, if one is to be haunted by the spectre of pollution from radioactive atomic wastes, which might have even worse long-range effects than chemical pollution. We shall never be able to tolerate the idea that atomic wastes can be injected into rivers or seas. What could be done is to purify them electrochemically. The principle of purification would be that of electrodeposition, as explained in the Section on electro-separation in Chapter 6. From the radioactive liquids associated with the reactor, one would get out the corresponding *solid* materials.

Thus, electrochemically purified atomic wastes would be compressed into a small volume. The storage of these relatively small packages of solid (but highly radioactive!) wastes in mine shafts for times of the order of hundreds of years is feasible. At longer range than this, it seems that people will be able to raise great masses from the earth into space by means of atomic rockets fairly easily and cheaply, so solid atomic wastes might be put into space, and sent back to where their nuclei originated, i.e., to our sun.

Meanwhile, we have to deal with the world as it is, a very dirty world becoming rapidly dirtier. Electrochemical processes seem to offer the best way in which the dirtying of the atmosphere, rivers, lakes, and seas may be stopped and reversed. It is not necessary for factories to be continuously supplied with water, which then, in a dirtier form, goes into a river or lake or sea, to give rise to evaporation, rain, storage, and recirculation to the factory. The water need never leave the factory, but can be electrodialysed on the spot and re-used (fig. 1.14).

Organic liquids containing non-ionic substances (only ionic substances are subject to electrodialysis) need not be rejected from factories but can be passed over electrodes and oxidized to carbon dioxide, or undergo a reaction to form hydrocarbons, which can then be vented off.

Sewage, too, can be treated electrochemically to convert it largely to carbon dioxide, which can then be converted to other more useful things by electrochemical means—to formaldehyde, for example; and even by way of the intervention of an enzyme and surrounding atmospheric nitrogen, to protein. These possibilities open up the imaginative prospect of the household as the ecological unit, with man as the main converter from food to the degraded products of sewage, which can then be electrochemically upgraded once more to available protein.

Rubbish need not be rejected into the sea, or allowed to ferment, thus taking up land, but could be electrochemically converted (again perhaps within each house) largely to carbon dioxide.

Lastly, an excellent example of how electrochemical science can alleviate pollution lies in the removal of discarded motor cars. At present there is only minimal re-use of iron and other metals in cars, because feeding the whole car back into a steel furnace gives rise to unwanted products in the steel. Electrochemically, it would be possible to dissolve the whole car in a bath containing ionic salts. Thereafter, by a process known as electro-extraction (see Chapter 6), the components of the cars can be deposited electrochemically, but separately, each being depositable by adjusting the electrode potential by means of a potentiostat. Calculations show that one car can be dissolved in about one week in a bath, and thereafter the material would give about £100 worth

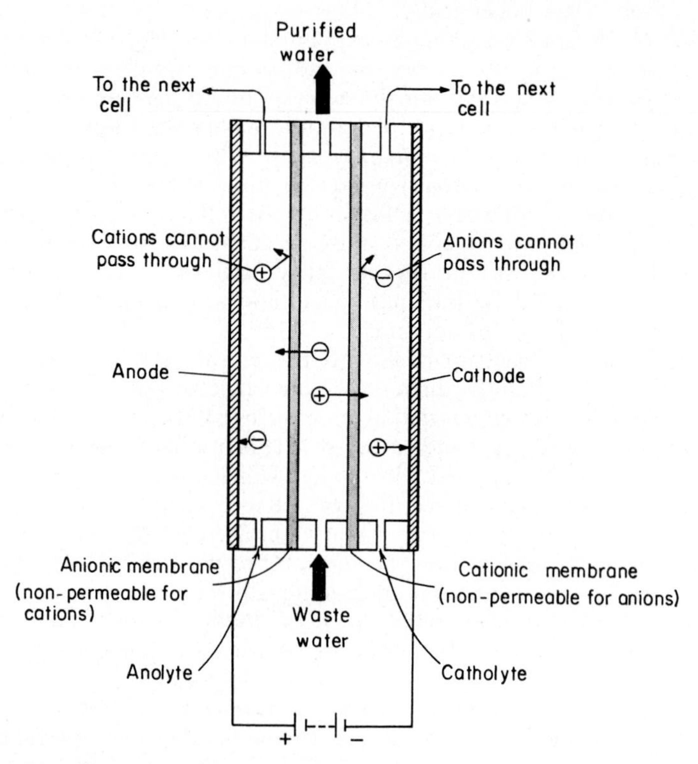

Fig. 1.14. Charged particles can be removed from waste water by electrodialysis.

of raw materials for re-use. About one-fourth of steel production could be eliminated by the re-circulation of iron in this way. Incidentally, the iron produced would be in the form of powder, just in the right form for re-use in powder-metallurgy.

Enough has been said already to show that electrochemical science is coming into its own to form the central part of our future in our supply of energy, the stability of our materials, their recycling, our syntheses, and so on (fig. 1.15).

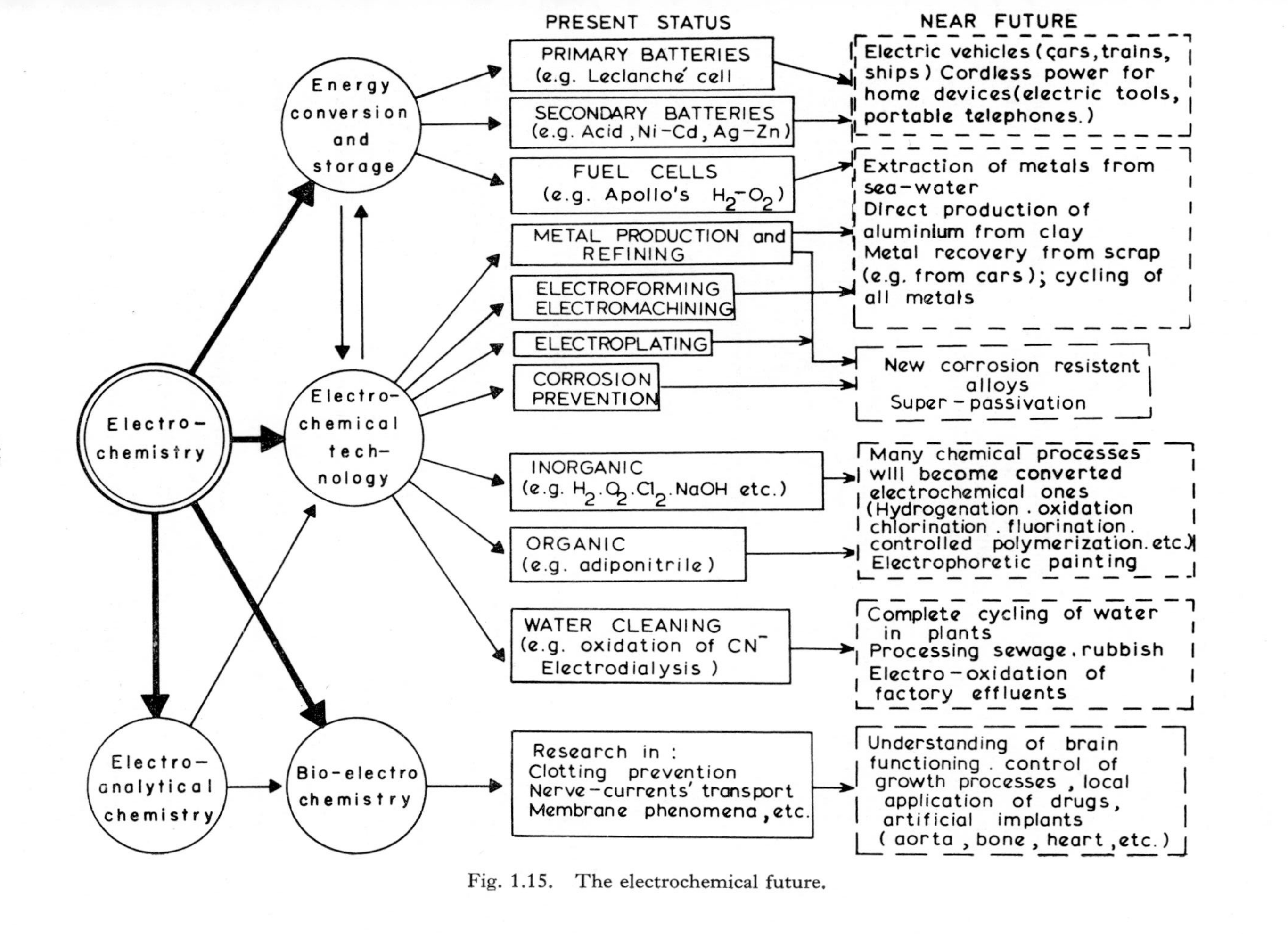

Fig. 1.15. The electrochemical future.

The Hydrogen Economy

As nuclear reactions develop as the main source of electric power, the question will be whether to distribute the energy by means of electric currents flowing through metallic wire conductors in a grid or whether to distribute it by other means. The difficulty of distribution by wires is that it costs a lot to send currents down wires because of the resistance they offer, which is responsible for the lost ('IR') volts and the wasted ('I^2R') power.

Superconducting materials (with *zero* resistance) are being developed, but all of those so far described are only superconducting while being maintained at very low temperatures. One approach is to seek for a superconductor that functions at ordinary temperatures.

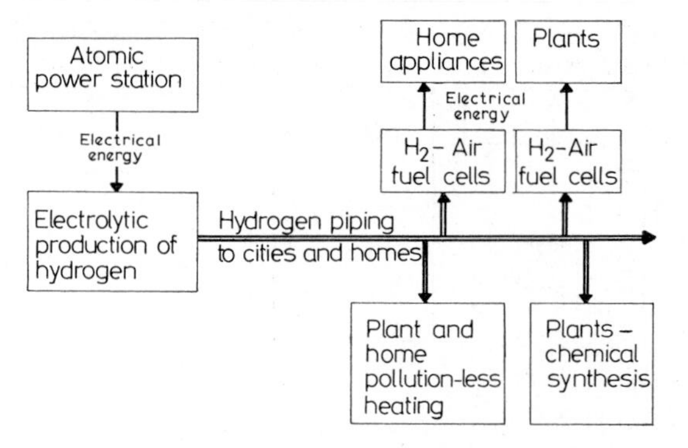

Fig. 1.16. The hydrogen economy.

An alternative approach is that, at the atomic power stations, the electrical energy be used to produce hydrogen on a large scale by the electrolysis of water. The hydrogen produced will be piped to the consumer (just like 'coal gas', a former domestic fuel, which was 50% hydrogen), where it will provide power by means of hydrogen–air fuel cells. The advantage is that the electrical energy will arrive where it is needed more cheaply than is possible by the use of wires, perhaps at about half the cost.

Biology and Electrochemistry

If electrochemistry is an underdeveloped science, then the most underdeveloped part of it is certainly in its applications to biology. There are two general problems in biology which can be attacked only with an increase in electrochemical knowledge. One of them is the fact that in biological systems the area-to-volume ratio is usually high. Many substances in biological systems are colloidal, existing as stable individual particles of radius 0·01–0·1 μm by virtue of bearing an excess electric charge which repels other similarly charged particles.

Under these circumstances, the properties of the surfaces are more important than the bulk properties in determining stability. The functioning of many colloidal systems depends upon the interphasial region and its electric charge. The electrochemistry of the interface of many biological systems holds the clue to their behaviour. It is a little-researched area in biophysics, where investigations are usually still over-influenced by the equilibrium thermodynamics of Nernst.

A broad topic in biology which is almost pure electrochemistry is that of processes associated with potential differences. Thus, there is a potential difference across membranes in body tissues. Encephalographic oscillations (which show variations of potential differences between parts of the brain) are associated with our various psychological states. Although the origin of these oscillations, in physiological terms, is as yet little understood, it seems likely that they have an electrochemical origin.

These are questions for the future. But man's ability to investigate them depends in turn upon the availability of knowledge in electrochemical science—a science still only awakening from a fifty-year hibernation.

Approaches to Electrochemistry

What has been said about the slow development of electrochemistry does not apply so much to *electroanalytical* chemistry, a branch of the subject which accounts for as much as half the chemical analysis done today. Many young electroanalytical chemists understand modern electrochemistry, and apply it with the help of electronic instrumentation.

The objective of the electroanalytical chemist is, understandably, chemical analysis; and he uses electrochemistry as a tool. His contributions to modern electrochemistry, which particularly in the U.S.A. are substantial, are incidental to the subject: he is improving a tool.

On the other hand, the electrochemical scientist is interested primarily in all aspects of science which contribute to his knowledge of the electrode–solution interface, and the processes which depend upon electron transfer across it, whether these be in Chemistry, Biology, Metallurgy, Engineering, or even dentistry, rock drilling, or the production of oxygen on the moon. Thus, he needs a knowledge of the solid state; of the structure of the solutions which form the 'other side' of the double-layer; and, of course, of the central event, the mechanism of the transfer of charge across the boundary, and the aspects of basic physics which control this. The branches of science that are most nearly related to electrochemical science are surface chemistry and surface physics, along with a knowledge of quantum mechanics and molecular structure.

There has also, of course, been great progress in the electrochemistry of ionic solutions and this must not confuse the point we are here trying to make. A review of the developments of the last twenty years reveals a radiant series of new electrochemical possibilities for a viable post-industrial society. However, the old electrochemistry itself produced a thriving present-day industry which indeed has existed for decades. Electroplating, storage batteries, some electrosyntheses, corrosion control, etc., are all areas in which there is a considerable industrial development, and which are well represented by the Electrochemical Society of the United States.

The tiny area of electrochemistry which is touched upon in chemistry courses in colleges concerns what is called 'the electrochemistry of ions in solution', such topics as pH, dissociation constants of acids and bases, and the interaction of ions in solution. Twenty or more years ago, at least in the U.K. and U.S., this was the substance of electrochemistry. However, these classical aspects of electrochemistry do indeed seem to be 'just a branch of physical chemistry'; and critics would be justified in claiming that there is no reason why they should be treated as a separate subject. They do not have a particular character of their own as do the highly interdisciplinary and many-sided processes occurring at the metal–solution interface. Absorption of the electrochemistry of solutions into *physical chemistry* seems the most likely classification for this subject, whilst the electrode-process side should go ahead to grow to a new, and individual, discipline, Electrochemical Science.

Is Electrochemical Science Predominantly an Applied Science?

If the reader thinks that the great stress placed upon the *utility* of the new Electrochemical Science means that the person whose scientific activities arise only from his pure, spontaneous curiosity, and not because he thinks of social value, will find little to inspire him in the New Electrochemistry, he would have misunderstood our intent. The approach of this first chapter arises because we feel that it is urgently necessary (*a*) to show to the reader that there is an important body of very relevant science which so far has not been recognized in school and university curricula, and (*b*) to direct the reader's attention to its application to these environmental matters which have begun to concentrate our minds and will certainly occupy his mind for the whole of his life.

Electrochemical science certainly contains very many problems of interest to physicists and chemists at the most fundamental level. In fact, research work by good theorists is perhaps the greatest of all the needs in the field at the present time. Atomic-scale theories of surface properties are wanting. Thus, during the last 25 years, the development of solid state physics has been largely limited to bulk properties, with little progress towards a non-phenomenological theory of electrical or non-electrical surface properties. At the same time, the great practical relevance of the subject may perhaps be an added attraction for those scientifically-minded students who believe that the direction of their work should involve some social relevance, in addition to being an expression of their spontaneous curiosity.

The theory of the electrical double layer, to be presented in the next chapter, is still at a level of achievement well below that at which, say, solid state theory enables the energy of a crystal lattice to be calculated. The theory of the charge transfer reaction itself, which must be in quantum mechanical terms, has been formulated, but the theories hitherto given are formalistic, and tend to look the other way at vital moments, as will be shown in Chapter 3. Correspondingly, when one gets on to the parts of electrochemistry which deal with the dependence of reaction rates upon the metal itself—electrocatalysis (see Chapter 5)—the theories given are so crude and non-predictive as to be as yet of little practical value to the electrochemical engineer who wishes to develop his plans for the achievement of certain practical goals with the help of reliable fundamental calculations.

Electrochemical Science is full of fundamental problems. But it does contain within it a deterrent to many modern theorists. Many of these like to work, as yet, on super-simple systems, which are usually difficult enough if these are to be tackled in a way which satisfies him psychologically. He, therefore, demurs: 'I haven't got much of a theory for electrons at the surface of mercury yet. How do you expect me to work out the basic theory of the surface of solid metals when there are complications of adsorbed water molecules, heterogeneity of the crystal lattice, and a strong electric field?' (He means, 'with all the complications of the electrochemical situation'.)

But it certainly would not seem to be helpful if chemical theorists chose to wait several decades more before trying to tackle the complexities inherent in surface systems. It seems probable that, ecologically, we haven't got that amount of time left.

This book is addressed above all to young people—those who might still be alive at the time when many of the ecological and sociological matters touched upon in this introductory chapter will either be solved by electrochemical methods, or not be solvable at all. Much of that decision will be made in the minds of the readers of this book.

CHAPTER 2

the structure of electric double layers

Interfaces and Interphases

THE previous chapter explained the importance of *electron transfer across charged interfaces*. To what do these electrons transfer? If the reaction is one in which the electrons are leaving the metal and entering a solution, they transfer either to ions:

$$Fe^{2+} + 2e \rightarrow Fe \tag{2.1}$$

or to molecules:

$$O_2 + 4H^+ + 4e \rightarrow 2H_2O. \tag{2.2}$$

There must, therefore, be a *region* across which the electron transfer occurs. We must distinguish between an *interface*, 'a *surface* in contact with another phase', and an *interphase*, which is 'the *region* of changing properties between two phases (and, indeed, between two interfaces)'.

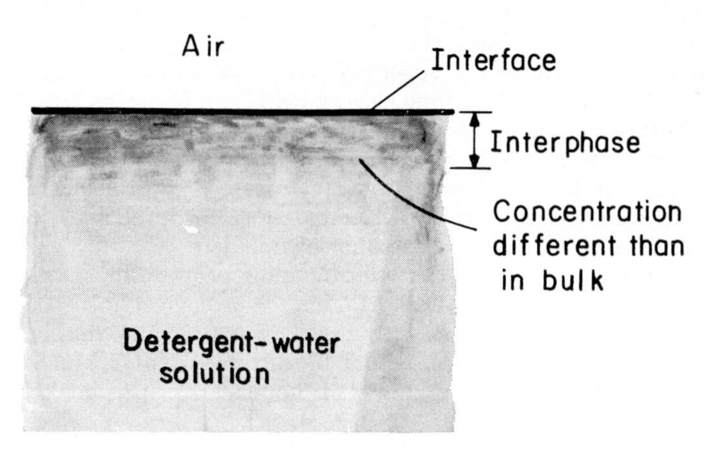

Fig. 2.1. Interface and interphase.

An interface is sharp and definite to within an atomic layer. An interphase is a less sharply definable region, which will range over at least two molecular diameters, but may extend over thousands of ångströms; it may be defined more fully as 'the region between two phases in which the properties have not yet reached those of the bulk of either phase'.

Why should we devote an entire chapter to discussing the 'electric double layer', a good descriptive term for these charged interfaces? The reason is that the properties of *this interphasial region* affect, and indeed, dominate, the charge transfer reaction.

Consider a very simple example: an imaginary very sharp interface in which the left-hand side consists of a line of excess electrons on a mercury surface, and the other consists of a line of *positive* charges in a solution which is imagined to be in contact with the mercury. When one refers to 'excess' charges like this, one is ignoring all the vast numbers of other charges present in the metal–solution interphase, on

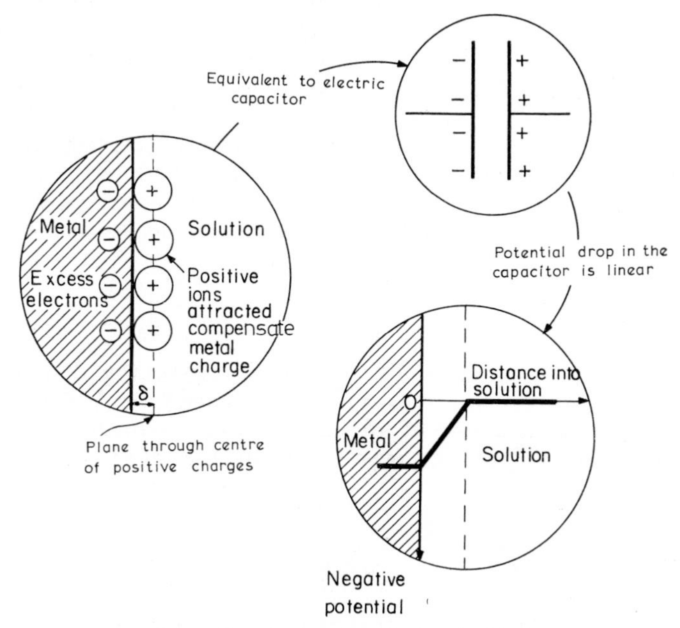

Fig. 2.2. The simplest-imaginable double layer.

the assumption that wherever there are positive ions, there will, on the whole, be negative ions very close by, so that their charges cancel. One is thinking only of the *excess* charges, which are not neutralized and which hence affect the electric situation.

The force per unit charge experienced at any point in an electric field is the electric field strength (measured in NC^{-1})† at that point. It is equal to the potential gradient (measured in $V\ m^{-1}$) at that point. At electrochemical interfaces, one is usually dealing with a potential difference of about 0·1 V to 1 V. A potential difference of 1 volt

† Electric field (in newtons per coulomb) equals the rate of variation of the potential with distance, $\partial\psi/\partial x$ (in volts per metre). If the variation is linear, we can just take the end values (or the potential difference) and divide by distance.

acting across the distance of about 1 Å = 10^{-10} m between the layers of charge in the double layer gives an electric field strength of about 10^{10} V m^{-1}.

It is this very strong field which causes the electrons to jump across the interface. As far as electrochemical reactions are concerned, it is not just a matter of how much charge there is upon each phase. It is the distribution of this charge—the distance between the various charged particles—which determines the *interfacial electric field strength* ($\partial\psi/\partial x$), and hence the speed of electron transfer between the two phases. So we must seek some kind of *molecular description* of what is going on in the region of the liquid phase near the metal. The figure of 1 Å cited above is really an underestimate; the distance is more like 5 Å for the region of *hot* activity. Regions of hundreds, occasionally even thousands, of ångströms are also sometimes of importance, more for secondary effects.

This chapter will therefore discuss the distribution of electrons within the metal, with respect to the metal surface; and the much more important question of the distribution of positive and negative ions in the solution. We are going to study the *structure of the double layer.*

The Electric Double Layer

Double layers are widespread in nature

It is easy to give examples of electric double layers (fig. 2.3), and one nearly always finds that a surface is accompanied by a double layer.

Not very much is known at present about the boundary between an insulator and a solution, and even less about the interface between an

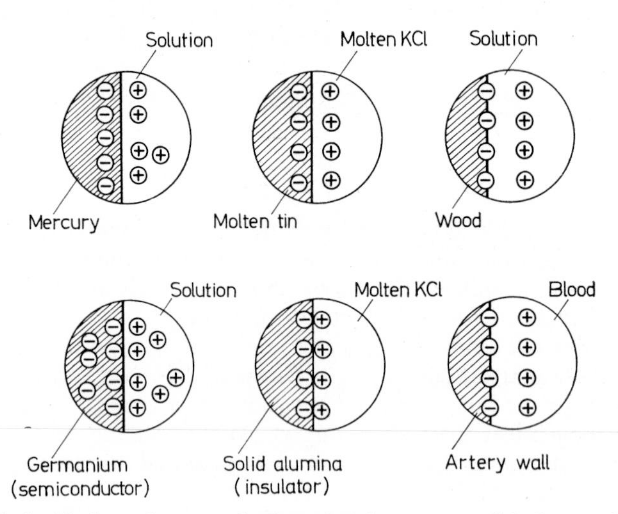

Fig. 2.3. A double layer forms at the boundary between a solid plane and an ionic solution.

artery wall and the colloidal particles of blood in contact with it. However, in both cases, there is plenty of experimental evidence for the importance of electrochemical (hence double layer-controlled) effects at such interfaces.

Double layers are always electrically charged

Let us imagine the two real interfaces of a mercury–solution system to be the two plates of a capacitor. When they are in equilibrium, there is an excess charge of q^{α} on one plate and q^{β} upon the other.

The charges (excess charges) on the two plates of a capacitor are equal in magnitude and opposite in sign, so $q^{\alpha} = q^{\beta}$.

If the interfaces did behave as though they were simple capacitances (they don't, but they nearly do occasionally, and the analogy is a good one), then $C = q^{\alpha}/V$, where V is the potential difference between the

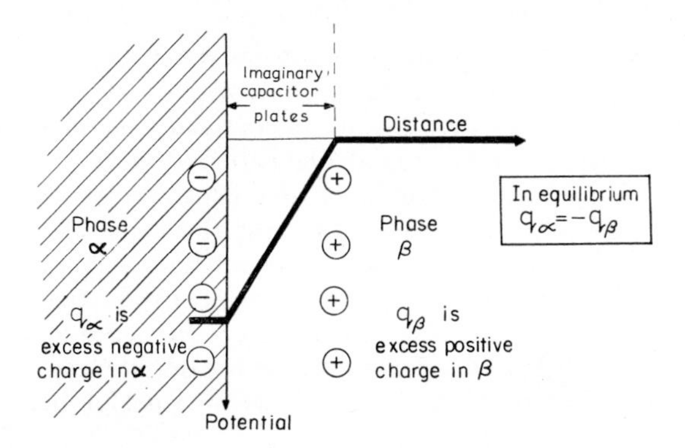

Fig. 2.4. Potential difference and 'excess charges' on a double layer.

plates of the 'capacitor'. More simply, charge separation produces an electric field in the space between the charges; with an electric field there is a potential gradient, and hence (between different points in the direction of the field) a potential difference. Wherever there is a double layer, there will be two equal and opposite layers of charge, *and a potential difference between them.*

Only tiny amounts of excess charge are needed to cause large changes in the actions of double layers

Let us calculate the resulting change in the velocity of a reaction—one in which an electron is emitted from the electrode to an ion in solution nearby—for a given change in the excess charge on the double layer. A typical excess charge on a double layer is $0{\cdot}1\ \mathrm{C\ m^{-2}}$. One mole of electrons carries $F = 96\,500\ \mathrm{C}$ = approximately 10^5 C, so $0{\cdot}1$ C represents 10^{-6} mol of electrons.

Hence, the 'amount' of excess electrons per unit area is approximately 10^{-6} moles of electrons per square metre. With the Avogadro constant taken roughly as 6×10^{23}, one finds that the number of excess electrons on one square metre of the surface which give them an excess charge of 0·1 C is 6×10^{17}. The number of atoms in one square metre of a typical surface works out to about 10^{19}, so that only about 6% of the atoms have to have excess electron-charges on them to provide the 0·1 C m^{-2}.†

Now, consider the effects that this mere 10^{-6} mol of electrons can bring about. It will later be shown (Chapter 3) that one of the most marked effects which an excess charge has upon a surface in contact with a solution is to cause reactions which occur at it to go at different speeds. The formula (derived in Chapter 3, equation 3.5) is

$$\frac{\text{rate at potential } V_2}{\text{rate at potential } V_1} = \frac{\exp(-\beta F V_2/RT)}{\exp(-\beta F V_1/RT)} = \exp(-\beta F(V_2 - V_1)/RT) \quad (2.3)$$

where F is the Faraday constant, R is the gas constant, T is the temperature in Kelvins, and β is a constant, often with a value near to $\frac{1}{2}$. To find out how much the reaction rate is changed by a change in excess charge of 0·1 C m^{-2}, one has to calculate the *potential difference* change due to the charge, keeping the layer as a capacitor of capacitance C‡ and using $V = Q/C$. The expression for the capacitance C for one square metre is $C = \varepsilon\varepsilon_0/t$, where ε_0 the permittivity of space is 8·85 F m^{-1} and ε the dielectric constant always > 1. From this, if $t = 1$ Å $= 10^{-10}$ m, C works out to rather more (depending on ε) than 0·1 F m^{-2}. It is found experimentally that the double layer capacitances are of the order 0·15 to 0·20 F m^{-2}. Assuming 0·17 F m^{-2} and using

$$V = Q/C,$$

we get for the *change in* ΔV in V,

$$\Delta V = \Delta Q/C$$

so that

$$\Delta V = -0{\cdot}1/0{\cdot}17 = -0{\cdot}6 \text{ V}.$$

Writing $\Delta V = -0{\cdot}6$ V for $(V_2 - V_1)$ in equation 2.3, and taking $R = 8{\cdot}317$ J mol^{-1} K^{-1}, and $\beta = \frac{1}{2}$,

$$\begin{aligned} \text{rate } V_2 &= \exp(-\beta F \Delta V/RT) \times \text{rate } V_1 \\ &= \exp(0{\cdot}5 \times 96\,500 \times 0{\cdot}6)/(8{\cdot}317 \times 298) \times \text{rate } V_1 \\ &\approx 100\,000 \times \text{rate } V_1. \end{aligned}$$

Thus, this 10^{-6} mol of electrons per square metre has changed the rate of the reaction by a factor of 10^5.

† This is $1/\pi r^2 \times 1{\cdot}25$, where 1·25 represents a rough and ready correction for the space not filled up by atoms taken as circles in contact. Thus, if $r \simeq 1{\cdot}5 \times 10^{-10}$ m, the number of atoms is $1/\pi \times 2{\cdot}25 \times 10^{-20} \times 1{\cdot}25 \simeq 1{\cdot}1 \times 10^{19} \simeq 10^{19}$ atoms m^{-2}.

‡ Note the symbols: C = coulombs; C = capacitance.

Other elementary calculations of the same nature can be made. They show that all the mighty changes which go on at interfaces are caused by the very tiny amounts of material changes, e.g., 10^{-6} moles of electrons per square metre having a mass of about

$$\left(\frac{1}{2\,.\,10^{3}}\right) 10^{-6}\, 10^{-3} = 5 \times 10^{-13}\ \text{kg m}^{-2}.$$

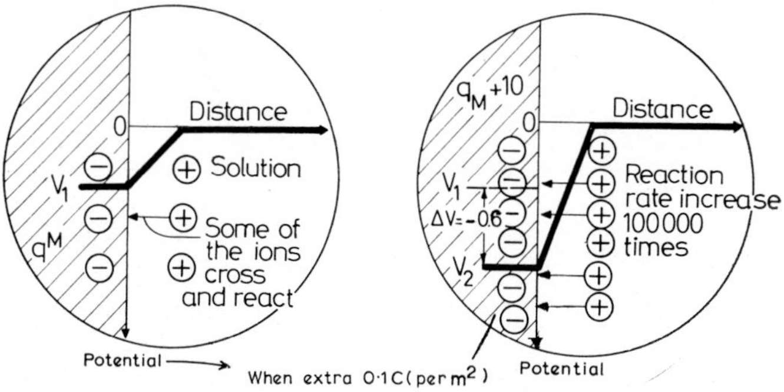

Fig. 2.5. An additional 0·1 C m^{-2} changes the rate of reaction by a factor 10^5.

Why does an interphasial potential difference change affect electrochemical reaction rates so greatly?

A very rough calculation was made above, where it was shown that the interphasial potential difference was some 10^{10} V m^{-1}; and then we demurred that this over-simple example had exaggerated the field-strength. However, it is entirely realistic to take electrochemical field strengths as being at least of the order 10^9 V m^{-1}.

No actual electric field strength of this magnitude can be set up in a situation outside the electrochemical one.

The reason is that a field strength of 10^9 V m^{-1} in a non-electrochemical situation, requires a dielectric which will withstand it. In practice, all dielectrics break down (by a process not unlike ionization by collision which leads to the spark discharge in air) at field strengths of the order of 10^6 V m^{-1}.

There cannot be any breakdown across double layers at electrodes, because the two opposing sheets of charge are not separated by more than *one or two* water molecule layers (the ions are *on either side* of these layers, and not in them) so that the cascade process of dielectric breakdown cannot occur.

Electrochemical double layers can give rise to a very high field strength, and therefore to a very large accelerating force on electric charges.

This large field strength, and the corresponding force it exerts on ions, is the origin of the effects which may take place across double layers.

There are two kinds of potential differences at electric double layers

The potential difference which gives rise to the electric field originates (fig. 2.6) in two ways.† Imagine (fig. 2.6) that there is a double layer just like our over-simple model (an excess of electrons on the

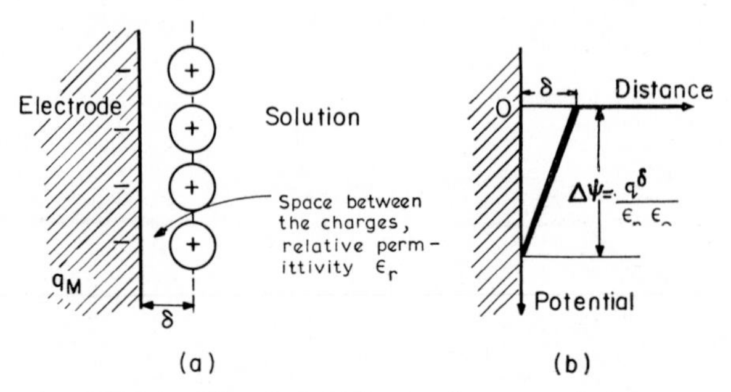

Fig. 2.6. Electric field due to the excess charge.

metal at charge density about $0{\cdot}1$ C m^{-2} and a corresponding excess of ions on the solution side). Now, we will not ask what lies between these charges, but will just consider it as a perfect dielectric. The potential difference, due to the excess charge on the 'capacitor' plates, is:

$$\Delta\psi = q\delta/\varepsilon_r\varepsilon_0, \tag{2.4}$$

where ε_r is the relative permittivity (dielectric constant) of the as yet very unclearly explained material between the plates, ε_0 is the permittivity of a vacuum ($8{\cdot}85 \times 10^{-12}$ F m^{-1}) and δ is the average distance between the excess electron layer and the counter-layer of excess charge in the solution (fig. 2.6). This is the potential difference *due to the excess charge.*

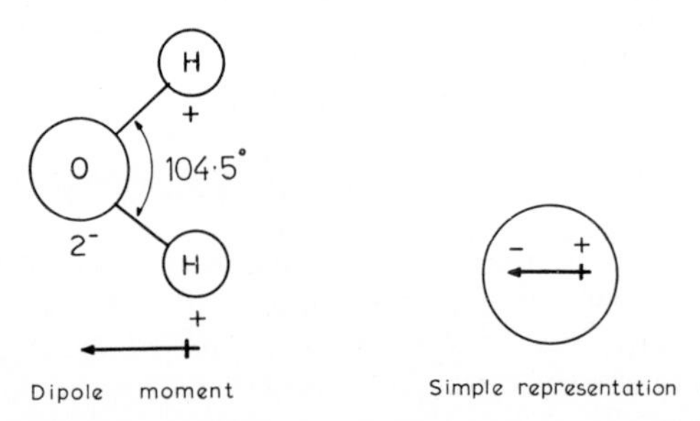

Fig. 2.7. The water molecule has two O–H bonds, polarization arising because the binding electrons ('2−') are closer to the oxygen atom. The electric dipole moment is $6{\cdot}20 \times 10^{-30}$ C m = $1{\cdot}86$ debye.

† The electrical potential inside a single phase is often called the Galvani or inner potential ϕ. The total potential difference between two phases in contact is called the Galvani potential difference, $\Delta\phi$. $\Delta\phi = \Delta\psi + \Delta\chi$, where $\Delta\chi$ is defined below.

However, there is another contribution to the potential difference across the double layer. It arises from the electric dipole behaviour of the molecules of the dielectric itself—usually water. We can imagine the water-molecule dipoles (fig. 2.7) to orient themselves as determined by the excess charge on the metal (fig. 2.8). If this is negative, water molecules will tend to orient themselves with their positive ends towards the metal, the negatively charged ends stuck out towards the solution. But of course there is a potential difference between the two 'separated' ends of the dipole itself! So a *layer of oriented dipoles* has a potential difference across it, and this will be *added* to the potential difference given in the equation above.

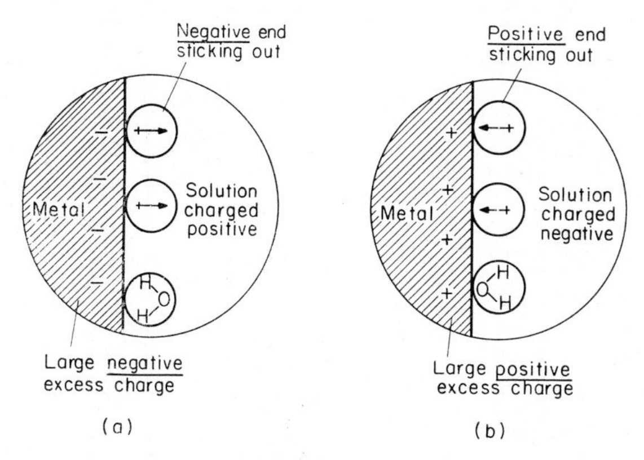

Fig. 2.8. Water molecules at a metal surface orient according to the sign of the excess charge on the metal.

It is easy to show, in a simple electrostatic model, that these oriented water molecules (fig. 2.9) give rise to a potential difference of:

$$\Delta\chi' = \mu(N_{\uparrow} - N_{\downarrow})/\varepsilon_r\varepsilon_0 \qquad (2.5)$$

where the $N_{\uparrow}$ represents the number of water molecules with their oxygens sticking out into the solution, the $N_{\downarrow}$, those in which the oxygen atom is touching the electrode, and μ the dipole moment of water (which, measured in the vapour phase, is $6{\cdot}2 \times 10^{-30}$ C m).

This dipole layer potential difference can be called a *surface* or adsorption potential difference. If, as will be seen, there are other substances adsorbed on the surface as well as water, their dipole moments will also contribute to the potential difference.

One can assume that adding new molecules to a solution, so long as they adsorb (for example, 2,6-dimethyl aniline) will interfere with the potential difference across the double layer—and hence (cf. eqn. 2.3) change the reaction rate. Raging corrosion (or electrodestruction) might, by a suitable additive, be moderated to dissolution at a negligible rate (see Chapter 9).

Let us recapitulate what has been established so far:

(1) There is an interphasial region of a few ångström where most of the action in electrochemistry occurs.

(2) Such interphasial regions, the electric double layers, are found wherever two phases adjoin; and there is always a potential difference across them which may range from a few millivolts to a volt or two.

(3) Further, 10^{-6} moles of excess charge per square metre is typical and gives rise to the tremendous electric field strength of 10^{9} V m^{-1}.

(4) There are two types of contribution to the potential associated with this field, one from the free charges at the interface, and one from the surface dipole layers.

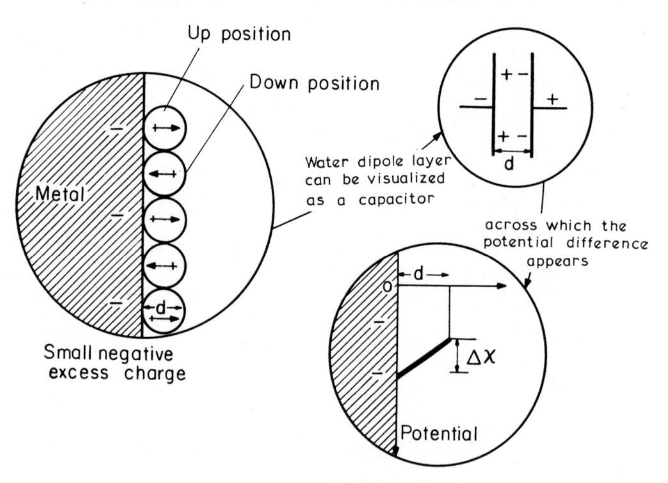

Fig. 2.9. The dipole layer at the surface gives rise to a surface potential difference $\Delta\chi$.

We must now consider a disturbing point: we cannot measure the absolute values of the potential differences of which we have been speaking so confidently. Picture the situation. One has, say, a sheet of copper dipping into a solution of hydrochloric acid; and one requires the potential difference (which we have asserted is in the range 10^{-3} V to 1·0 V) between the copper and the solution. The first thing, of course, is to connect one terminal of a high resistance voltmeter to the copper (fig. 2.10).

The trouble arises when one thinks what one has to do with the *other* voltmeter terminal, which is obviously to put another electrode (say, platinum) into the solution and connect it to that.

If we now read the voltmeter, it shows the *sum* of *three* potential differences, one at the copper–solution interface (the one we set out to measure), one at the platinum–solution interface, and one which is the contact potential difference between the copper and the platinum which effectively make contact through the external circuit.†

Of course, we could find the potential difference at the copper–solution interface if we knew each of the other two, or just their sum. But the trouble is that to measure either of the other two potential differences across phases (the platinum–solution one, or the platinum–copper one) would involve us in just the same series of vain attempts as the evaluation of the platinum–solution one we are talking about here! Each time we attempted to measure *one* interphasial (or double-layer) potential difference, we should involve two more.

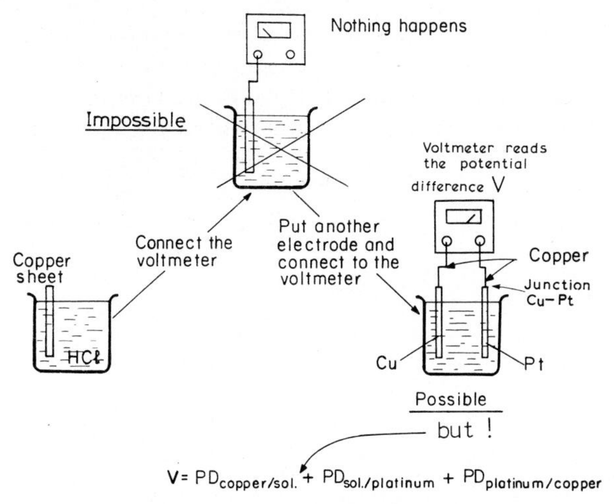

Fig. 2.10. Potential difference at *one* metal–solution interface cannot be measured. Only the potential *difference* between two electrodes can be measured; this includes *at least three* potential differences.

That we cannot actually measure absolute potential differences between interfaces, or across interphases, may seem to defeat the objective of applying solid state physics to electrochemical systems. But although we cannot actually measure the value at a metal–solution interface, we *can* measure the changes in it which accompany changes in the excess charge.

It is difficult to explain how we can measure a *change* in potential difference across a phase; but as it is basic to our discussion we must attempt it. Consider fig. 2.11, which shows a two-electrode system. It contains two instruments. One is a power source, which we can change at will, sending electrons into electrode B or extracting electrons from it. For this we use the other electrode, B. Electrode A is

† The same applies even more generally, when the other electrode is not copper, but, e.g., gold. Then, at the contacts of the copper wires from the instrument with the electrodes two potential differences appear. After summing, the effect of copper cancels out.

separated from electrode B, the one whose interface we propose to measure, by a high-impedance vacuum tube voltmeter. This instrument takes so small a current that it cannot have any appreciable effect on the potential of B.

At this point we introduce a new idea. The two double layers at A and at B behave differently towards electrons. It is difficult for electrons to cross the interface at B, while it is easy for them to cross at A. We are just supposing this at present; we shall give more explanation in Chapter 3. Also the contact potential difference between two metals (e.g., p.d. platinum/copper in fig. 2.10) is effectively independent of the current.

Now we change our power source so that enough electrons go into the circuit power-source → B → solution → A in such a way that *if they all piled up in B*, the change in B would be about one volt. Then, so long as we know that the electrons which we have sent from the

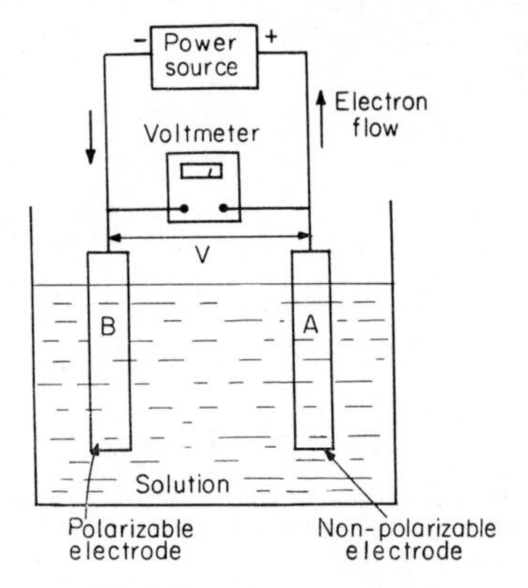

Fig. 2.11. Change of potential difference at one electrode can be measured by a voltmeter if the other electrode is a non-polarizable one, and if the change is caused by an external electric power source.

power source *do* all pile up at B, but pass very easily across A, we can say that the *change* in the potential difference applied by the power source is equal to the *change* in the potential difference across the double layer at B. We can forget altogether about the change applied to A, because we are assuming that when we apply an extra potential difference to A, the electrons just go straight across the double layer and don't accumulate to change the potential difference at A at all. (We have plenty of experimental reasons to believe that we can find a convenient interface of this kind.)

Two technical terms are introduced here:

Double layers such as that at B (resistive, difficult to get across) are called *polarizable*; and double layers such as that at A (conductive, easy to get across) are called *non-polarizable*.

A non-polarizable electrode, with the double layer in which the potential difference does not change with the passage of current across it, can be taken as a reference electrode for measuring the *change* of potential difference (which is often called just 'the potential'), at the polarizable electrode.

In reality, nearly all electrodes are more or less polarizable. There are only a few suitable (i.e., sufficiently non-polarizable) electrodes, one of which is the *saturated calomel electrode*, which consists of liquid mercury covered with calomel (Hg_2Cl_2) suspended in saturated KCl solution. This is non-polarizable if the current-density through it is sufficiently low (say, less than 10^{-1} A m^{-2}). The arrangement of fig. 2.11 can be used only in special cases, when a suitable reference electrode A can be found, and only for the very small currents at which it will remain polarizable.

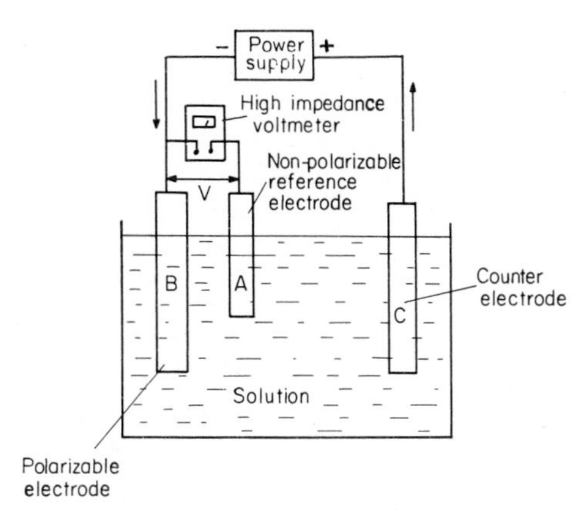

Fig. 2.12. Change of potential difference at the polarizable electrode, B, is usually measured in this way. The change is caused by passing current from the external power source by means of a counter electrode C, while its value is measured between B and A.

When the current is much larger, or when it is not possible to find a suitable non-polarizable electrode, we can use a three-electrode system (fig. 2.12). The current from the power supply does not pass through the non-polarizable reference electrode A, but goes through B and C, where C is an auxilliary counter-electrode. Now, the change in the current from the power source, produces changes of potential differences at the B and C interphases, but not at A. If we connect the vacuum-tube voltmeter between B and A, the change of reading ΔV on the voltmeter will now correspond to the change at B only, since there is no change at A.

So if we do have a polarizable electrode (B) suitably coupled with a non-polarizable one (A), we can measure the change in the potential difference of the polarizable electrode as recorded on the voltmeter. But what series of potentials does this change in voltmeter reading mean?

As shown previously (fig. 2.10) when we measure the e.m.f. of a cell the reading on the voltmeter represents the resultant of at least three separate potential differences:

$$V = \text{p.d.}_{M/\text{sol}} + \text{p.d.}_{\text{sol}/R} + \text{p.d.}_{R/M'}. \tag{2.6}$$

The same situation is shown in slightly different form in fig. 2.13. $\text{p.d.}_{M/\text{sol}}$ is the potential difference across the double layer of the working electrode (electrode B in figs. 2.11 and 2.12), $\text{p.d.}_{\text{sol}/R}$ is the potential difference at the reference electrode, $\text{p.d.}_{R/M'}$ is the potential difference at the contact of two metals R and M' (M' indicates that the metal M here is not at the same potential level as M), while V is the reading on the voltmeter.

What is, then, the meaning of a relative electrode potential? If we use the standard hydrogen electrode (SHE)† as the reference electrode for the relative electrode potential scale, what potentials are maintained constant when one measures a number of electrode potential in cells which always contain a standard hydrogen electrode?

The answer to this question is relatively simple if one breaks down the p.d. into the differences of two ϕ potentials (ϕ_α is the inner or Galvani potential of the phase α)

$$V = (\phi_M - \phi_{\text{sol}}) + (\phi_{\text{sol}} - \phi_R) + (\phi_R - \phi_{M'}). \tag{2.7}$$

This equation can be rearranged in the following way:

$$V = (\phi_M - \phi_{\text{sol}} - \phi_{M'}) - (\phi_R - \phi_{\text{sol}} - \phi_R). \tag{2.8}$$

† Platinum in a solution containing H^+ ions saturated with gaseous hydrogen under pressure of 1 atmosphere changes its potential with the change of H^+ ion activity (activity = concentration × activity coefficient) according to the Nernst equation

$$V_{H_2} = V^\circ_{H_2} + \frac{RT}{F} \ln a_{H^+}$$

and it is often called the equilibrium or reversible hydrogen electrode. The standard hydrogen electrode (SHE) is the hydrogen electrode in the solution with $a_{H^+} = 1$ at 298°K. It has the potential $V^\circ_{H_2}$. By convention this electrode is taken as the reference for the relative electrode potential scale, assuming that its potential $V^\circ_{H_2}$ is equal to zero. If the standard hydrogen electrode is connected with some other electrode to form a cell (as in fig. 2.11), and the reading on the voltmeter measuring the cell voltage is V, it is said that this other electrode has potential V versus the standard hydrogen electrode, or a potential V on the standard hydrogen potential scale. This potential V might be positive or negative, depending whether this electrode is the positive or negative electrode of the cell. For example, if the saturated calomel electrode (see table 5.3) is connected with SHE it is the positive electrode of the cell, and one can read $V = 0{\cdot}245$ volt on the voltmeter. Therefore, the saturated calomel electrode is said to have a potential $V_{\text{cal}} = +0{\cdot}245$ volt. However, a zinc electrode in solution with $a_{Zn^{2+}} = 1$ is the negative electrode in a cell with an SHE. The voltmeter reading is found to be $V = 0{\cdot}736$ volt. Hence, the zinc electrode potential versus SHE will be $V_{Zn} = -0{\cdot}736$ volt.

The potential difference at the metal–metal junction is constant, i.e., independent of a passage of current from the power source (fig. 2.12). Therefore, when we measure *changes* of electrode potentials, it is the changes of the *metal–solution* potential differences that we really find.

It appears reasonable, therefore, to identify the value of the *electrode potential* with the sum of the inner potentials in each bracket. The

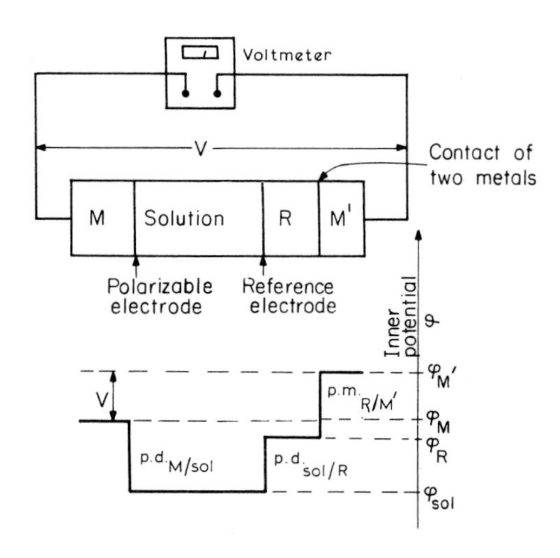

Fig. 2.13 The potential differences which contribute to the measured voltage V of an electrochemical cell with electrodes of two different metals M and R.

terms in the brackets show that the 'electrode potential' includes, besides the solution–metal potential difference, also a part of the contact potential difference between the different metals in the circuit

$$V = (\text{p.d.}_{M/\text{sol}} - \phi_{M'}) - (\text{p.d.}_{R/\text{sol}} - \phi_R). \tag{2.9}$$

For the reference SHE,

$$\text{p.d.}_{R/\text{sol}} - \phi_R = 0. \tag{2.10}$$

An electrode potential is not a metal–solution potential difference, it is a combination of two potential differences, one being that at the metal–solution interphase and the other being *part of* the metal–metal potential difference in one cell.

The structure of an interphase

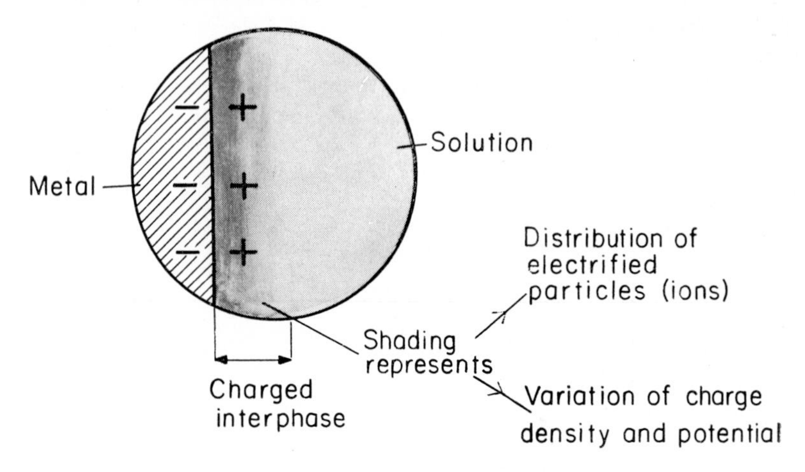

Fig. 2.14. Structure of the interphase.

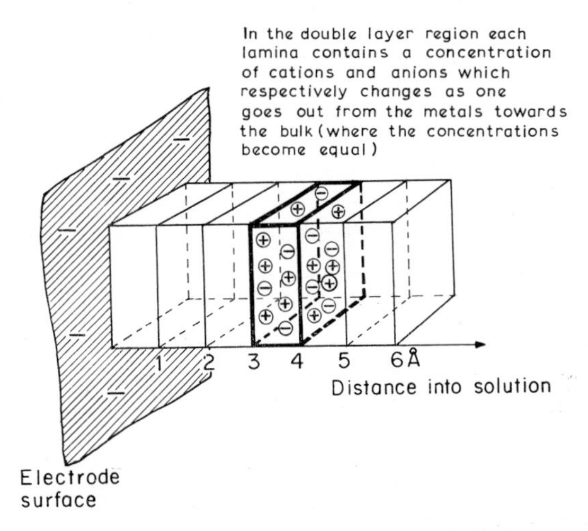

Fig. 2.15. Change of distribution of +ve and −ve ions is caused by the presence of excess charges at the electrode.

We shall try to determine how the concentration gradient of cations—and, quite separately, the concentration gradient of anions—varies as one goes outwards from the metal towards the bulk of the solution, where (far enough away from the electrode) there will be equal concentrations of both kinds of ion (fig. 2.15).

Thus, a perfectly-determined double layer structure would be one in which we knew the average concentration of cations and the average concentration of anions in each of the 1 Å thick layers all the way from the electrode to the main solution where the concentrations of cations and anions become equal, and the presence of the electrode has no effect.

Knowledge of the structure of the double layer is important in relating the potential difference between metal and solution to the *electric field strength* in the interphasial region. As we have said, the electric field strength determines the speed of electrochemical reactions.

Adsorption at the gas–metal and at the solution–metal interfaces

Adsorption is a well-understood effect in surface chemistry. When atoms form bonds with the metal on which they adsorb, it is known as chemisorption. A typical example is the adsorption of hydrogen upon the metal tungsten. Hydrogen molecules approach the metal from the gas phase, dissociate upon it and become strongly adsorbed in the form of atoms, bonded to the metal. In this system, the difference between the hydrogen in its own hydrogen gas phase (H bound to H as molecules) and the hydrogen adsorbed upon the metal (H atoms bound to W atoms) is distinct. The change takes place over a distance of about 1 Å as the hydrogen molecules come into contact with the metal and dissociate, bonding to the metal.

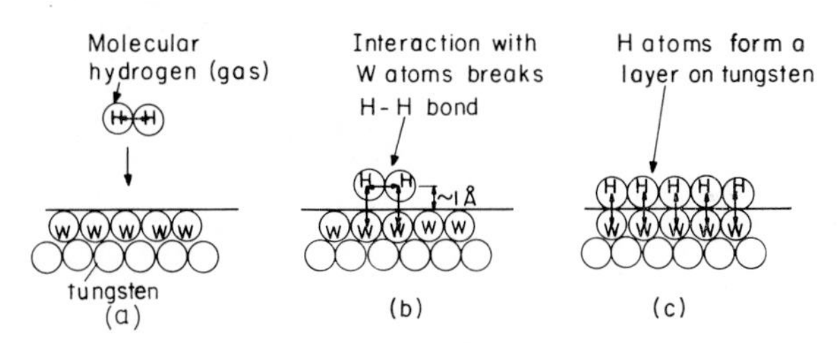

Fig. 2.16. Adsorption of hydrogen on tungsten.

The meaning of the term 'adsorption' in an electrochemical system is far less clear-cut. Thus (fig. 2.17), the changes in the concentration of the materials in the solution start *well before* the ions from solution are in contact with the metal. The electric field stretches a long way out from the electrode into the solution. It may be that the energy of interaction of the field of the electrode with an ion is significant compared with the thermal energy of that ion even at as much as 1000 Å away from the boundary upon the metal interface. Hence, even ions 1000 Å away from the metal side of the double layer may be preferentially affected by the electrode's field. If the interface of the metal has a *deficiency* of electrons on it (and so is positively charged), anions will be attracted, and cations will be repelled, and vice versa (fig. 2.17).

Actually within an ångström or two of the metal itself there will be something similar to the hydrogen–tungsten adsorption, that is, some degree of chemisorption, some *bonding* between an ion actually in contact with the metal, and the metal itself. The point is, that one

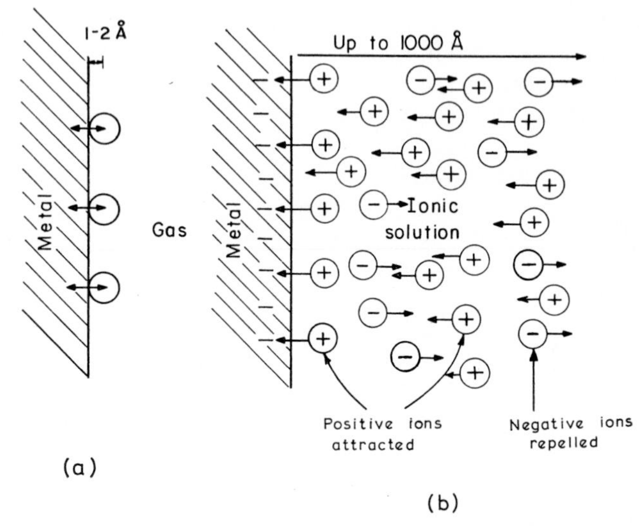

Fig. 2.17. (*a*) In gas–metal adsorption the interaction is limited to a few ångströms distance from the metal. (*b*) In adsorption from ionic solution the interaction extends further from the metal.

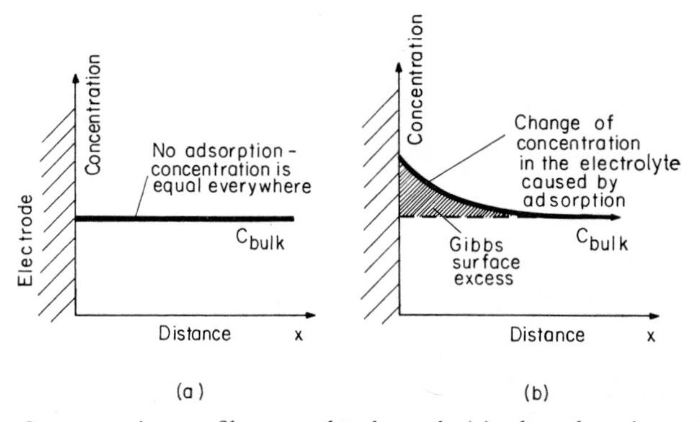

Fig. 2.18. Concentration profiles near the electrode (*a*) when there is no adsorption, and (*b*) when positive adsorption occurs.

cannot simply count up these chemisorbed particles and say, 'This is the adsorption.' One has also to take into account the other type of adsorption, the preferential sorting-out in solution which is illustrated in fig. 2.17. In this sense, then, electrochemical and chemical adsorption situations differ substantially.

Figure 2.19 shows an imaginary concentration profile for the preferential adsorption of, say, a chloride ion and the repulsion of, say, a sodium ion. Let us be imaginative and suppose that we could go on photographing 'time-average laminae' in the solution, as represented in fig. 2.15, and obtain information on how many ions of each type were in each particular lamina. Willard Gibbs suggested that a reasonable way

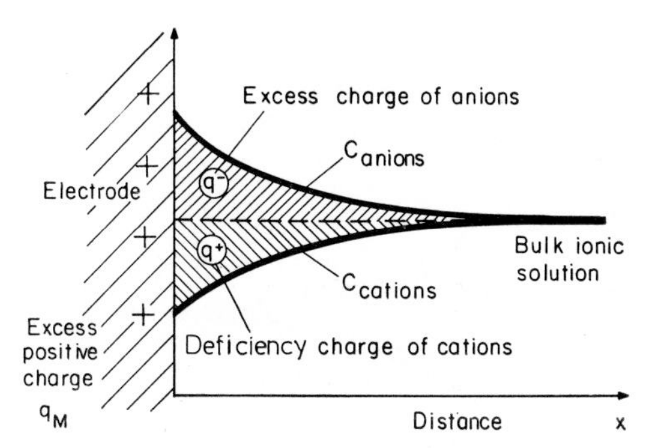

Fig. 2.19. In the double layer there is usually an excess of negative ions, and a deficiency of positive ions, if the electrode is positive. The curves $c_+(x)$ and $c_-(x)$ are not necessarily symmetrical.

of measuring the total adsorption at the interface would be to consider each lamina and the number of ions in it—with an area, say, 1 m²—and subtract the ions which would be there anyway if there had been no electrode on the left. He then summed the excesses (or deficiencies) in each lamina. We call the sum of the excesses the 'Gibbs surface excess', Γ_i, given by

$$\Gamma_i = \int_0^\infty \{c_i(x)-c_i^\circ\}\,\mathrm{d}x = \frac{1}{A}\int_0^\infty \{c_i(x)-c_i^\circ\}\,\mathrm{d}v = \frac{1}{A}\int_0^{n_i-n_i^\circ} \mathrm{d}(\Delta n_i)$$

$$= \frac{n_i}{A}-\frac{n_i^\circ}{A}, \qquad (2.11)$$

where $c_i(x)$ is the actual concentration at distance x and c_i° the concentration in the bulk of species i, n_i is the actual number of moles of species i in the interphase region, n_i° is the number of moles that would have been there if there had been no double layer, v is volume and A is the area of the interface.

We see from this equation that Γ_i can be either positive or negative, depending whether n_i is larger or smaller than n_i°.

There are two kinds of adsorption at the interface: electrostatic and 'contact'

In an ideal physicist's world, where the complications of chemical bonds did not exist, one might expect that the following would happen if one brought a solution into contact with a metal. As one increased the excess charge on the metal (making it, say, more negative) cations would be attracted and anions repelled, all nice and symmetrical, and the entire proceedings could be dealt with in terms of electrostatics. The Maxwell–Boltzmann distribution law would apply, with the energy

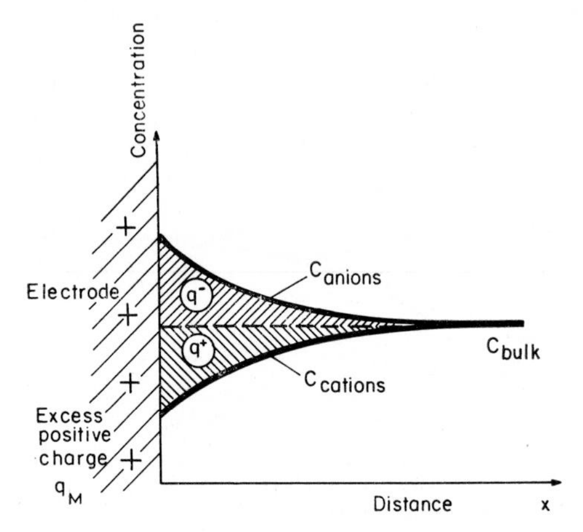

Fig. 2.20. Oversimple (idealized) picture of adsorption at an interface: anions are attracted and cations repelled.

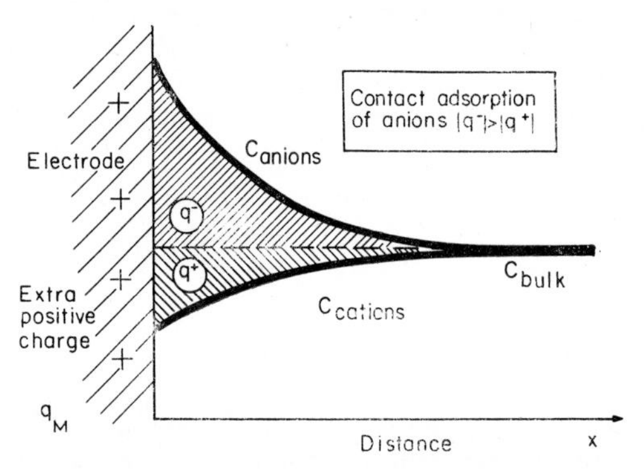

Fig. 2.21. The arrangement when there is also contact adsorption: anions are attracted in amounts greater than that needed to counter the +ve charge on the electrode. An excess of cations arises to make the charge on the solution side equal in amount (opposite in sign) to that on the electrode.

term containing an electrostatic interaction between the field due to the electrode and the solution. In fact, the physicist's simple idea nearly happens in some cases; and when the adsorption at electrodes takes place in this very simple way, we call it 'electrostatic adsorption' (fig. 2.20).

But real situations seldom turn out as simply as this, because at the interface there is some kind of *special* adsorption between metal and ions in the solution which is not subject to a discussion in terms of simple physics.

Let us not ask for the moment about just what other force is responsible for shattering the simplicity of an electrostatics approach. Let us note, however—for experiment indicates this—that there *is* such a specific (i.e., ion-dependent) force in operation at many interfaces. For every ten excess electrons in the surface of the metal, there will be a net excess of ten positive charges in the solution. But the point is, this is a *net* excess, and *it may not be arranged in a simple way* (fig. 2.21).

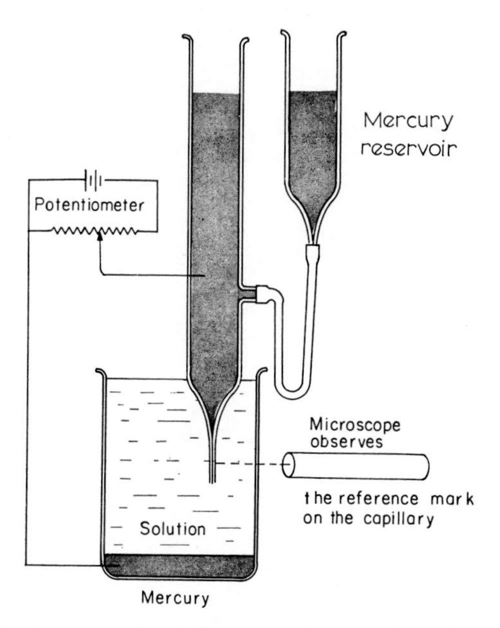

Fig. 2.22. Apparatus for rudimentary electrocapillary determination.

Surface tension–potential curves and determination of the excess charge at interfaces.—If one takes a column of mercury in a capillary tube and immerses it in a solution, it is found that with the electrical arrangement of fig. 2.22, the mercury can be made to go up and down at will by varying the potential difference applied between the mercury and the solution.

Elementary explanations of capillarity in terms of van der Waals molecular attraction are often pretty bogus, but it is certain that the depression of mercury in a capillary tube, and hence its position in the capillary of fig. 2.22, is directly related to the tendency of the free surface to occupy the smallest area that it can because of the attraction of the surface layers of molecules into the body of the liquid, and we need here delve no deeper than to say that this 'surface tension' (or 'interfacial tension' if another liquid is above the mercury) is a surface-shrinking effect.

However, in the electrochemical situation, we have not only the natural surface tension of the mercury but also the excess charge per unit area, with 100 mC m^{-2} as a typical value. The ions comprising the excess charges will hence *repel* each other, and try to expand the surface as much as possible. They are, therefore, acting *against* the tendency of interfacial tension to contract the surface. Hence, the more excess charge we send on to the surface, the more we lower the effective surface tension exhibited by the interface concerned, and the more we affect the capillary depression. This is the basis of the rise and fall of the mercury column in an electrocapillary device, as we send in or take out net charge. We are changing the *net* surface tension by giving charge to or extracting charge from the surface when we vary its potential by flowing charge in and out of it from a power source.

Figure 2.23 shows an ideal electrocapillary curve.

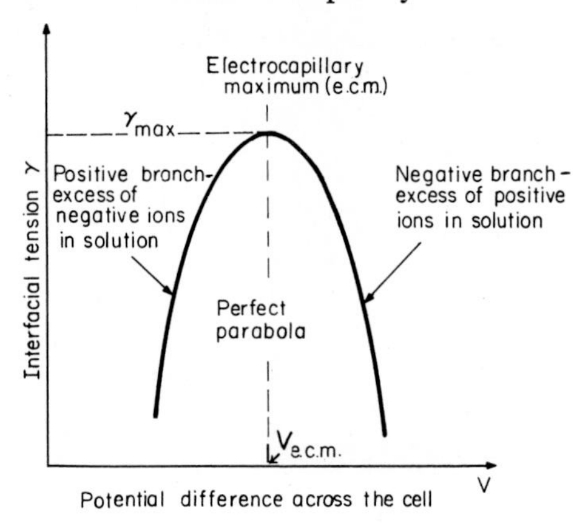

Fig. 2.23. The ideal electrocapillary curve.

It can be shown that the excess charge on the metal surface is given by

$$q_M = -\left(\frac{\partial \gamma}{\partial \Delta\phi}\right)_{T,p,N} \tag{2.12}$$

where q_M is the excess charge per unit area, γ the interfacial tension between metal and solution, and $\Delta\phi$ the potential difference between the metal and the solution.† (2.12) is known as the Lippmann equation.

† Since it is only *changes* here which we need, we are not affected by our inability to know the absolute value of $\Delta\phi$. Also, as shown on p. 34, for an experimental arrangement such as that of fig. 2.12 (or, if the current density across A is sufficiently small, that of fig. 2.11) the changes on the voltmeter reading are equal to the change of p.d.$_{M/\mathrm{sol}}$ or $\Delta\phi$ across this (*one*) interphase. In fig. 2.22, this would be the interphase in the capillary.

The electrocapillary curve for 0·1 M KCl solution is shown in fig. 2.24. A tangent was drawn at the point corresponding to +0·1 V. It has the slope

$$\frac{\Delta\gamma}{\Delta V} = \frac{17{\cdot}8\times 10^{-3}\ \mathrm{J\ m^{-2}\ V^{-1}}}{-0{\cdot}2} = -89\times 10^{-3}\ \mathrm{J\ m^{-2}\ V^{-1}}.$$

To get the excess charge q_M in C m^{-2}, one has to recall that 1 J V^{-1} $\equiv$ 1 C, so:

$$q_M = -(\text{gradient}) = 89\times 10^{-3}\ \mathrm{J\ V^{-1}\ m^{-2}}.$$

Computed in this way, Table 2.1 gives the charges for different potentials.†

The experimental electrocapillary curve (fig. 2.24) *is not quite an ideal parabola.* The experimental values for interfacial tension are *smaller* than expected when anions are in excess in the double layer (positive branch of the electrocapillary curve). The effect depends on the concentration of the solution (fig. 2.25) but also on the type of anions in the solution. In fig. 2.26 a series of curves for different kinds of solutions is given. On the negative branch, where cations are in excess in the solution, it makes no difference whether these are K^+ or Na^+. However, on the positive branch of the curve, anions exhibit the effect in the following order:

$$I^- > Br^- > Cl^- > OH^-.$$

One further point should be mentioned here. Since the gradient of the electrocapillary curve gives the value of the charge density (eqn. 2.12), and the value of the gradient at the electrocapillary maximum is zero, it follows that the excess q_M, at the electrocapillary maximum (e.c.m.) is also zero. Therefore, the potential at the e.c.m. is often called the *potential of zero charge* (p.z.c.), an important basic concept, firstly introduced by A. N. Frumkin. Figure 2.26 shows that the p.z.c. is different for different solutions, even when the same metal is used. It also depends on the metal.

† Electrode potentials are often referred to the reversible hydrogen electrode (RHE) in the same solution in which the measurement is done, instead of to the standard hydrogen electrode (SHE) (see footnote, p. 34), especially if a platinized platinum–hydrogen electrode in the same solution is used as the reference electrode. Usually, this is done to avoid errors in recalculation to the standard hydrogen potential scale, for which knowledge of the activity of H^+ ions in the solution is necessary. If the activity a_{H^+} is known the potential of the RHE can be readily calculated by using the Nernst equation: $V_{H_2} = 2{\cdot}3RT/F \log a_{H^+}$ ($V^{\circ}_{H_2} = 0$ by convention), and the measured electrode potential corrected for the difference. For example, the potentials of the mercury electrode given in Table 2.1 and fig. 2.24 can be recalculated to the standard hydrogen potential scale. Assuming that $a_{H^+} \approx 0{\cdot}1$ in 0·1 M HCl, $V_{H_2} = 2{\cdot}3RT/F \log 0{\cdot}1 \approx -0{\cdot}059$ volt.

To express mercury electrode potentials in fig. 2.24 on the standard hydrogen scale, all the potentials should be corrected for the difference $V_{H_2} - V^{\circ}_{H_2} = -0{\cdot}059$ V, i.e. all the values should be larger by 0·059 V.

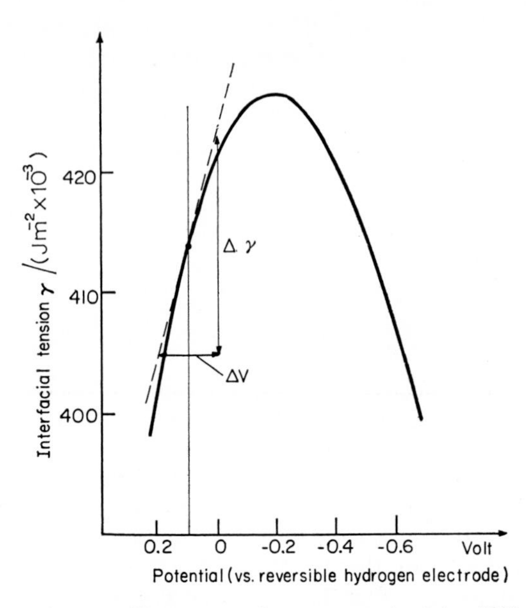

Fig. 2.24. The electrocapillary curve for mercury in 0·1 M HCl solution. The gradient at any potential gives the excess charge for that potential.

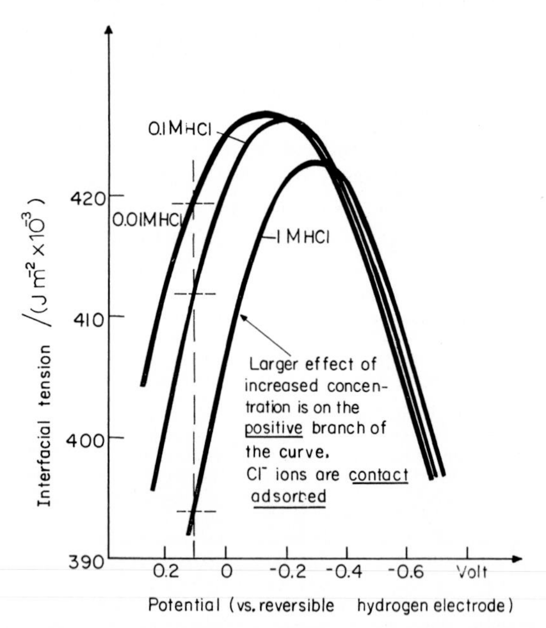

Fig. 2.25. The effect of concentration of HCl on the shape of the electrocapillary curve. For the same potential interfacial tension is different if anions are present at different concentrations.

The surface tension–concentration curve.—If we can determine the electrocapillary curve (fig. 2.24) for one concentration, we can determine it for a number of others. The only requirement for obtaining the charge is that for any given electrocapillary curve, the concentration (and temperature and pressure) be constant. Figure 2.25 shows a number of electrocapillary curves taken at different concentrations.

Table 2.1. Variation of charge density with potential difference of a mercury electrode in contact with 0·1 M HCl solution

Potential difference/V (vs. rev. hydrogen electrode)	Electrode-charge density, $q_M/10^{-2}$ C m^{-2}
0·2	13·8
0·1	8·9
0·0	6·5
−0·1	2·5
−0·2	−1·0
−0·3	−3·8
−0·4	−5·5
−0·5	−7·1
−0·6	−8·5
−0·7	−10·0
−0·8	−11·5

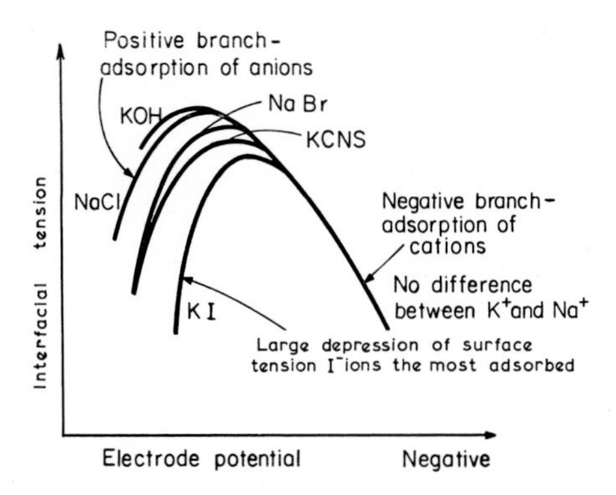

Fig. 2.26. Electrocapillary curves for various solutions.

Reference electrodes have already been met, in figs. 2.12 where electrode A has been described as 'reversible', and this means that thermodynamics *does* apply to it. However, a reference electrode reacts only with respect to one ion. Taking the 'hydrogen electrode': hydrogen gas is dissolved in the solution, diffuses up to the substrate (often a noble metal) with which hydrogen exchanges electrons, and dissociates, giving rise to adsorbed hydrogen atoms. These adsorbed hydrogen atoms then give up a charge and dissolve as hydrogen ions in solution. The opposite series of changes also occur and at the same rate so that the reaction is in equilibrium. The reversible hydrogen electrode, is said to be 'reversible with respect to hydrogen ions'. Correspondingly, there are electrodes which are reversible with respect to, say, chloride ions.

Now the point here is that the information that one gets from plots of electrocapillary curves at various concentrations can be shown to depend upon whether the reference electrode is reversible with respect to a cation, or to an anion.

Let us go back to the electrocapillary curves of fig. 2.25. Suppose that potential in this diagram means the potential of a cell in which the reference electrode is reversible with respect to a cation. Then, we draw a perpendicular to the abscissa at say $-0{\cdot}1$ volt. We take all the

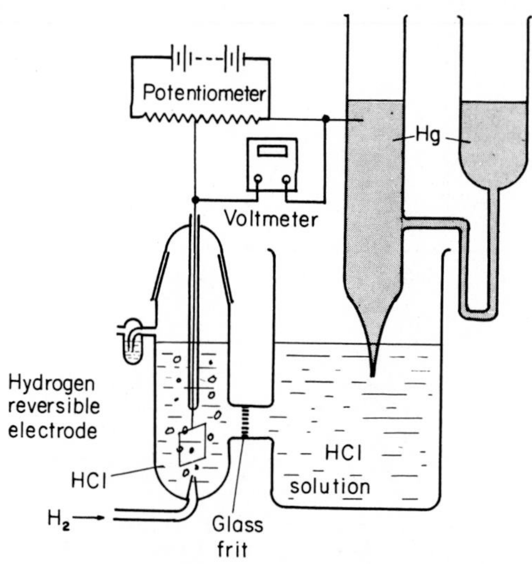

Fig. 2.27. Experimental arrangement for electrocapillary curves, with the reversible hydrogen electrode as the reference electrode. The interphase to which the following discussion applies is that in the mercury solution boundary in the capillary.

interfacial tension (γ) points which this perpendicular passes through, and plot log γ against the logarithm of the concentration of the ion in solution, the adsorption of which we would like to know (see fig. 2.28).

The relevant thermodynamic equation for determining the adsorption of either of the ions, (e.g., 'i') can be shown to be:

$$(\Gamma_i)_V = -\left(\frac{\partial \gamma}{2RT\, \partial \ln a_i}\right)_{p,T,j}. \tag{2.13}$$

This differential equation means the following: The Gibbs surface excess (p. 39) of the ion of species i at certain potential V is given by the slope of the interfacial tension at that fixed potential as a function of logarithm of the concentration of the ion, i. But for this information to be correct, at the reference electrode, the ion which reversibly discharges across the interface must be 'j' (and not i).

In a metal dipped into an HCl solution, if it is desired to obtain the surface excess of Cl^-, the reversible reference electrode in a cell such as 2.27 must be reversible with respect to H^+.

One can get the Gibbs surface excess at another potential by just moving over the potential scale (fig. 2.25), graphically obtaining $(\partial\gamma/\partial \log c)$ again for the next potential, and applying this value in equation (2.13), and so on. One can do this at any chosen potential, and thus get a plot of $(\Gamma_i)_V$ against V, so obtaining the Gibbs surface excess as a function of potential.

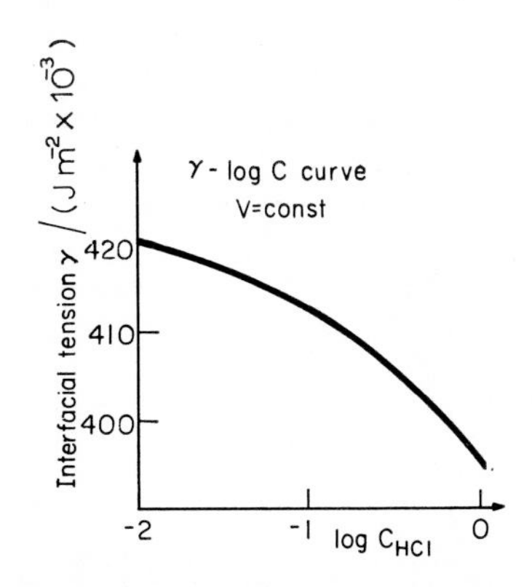

Fig. 2.28. Interfacial tension at constant potential, γ, versus log c.

So far we have shown how to get the Gibbs surface excess of one of the ions, say Cl^-, in the solution. To obtain its value for the other ion (assuming only, e.g., HCl to be present), we take the total excess charge on the solution, q_s, and apply the equation:

$$q_s = z_+F\Gamma_+ + z_-F\Gamma_-, \tag{2.14}$$

(since the Gibbs surface excess in the solution must consist of the surface excesses of cation and anion). Hence, if we have obtained the surface excess of the anions, Γ_-, the Cl^- in the HCl solution in contact with, say, mercury, and if we know from the equation

$$q_M = -\left(\frac{\partial \gamma}{\partial V}\right)_{T,p,N} \tag{2.12}$$

the total charge on the metal (or $-q_s$), we can obtain the surface excess of the cation, Γ_+, using

$$z_+F\Gamma_+ = q_s - z_-F\Gamma_-. \tag{2.14 a}$$

In fig. 2.29 typical plots of Γ_+ and Γ_- as a function of potential are shown.

Extricating the contact adsorption in the double layer from the total Gibbs surface excess.—So far, we have explained how we can get Γ_+ and Γ_-, the surface excesses of the cation and anion at the interface, respectively. These are totals, i.e., surface excesses (cf. eqn. 2.11) due both to electrostatic and other kinds of adsorption.

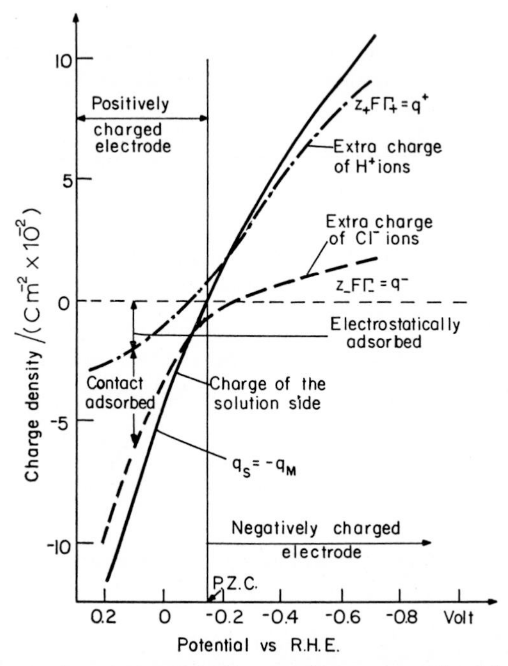

Fig. 2.29. Excess charge–potential diagram for mercury in 0·1 M HCl solution. Full line: total excess charge q_s; broken lines: excess charges due to cations and anions. The excess of Cl^- ions is larger than the deficiency of H^+ ions, because of contact adsorption of Cl^- ions.

This is all very well, but Γ_i is a macroscopic quantity, a typical thermodynamic quantity that does not invoke structures. If we determine the free energy change in a reaction we get an overall total value, and we know nothing about the contributions to it of various molecular bonds, their vibrations and rotations, which contribute to the total free energy which we determine thermodynamically. Likewise, the Gibbs surface excess by itself tells us nothing about the spatial distribution of particles in the solution.

How the Gibbs surface excess can be resolved into something *structurally* meaningful is a beautiful piece of reasoning, worked out originally by D. C. Grahame in the 1950's. First, one makes the assumption that the Gibbs surface excess for the *cation* is free of *contact* adsorption; it consists of electrostatic adsorption only, and has none of the specific adsorption referred to on page 40. There is a good reason behind this assumption. It is that if one takes electrocapillary curves for a series of solutions in which there is one anion and a series of different cations, the curves are all identical at the same concentration of salt. Hence, there is nothing *specific* about electrocapillary curves if the cations only are changed: it is when the anions are changed that one gets a change of electrocapillary curve characteristic of the ion (see fig. 2.26 where the −ve side is seen to be identical though different cations are adsorbed on it: the +ve side differs with the anions.)

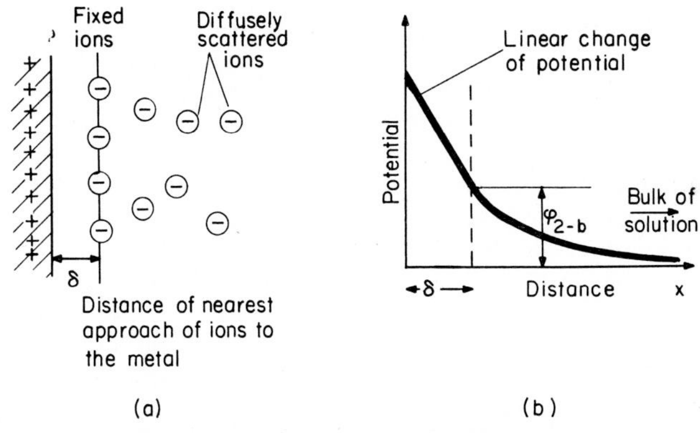

Fig. 2.30. Stern's model of the double layer. (*a*) Most of the ions are close to metal but some are also diffusely scattered further from the surface. (*b*) Potential–distance relation in Stern layer.

Figure 2.30b shows the supposed distribution of potential in the double layer. The sharp break in the potential–distance relation corresponds to the potential ϕ_{2-b}, the potential at the distance of nearest approach of cations to the metal, with reference to the solution. This physical meaning is 'the potential associated with electrostatic adsorption only'.

If we know the electrostatic relationship between Γ_+ and ϕ_{2-b}, then Grahame's assumption that Γ_+ is associated only with electrostatic adsorption allows us to get ϕ_{2-b} corresponding to any potential of the cell shown in fig. 2.27.

Thus the equation which relates ϕ_{2-b} to the adsorption (or, rather, to the Gibbs surface excess) involves Grahame's assumption about the cation being adsorbed on mercury *entirely* by electrostatic (long-range, coulombic) forces and having, therefore, no short-range attachment between ion and electrode. The equation which follows from this assumption relates the electrostatic charge in the diffuse layer (i.e., the total number (per m²) of *excess* cations) to the value of ϕ_{2-b}. It can be shown to be:

$$q^{+}{}_{\text{diffuse}} = +\left(\frac{\varepsilon_r \varepsilon_0 n^{\circ} kT}{2\pi}\right)^{1/2}\left[\exp\left(\frac{-z_{+}e\phi_{2-b}}{2kT}-1\right)\right] \tag{2.15}$$

where n° is the concentration of the salt (e.g., KCl, HCl, etc.) in the bulk of the solution in number of ions per m³, ε_r the dielectric constant in the double layer, z_{+} the number of positive charges on the cation, 1 for K^{+}, e the electronic charge, and k the Boltzmann constant.

So long as the conditions—concentration, temperature, etc.—are known, the diffuse layer charge, $q^{+}{}_{\text{diffuse}}$, is determined when ϕ_{2-b} is known. Now, we *don't* know ϕ_{2-b} as yet. But, if Grahame's assumption is true,

$$q^{+}{}_{\text{diffuse}} = z_{+}F\Gamma_{+}.$$

Now, we do know Γ_{+} from equation (2.14 *a*), based on the Gibbsian thermodynamic equation (2.13). Hence, we know $q^{+}{}_{\text{diffuse}}$. Thus, we obtain, from (2.15), ϕ_{2-b}. We can do this for any value of Γ_{+} and hence obtain a series of values of ϕ_{2-b}'s, each one corresponding to a different potential of the cell of fig. 2.27, and hence to the potential across the mercury-solution interphase of that cell.

Anions are supposed, on the Grahame picture, to be adsorbed in *two* modes.

One mode is electrostatic, like the cations. The anions which are thus adsorbed distribute themselves out into the solution, away from the electrode.

As to the other mode of adsorption for anions, they are adsorbed on contact with the electrode, something which does *not* appear to happen to cations. The adsorption of anions in contact with the electrode is called *contact adsorption* (also specific adsorption). Now Γ_{-} (the *anion total* Gibbs surface excess) is obtainable from the thermodynamic argument (eqn. (2.13)).

Then, $(\Gamma_{-})_{\text{electrostatic}}$ is obtainable by using:

$$q^{-}{}_{\text{diffuse}} = z_{-}F(\Gamma_{-})_{\text{el.st.}} = -\left(\frac{\varepsilon_r \varepsilon_0 n^{\circ} kT}{2\pi}\right)^{1/2}\left[\exp\left(-\frac{z_{-}e\phi_{2-b}}{2kT}-1\right)\right]^{1/2} \tag{2.16}$$

with the ϕ_{2-b} from a knowledge of Γ_{+} and the equation (2.15).

To obtain the amount of the anion *adsorbed in contact with the electrode*, i.e., not electrostatically distributed out into the solution but stuck to the metal, by forces characteristic of the anion, we take the difference

$$(\Gamma_{-})_{\text{contact}} = \Gamma_{-} - (\Gamma_{-})_{\text{el. st.}}$$

Thus,

$$\Gamma_{-} = (\Gamma_{-})_{\text{el. st.}} + (\Gamma_{-})_{\text{contact}}$$

Or:

$$\Gamma_- = (\Gamma_-)_{\text{distributed into solution}} + (\Gamma_-)_{\text{ion in contact with electrode}}$$

Thus:

$$\Gamma_{-\text{obtained from electrocapillary curve}}$$
$$= (\Gamma_-)_{\text{obtained from knowledge of } \phi_{2-b}} + (\Gamma_-)_{\text{contact}}.$$

Hence, $(\Gamma_-)_{\text{contact}}$ is obtained and for any potential for which Γ_+ and Γ_- thermodynamic data are known.

We can summarize the above arguments.

The thermodynamic equations (2.12), (2.13) and (2.14) allow us to find the charge upon the electrode and the Gibbs surface excess of each ion in solution from experiments on interfacial tension as a function of potential.

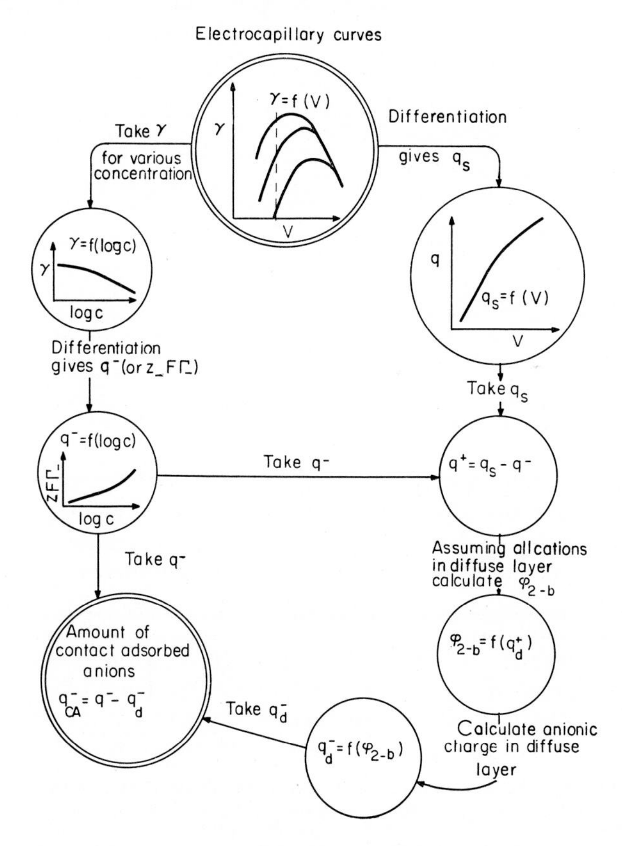

Fig. 2.31. Measurements and calculations involved in determining the contact adsorption of anions.

The reasoning is thermodynamical; and as long as the experimental conditions required by thermodynamics are followed, there is no doubt about the validity of the values of Γ_+ and Γ_-. When it comes to determining how much of Γ_+ and Γ_- are to be taken, from the structural point of view, as representing ions distributed out into the solution or as adsorbed in contact with the electrode, things get more difficult and less certain. However, by an argument in which it is assumed that the Gibbs surface excess for *cations* is electrostatic only, whilst that for *anions* is partly electrostatic and partly 'chemical' (or specific, or contact), it is possible to deduce from a value for the *total* Gibbs surface excess for anions to a value which is broken up into a contribution from anions stuck to the electrode, and a contribution from those distributed out into the solution.

We can now determine the structure of the double layer.—We have thrown in an assumption or two above, and hence what is now going to be stated should be looked at not as some kind of certainty, but as a rather probable piece of fairly mature electrochemistry, with some doubts still to be answered.†

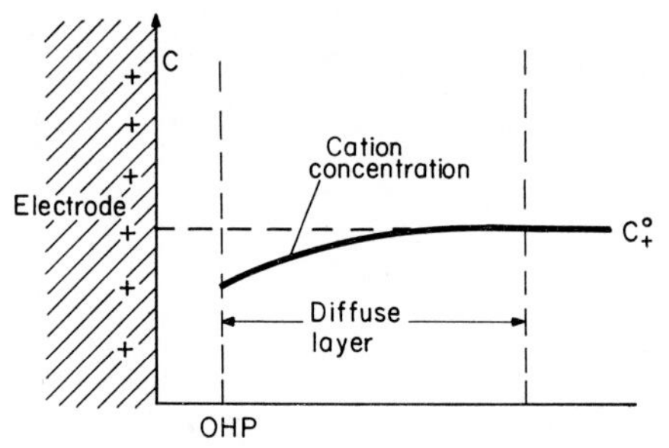

Fig. 2.32. Cation concentration profile in the diffuse part of the double layer. The 'outer Helmholtz plane' (OHP) begins the diffuse layer.

If we know the Gibbs surface excesses, Γ_+ and Γ_-, suitably broken up into contact and electrostatic adsorption, we can 'map' the double layer, in the sense that we can plot the concentration of ions as a function of distance from the layer. The arguments which lead to such a map are a bit complicated, but they can be sketched qualitatively.

First, consider the cations. We know the total amount of cationic charge by using the equation for Γ_+ and the total value of q_M. To fix the concentration of cations as a function of distance, one assumes the cations are distributed only electrostatically; this is justified because for a given anion one gets the same electrocapillary curve whatever

† The doubts are, of course, associated with Grahame's assumption. It does apply to cations of Group IA and IIA of the Periodic Table, except that it begins to break down a little for Cs^+. Its applicability to Tl^+ is limited; and to tetra-alkyl ammonium cations negligible. The present account is hence an approach and not a complete solution to double layer studies.

cations are present (fig. 2.26). One then invokes an equation for the dependence of the distribution of ionic concentration on distance, which is purely electrostatic, and this gives the *difference* of the anion and cation concentration as a function of distance. Knowing the value in the bulk (where they must be equal) one obtains the concentration as a function of distance. The result of such a plot is shown in fig. 2.32.

When it comes to plotting for the anion, one has to take into account the division of *its* adsorption into contact adsorption and purely electrostatic adsorption. One takes first the electrostatic part and plots that (on the basis of electrostatic charge–distance equations). Then the part which is 'in contact' with the electrode is considered to be placed at a distance from the electrode which corresponds to the radius of the anion. Thus, one has a map of the double layer, which shows its cation concentration and its anion concentration as functions of the distance from the electrode. Of course, any distribution of this type refers to one potential.

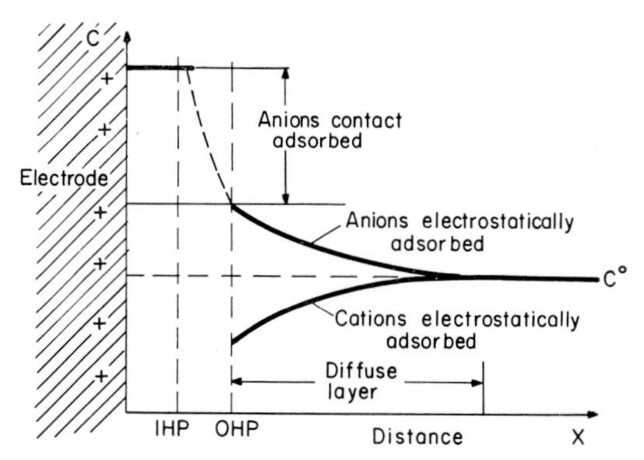

Fig. 2.33. Concentration profile for cations and anions inside the double layer. The inner Helmholtz plane (IHP) passes through the centres of the anions contact adsorbed.

How can we measure the adsorption of ions on solid metals involved in double layers?—The method which we have just outlined for mapping the structure of the double layer only applies if one can measure the interfacial tension between metal and solution.

This is clearly not helpful, however, to a metallurgist who wants to know why the addition of chloride ions to a solution in contact with iron breaks the protective film which can be made to form upon this metal, and causes it to corrode so violently. He wants to know what is the adsorption of chloride ions on iron containing a passive film.

A method for measuring the interfacial tension, and thus the Gibbs surface excess, upon *solids* is therefore one of great importance.

Such methods were not developed until the 1970's, when Beck; Gockstein; and Fredlein and Damjanovic all described methods whereby the *change* of surface tension with potential and concentration could be measured (cf. eqn. (2.13)). Only that of the latter workers will be described here. Its principle is as follows: If one takes a sufficiently thin electrode (a thin sheet), then that part of the surface energy which varies with the electric charge on the metal will affect the mechanical properties of the whole body. The surface skin of metal becomes more contractile, when the charge upon the surface is reduced; this contraction can be measured, and the surface tension then evaluated as a function of the potential. If the relation between surface tension and potential is known, the charge can be calculated (eqn. (2.12)).

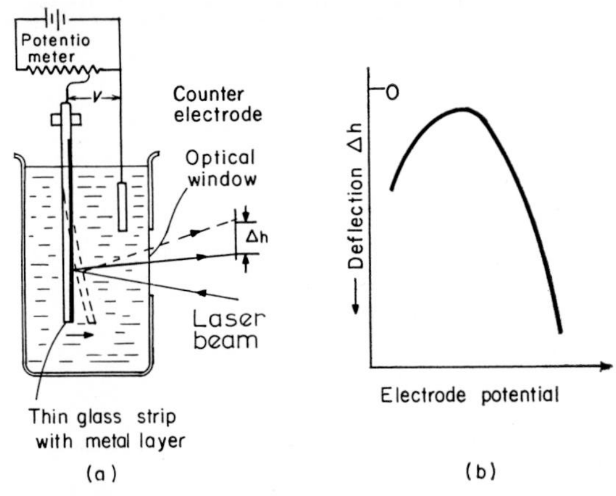

Fig. 2.34. (*a*) Apparatus for measuring the adsorption of ions at the solid–solution interface. (*b*) Deflection–potential curve for a solid is equivalent to an electrocapillary curve for mercury.

The apparatus is shown in fig. 2.34 *a*. It turns out that the base material on which the metal is sputtered has to be thinner than about 0·01 cm. The sputtered metallic layer is about 100 Å. Under these conditions, a change of charge of Δq causes a change in the length of the electrode, which gives a deflection of the reflected laser beam on the screen, Δh (fig. 2.34 *b*). Of course, once the change of surface tension has been obtained as a function of potential, the same kind of equations as have been used above for Hg can be applied to get the surface charge. Correspondingly, the electrocapillary curves can be repeated as a function of concentration, and the entire method of approach sketched above for mercury can be applied to the solid–solution contact. Hence, for this interface the same kind of information can be obtained as that for mercury.†

† But the possibilities are still less good than with Hg, because H and O tend to deposit on solid metals, thus interfering with the thermodynamic equations. Recent discussions of electrocapillary equations on solids, by Frumkin, and by Mohilner, may aid this situation.

The potential of zero charge (p.z.c.)

The potential of zero charge (p.z.c.).—The electrocapillary curve of fig. 2.24 has a maximum at which the gradient of the γ–V line is zero. Correspondingly, from eqn. 2.12,

$$q_M = -\left(\frac{\partial \gamma}{\partial V}\right)_{p,T,N} \tag{2.12}$$

and as we have seen, the potential of the maximum of an electrocapillary curve is the potential at which there is zero excess charge upon the metal (fig. 2.35).

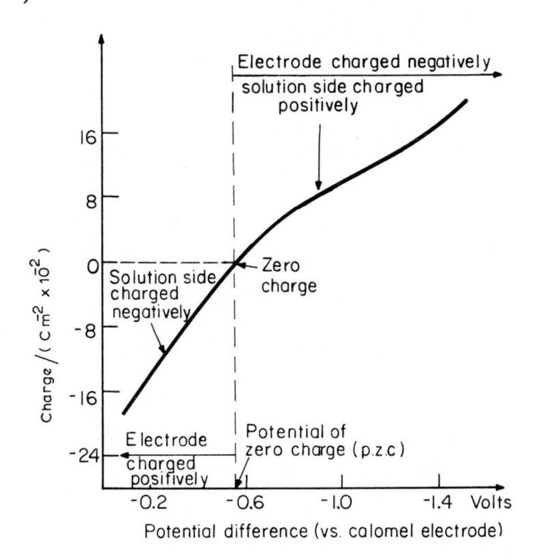

Fig. 2.35. A typical relation of the excess charge and electrode potential. Hg electrode in 0·3 M NaCl.

Why is this a potential of great importance? If we consider the adsorption of a cation, this will tend to be adsorbed at an electrode if its potential is negative, with respect to the potential of zero charge, but to be desorbed if its potential is positive. The potential of zero charge tends to represent the dividing line between adsorption and desorption for given ions at the particular electrode.

However, the potential of zero charge has a more general significance. It is the potential at which there is *no excess charge upon the metal electrode.*

Potentials of zero charge for various metals have not been determined extensively at the present time. Their determination was regarded as difficult until the 1970's. It is likely that the potential of zero charge will gradually establish itself as the principal reference potential in electrochemical science. There is already a tendency to speak of potentials of electrodes referred to the potential of zero charge as 'rational potentials'.

Table 2.2. The potential of zero charge on metals

Metal	Solution	$E_{p.z.c.}/V$ vs. SHE
Aluminium	0·01 M KCl	−0·52
Antimony	0·5 M Na_2SO_4	−0·20
Bismuth	0·01 M KCl	−0·36
Cadmium	0·01 M KCl	−0·92
Chromium	0·05 M H_2SO_4	−0·45
Cobalt	0·01 M Na_2SO_4	−0·32
Copper	0·01 M Na_2SO_4	+0·03
Gold	0·01 M Na_2SO_4	+0·23
Iron	0·005 M H_2SO_4	−0·37
Lead	0·01 M KCl	−0·69
Mercury	0·1 M NaF	−0·19
Platinum	0·003 M $KClO_4$	+0·41
Silver	0·05 M Na_2SO_4	−0·7
Zinc	0·5 M Na_2SO_4	−0·65

Can we now derive a model for the double layer?

The simple Helmholtz–Perrin model.—A simple model of the double layer was suggested by Helmholtz and Perrin at the end of the nineteenth century. This represents the double layer in terms of the simple 'plates of a capacitor' point of view. The metal, with its excess charge, is one side of the double layer; and the solution, with *its* excess

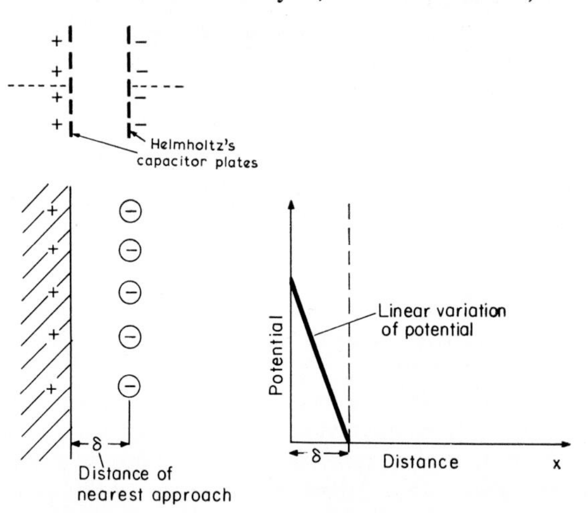

Fig. 2.36. Helmholtz's parallel plate capacitor model of the double layer.

counter charge, is the other side of the double layer (fig. 2.36). Of course, there *is* no real plate on the solution side, but it is imagined that the excess charges in the solution make up a layer of charge just as if they were attached to a plate there.

We already know that this picture is over-simplified, because only *some* of the charge in the solution is near to the metal and in the form of a plate; the rest is distributed out into the solution.

Let us start off with Lippmann's equation, equation (2.12), $q_M = -(\mathrm{d}\gamma/\mathrm{d}V)_{T,p,N}$, and integrate it. Then

$$\int \mathrm{d}\gamma = -\int q_M\,\mathrm{d}V. \tag{2.17}$$

But is q_M a function of V? For a simple Helmholtz double layer, we can assume that the analogy of the parallel plate capacitors will hold, and so,†

$$V = \frac{\delta}{\varepsilon_r \varepsilon_0} q_M, \tag{2.18}$$

where ε_0 is the permittivity of a vacuum, δ is the distance between the plates and ε is the relative permittivity of the material between the plates. Hence,

$$\mathrm{d}V = \frac{\delta}{\varepsilon_r \varepsilon_0} \mathrm{d}q_M. \tag{2.19}$$

Substituting for $\mathrm{d}V$ in equation 2.17, and integrating,

$$\gamma + \text{constant} = \frac{1}{2}\frac{\delta}{\varepsilon_r \varepsilon_0} q_M{}^2. \tag{2.20}$$

At the potential at which γ is a maximum $(= \gamma_{\text{max}})$, $q_M = 0$. So,

$$\gamma = \gamma_{\text{max}} - \frac{\varepsilon_r \varepsilon_0}{2\delta} V^2. \tag{2.21}$$

Now, the point of this deduction (due to Reddy), is to show that the simple Helmholtz model does contain a fair degree of truth: it gives an interpretation of the basic, idealized electrocapillary curve, a parabola.

Inconsistencies in the parallel plate model.—For one thing, as has been hinted, real electrocapillary curves are seldom symmetrical (cf. figs. 2.24 and 2.26). Therefore, there must be something incomplete about the Helmholtz–Perrin model for it to yield an inconsistent prediction on this important phenomenological detail. We shall learn later on that the model has not taken into account the *contact* adsorption of ions, which is *specific*, and which does not depend simply on something very simple such as the excess charge on the metal. Contact adsorption occurs largely when the electrode is positive, when the ions which adsorb are predominantly negative ions. In a more mature theory of the double layer than that of Helmholtz's first model, one must make some changes so that the anion-dependent shape in electrocapillary curves comes understandably out of the model.

† Here, the potential is referred to the potential of zero charge, i.e. $V = 0$ at $V_{\text{p.z.c.}}$

The other inconsistency is that, according to the Helmholtz–Perrin model, the capacitance would be independent of potential. One can see this by differentiating q_M in equation 2.18 with respect to V,

$$C = \frac{\mathrm{d}q_M}{\mathrm{d}V} = \frac{\varepsilon_r \varepsilon_0}{\delta} \tag{2.22}$$

Now ε is the relative permittivity and δ the distance between the plates; and in terms of Helmholtz model neither of these should vary with the potential of the electrode, the capacity of which is being measured. In reality, however, capacitances of the double layer are *not* constant with potential: a typical plot is given in fig. 2.37. This inconsistency shows we must change the model quite a bit before we can consider that we have a theory of the double layer consistent with the main facts.

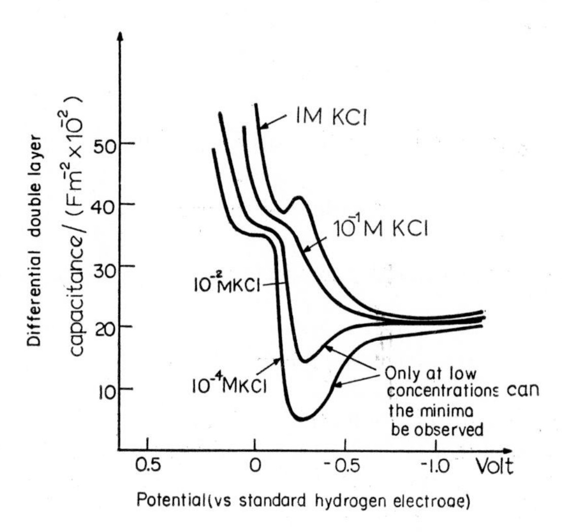

Fig. 2.37. Differential capacitance/mercury electrode potential relation for KCl solutions.

The charge cloud.—One approach to the structure of the double layer was made by Gouy and Chapman. They assumed that there would be no *sticking* of the ions to the electrode at all—no contact adsorption—and suggested that the rigidity of the Helmholtz theory, in which the excess charge on the solution was placed all in the same plane, and all in contact with the electrode, should give place to a *diffuse charge* model.

The Gouy–Chapman diffuse (or space charge) model of the double layer cannot be regarded as a complete theory. One discrepancy is that the calculated capacitance of the double layer to which the model gives rise varies too sharply with potential, and in the wrong way (fig. 2.39). However, we must not discard the Gouy–Chapman charge cloud theory, because it *will* apply to those ions which (fig. 2.30a) are *not* stuck to the double layer; for these the energy of interaction of the electrode's electric field with the ionic charge is of the same order as the thermal energy of interaction. For a treatment of the diffuse, or entirely electrostatic part of the double layer, in fact, the Gouy–Chapman model is fine.

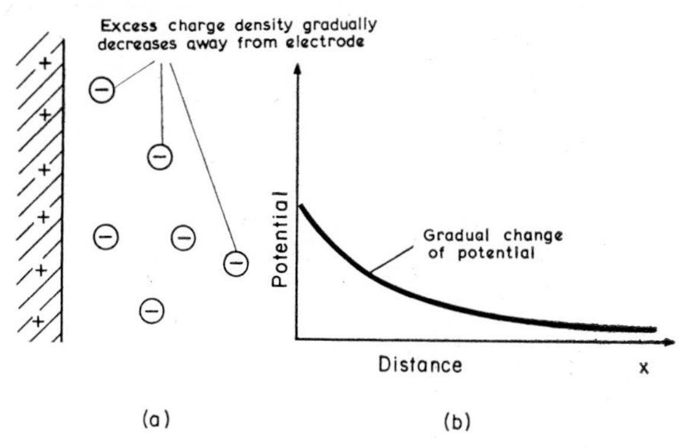

Fig. 2.38. Gouy–Chapman model of the double layer.

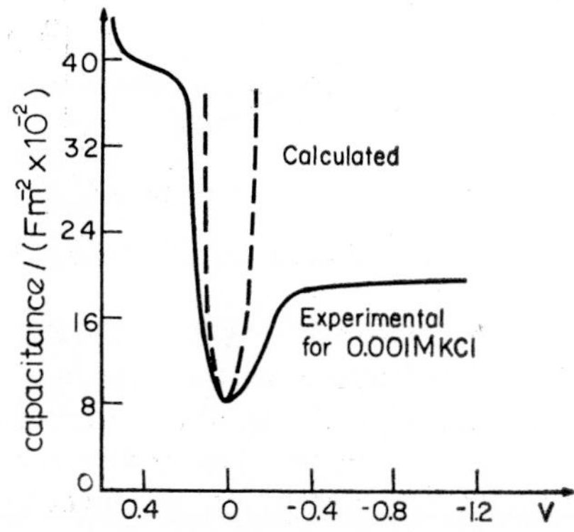

Fig. 2.39. Experimental capacitance–potential curve, and that calculated using the Gouy–Chapman model. Close to the minimum of the curve, agreement is fairly good. Potentials are referred to the reversible hydrogen electrode.

We quote here two equations from the Gouy–Chapman theory because they will be useful to us later on. One is the equation for the dependence of potential upon distance:

$$\phi_x = \phi_{2-b} \exp(-\kappa x), \tag{2.23}$$

where ϕ_x is the potential at a distance outside the plane which runs through cations at their distance of closest approach to the electrode, (O.H.P.), κ is a parameter which is calculable if the concentration of ions in the solution is known, and x is the distance out from the electrode into some lamina in the solution (see fig. 2.40).

The second equation relates the net electric charge on the diffuse layer to the potential at the plane of nearest approach of the hydrated ions to the electrode, ϕ_{2-b}. When we were finding the difference between the contact and electrostatic parts of the anionic charge (p. 50), we had to express the charge on the diffuse layer as a function of ϕ_{2-b}, and this enabled us (knowing ϕ_{2-b} from Γ_+) to split up the total anion excess into that due to contact adsorption and that out in the diffuse layer. Now, there is also an equation for the *net* charge on the diffuse layer, taking into account both cations and anions. This is

$$q^{\pm} = -2\left(\frac{\varepsilon_r \varepsilon_0 n^{\circ} kT}{2\pi}\right)^{\frac{1}{2}} \sinh\left(\frac{ze\phi_{2-b}}{2kT}\right). \qquad (2.24)$$

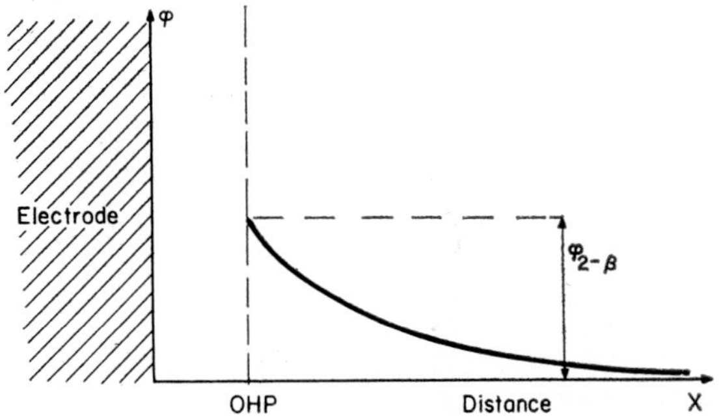

Fig. 2.40. Change of potential with distance in the diffuse part of the double layer.

Water structure on the electrode.—It has already been mentioned (p. 29) that the potential difference at the interface involves not only the contribution due to the ionic charge at and near the surface, and the potential difference described in the Helmholtz theory; there is also the effect of water molecules present on the electrode. These water molecules can be regarded as dipoles,† oriented one way or the other according to whether the electrode is positive or negative with respect to the potential of zero charge (fig. 2.8).

The electric capacitance of the double layer.—In fig. 2.37, for the capacitance–potential plot, one sees that it is only over a certain potential range on the negative side that the capacitance has a constant value,

† The structure may well be less simple than this. For example, there may be structure among the dipoles, perhaps dimerization, or some two-dimensional network formation. But as a starter, individual dipoles oriented in two positions ('up' and 'down') by the electrode charge, seems worth a try.

independent of the potential. This value is called by electrochemists 'the capacitance of the double layer'. The associated potential range, at least on mercury electrodes, is large, as electrochemical potential ranges go, as much as 1000 mV (see Table 2.3). Moreover, there is something very interesting about the value of the capacitance in the constant double layer region. The value is *independent* of the ions which make up the 'other side' (the solution side) of the double layer.

Table 2.3. The differential capacitance for mercury electrode in 0·001 M NaF solution on the negative side of the potential of zero charge

Potential/V (vs. normal calomel electrode)	Capacitance/(F $m^{-2} \times 10^{-2}$)
−0·8	16·2
−0·9	16·0
−1·0	15·5
−1·1	15·0
−1·2	14·8
−1·3	15·0
−1·4	15·3
−1·5	16·0
−1·6	16·1
−1·7	17·0
−1·8	18·0

Now, this is not what one would expect. According to the Helmholtz picture of equation 2.18, one would think that δ would be the distance between the electrode and the centres of the ions on the solution side, and this would *vary with the radius of the ions*. How can the constancy of the capacitance be explained?

What we would seem to need is a layer of water molecules around the ions of a thickness such that it compensates for the varying radii of the ions. However, the radii of ions taking part in double layer capacitances vary from about 0·66 Å to about 2·2 Å. An equivalent variation of some other factor to make the thickness of the double layer, δ, in equation 2.18, come out 'just constant'—so that the double layer capacitance would indeed be constant as observed—seems improbable.

Suppose that we complicate the picture a little. This may enable us to discover why it is that the capacitance is always about 160 mF m^{-2}, although the ionic radius would seem to vary quite widely. Let us suppose that our layer of water molecules is there (see p. 29); and also that the ions themselves, at least those cations which take part in the double layer, are hydrated (in fig. 2.41).

Now, let us assume that this configuration is changed into what may be called 'two double layers in series'. The idea is shown in the diagram. To the first (water) dielectric, let us assign a relative permittivity (dielectric constant) of, say 5. To arrive at this, we imagine that for the most part the water molecules on the electrode side are 'saturated'. Hence, they give a relative permittivity which is less than if they were free to turn under an applied field as they are in water.

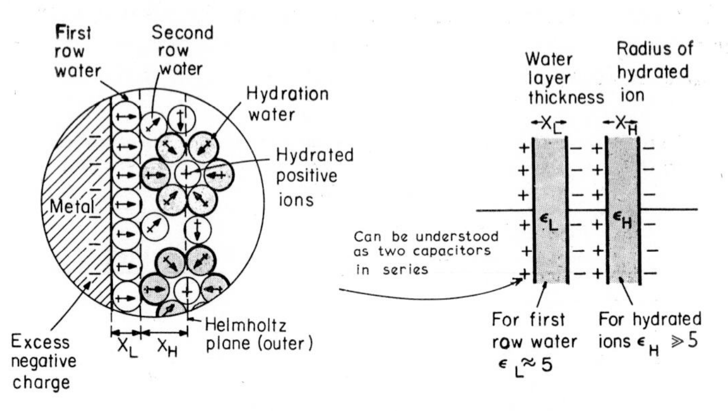

Fig. 2.41. Double layer consisting of a layer of water dipoles and ions is equivalent to two capacitors in series.

This is the sort of value for the dielectric constant which one would observe if one attempted to measure it at very high frequencies, above the range in which there would be an orientation of water dipoles. Orientation can take place only if the applied alternating frequency is less than about 10^9 Hz†, so that at about 10^{11} Hz we shall measure the relative permittivity we want, unaffected by orientation polarization, and hence fitting for the dielectrically-saturated water on the electrode. This has the value about 5, as shown by Smythe and others.

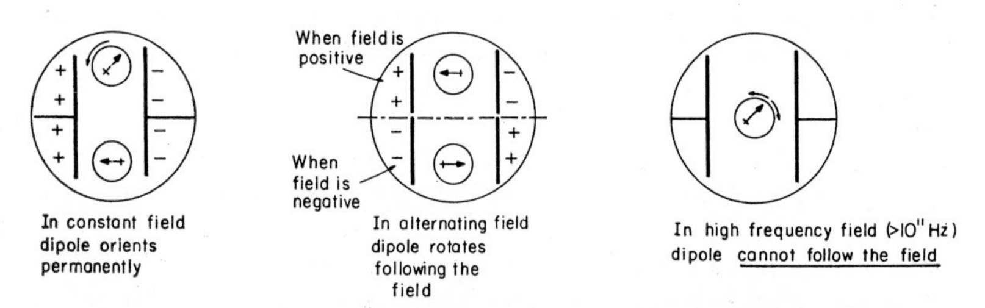

Fig. 2.42. Orientation of dipoles in constant and alternating fields.

The relative permittivity in the second layer, and further layers of water out from the electrode, will be greater and vary with distance. If we go far enough out, it is bound to rise to the ordinary relative permittivity of water, which is 80 at 25°C. But near enough to the

† At frequencies *lower* than this the dipoles are able to dance to the tune of the field. At higher frequencies, they cannot keep up.

electrode, some partial saturation of the dielectric will remain, and then we shall find a value much less than 80 (fig. 2.43).

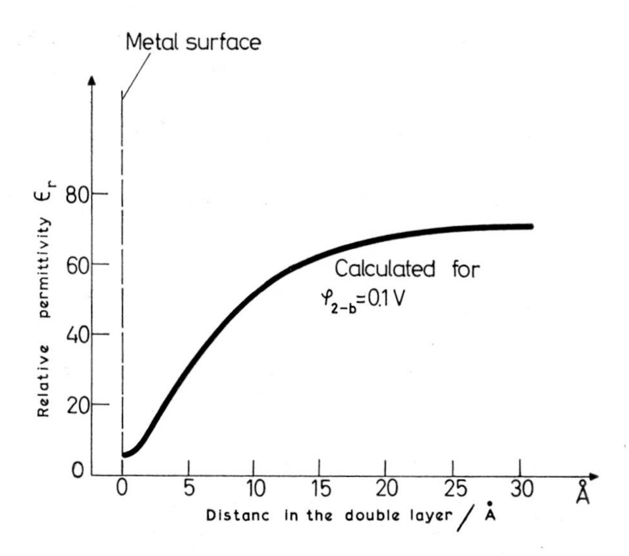

Fig. 2.43. Relative permittivity as a function of distance in the double layer.

The effective capacitance C of two capacitances C_1 and C_2 in series is given by $1/C = 1/C_1 + 1/C_2$. Thus, if the overall differential capacitance of the double layer is C, then, using equation (2.22) for each capacitance (fig. 2.41)

$$\frac{1}{C} = \frac{1}{C_{\text{water layer}}} + \frac{1}{C_{\text{Helmholtz layer}}} = \frac{d_{H_2O}}{\varepsilon_0 \varepsilon_{H_2O}} + \frac{(\delta - d_{H_2O})}{\varepsilon_0 \varepsilon_H} \quad (2.25)$$

or

$$\frac{1}{C} = \frac{1}{\varepsilon_0}\left[\frac{d_{H_2O}}{\varepsilon_{H_2O}} + \frac{(\delta - d_{H_2O})}{\varepsilon_H}\right]. \quad (2.26)$$

Here, ε_{H_2O} is the relative permittivity of adsorbed water dipole layer ($\varepsilon_{H_2O} \approx 5$), ε_H is that of the medium between the water layer and outer Helmholtz plane ($\varepsilon_H > 40$), d_{H_2O} is the thickness of the water dipole layer, and $(\delta - d_{H_2O})$ is the thickness of the remaining layer, representing the second capacitor.

We now begin to understand something about the constancy of the capacitance, for if $\varepsilon_{H_2O} = 5$ its value is much smaller than ε_H outside the first layer of water molecules (fig. 2.43). Consequently, $(\delta - d_{H_2O})/\varepsilon_H$ is substantially less than $d_{H_2O}/\varepsilon_{H_2O}$, so as an approximation one can omit the second term in the bracket of equation (2.26.) Then, in so far as the first term only is significant, we just have a water capacitor. This argument explains why the capacitance of the double layer does not depend on the ion present (cf. Watts–Tobin, Parsons and Mott).

In the approximate equation $1/C = d_{H_2O}/\varepsilon_0\varepsilon_{H_2O}$, if we take $\varepsilon_{H_2O} = 5$ and $d_{H_2O} = 2{\cdot}8 \times 10^{-10}$ m, then since $\varepsilon_0 = 8{\cdot}85 \times 10^{-12}$ F m^{-1} we get

$$C = \frac{5 \times 8{\cdot}85 \times 10^{-12}}{2{\cdot}8 \times 10^{-10}} = 159 \times 10^{-3} \text{ F m}^{-2},$$

which is very close to the experimental value.

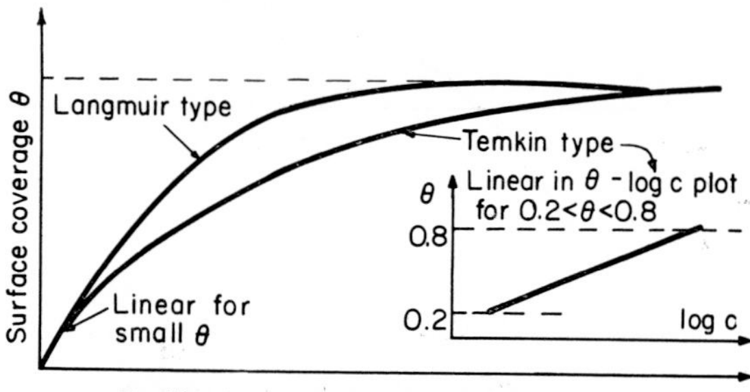

Fig. 2.44. The Langmuir type isotherm and the Temkin type isotherm.

Isotherms for Ionic Adsorption on Electrodes.—An adsorption isotherm is a relation between the degree of coverage on an electrode and the concentration of ions in solution. Its general shape is as shown in fig. 2.44. Adsorption isotherms are the real test of the physical chemistry of adsorption. However, in an electrochemical situation one has not only the coverage–concentration relation to compare with experiment, but also the coverage–electric charge relation at constant concentration in the solution. Adsorption isotherms should, therefore, be a rather better test in an electrochemical than in a chemical situation, of the model-assumptions which one makes beneath them.

An isotherm which has been used as a test of double layer theories is that based upon some work carried out by Bockris, Devanathan, and Muller (B.D.M.) in 1963, and improved by Wroblowa, Kovac, and Bockris in 1965. This isotherm begins with a great simplification; the charge-cloud part of the double layer is left out of things, and all the charge is assumed to be either in the 'outer Helmholtz plane' (fig. 2.45) or in the 'inner Helmholtz plane'. But a distinction is made between contact-adsorbed ions and those which are adsorbed electrostatically out of direct contact with the electrode (although, for simplicity, we assume that they are all on a layer close to the electrode†).

† It can be shown that this is in fact how things are: most of the electrostatically adsorbed ions do get compressed to a layer near, but not in contact with, the electrode, when the solution concentration is above 1 M.

The best-known isotherm is Langmuir's. It states that the relation between the fraction, θ, of a solid surface covered with some entity, i, and the concentration of particles in the gas phase (or solution), c_i, will be:

$$\theta = \frac{Kc_i}{1+Kc_i}, \tag{2.27}$$

where K is an equilibrium constant. Langmuir's model is essentially simple. The particles land on the electrode from the gas or the solution and stick to the electrode. But they also evaporate back into the solution or gas atmosphere. If the two rates, of evaporation and of condensation, are equal, we get equation 2.27.

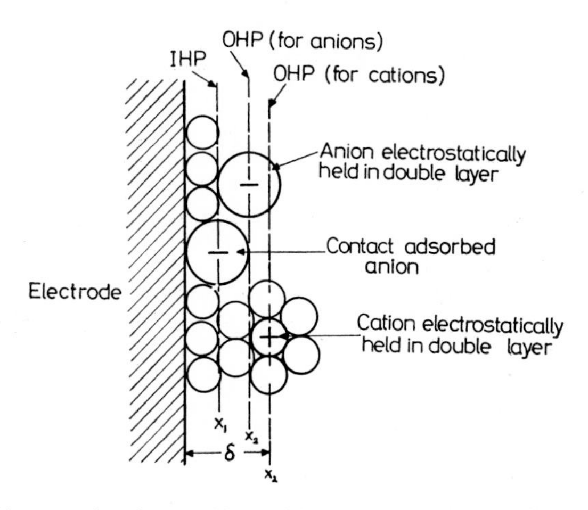

Fig. 2.45. Diagram showing position of ions at beginning of discussion of BDM isotherm.

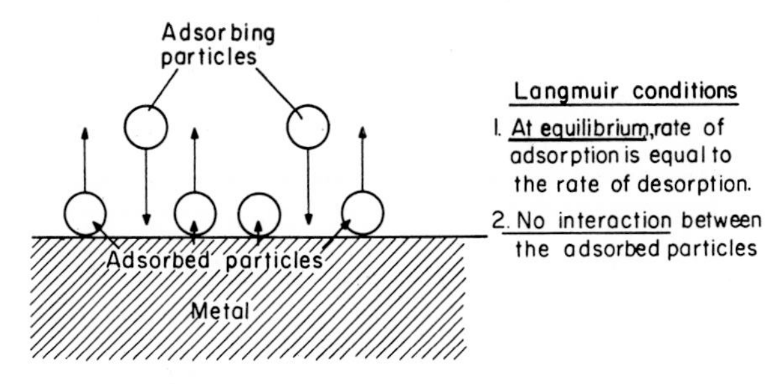

Fig. 2.46. Langmuir type adsorption.

In Langmuir's model, the ions are assumed not to interact with each other. Thus, if θ increases and the interionic or intermolecular forces between the ions get more intense, K does not change; it is independent of the concentration of ions in solution, and the coverage of the electrode.

Some authors, including Langmuir himself and in particular Frumkin and Temkin, tried to take into account the dependence of the K (in eqn. 2.27) upon potential and θ. If we can take into account the interactions between the adsorbing ions (fig. 2.47), we can perhaps modify the simple Langmuir isotherm, and obtain a θ-concentration relation (cells of an 'isotherm') which could be expected to apply to the adsorption of ions. Thus, Langmuir's isotherm would not apply because clearly ions *do* interact with each other when they adsorb, and hence K will not be constant.

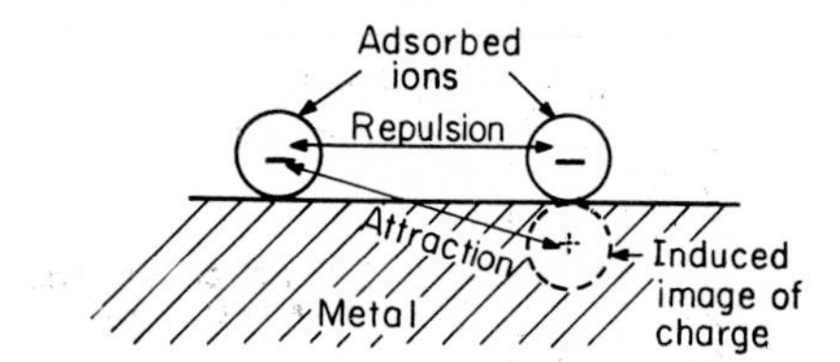

Fig. 2.47. Interactions between two adsorbed ions.

What will be the energy required to promote ions from the layer in the outer Helmholtz plane in fig. 2.48 to the inner Helmholtz plane?

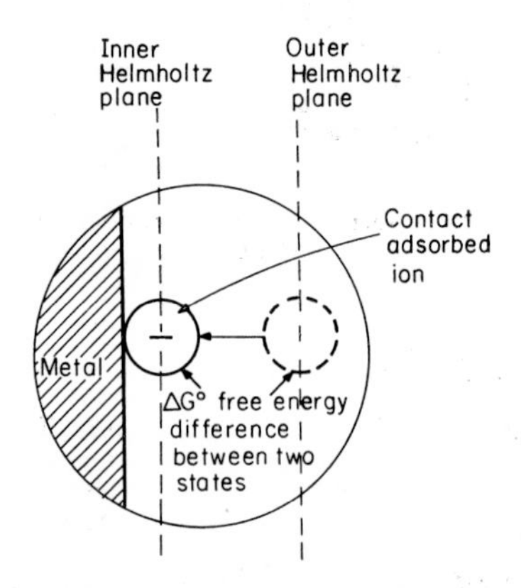

Fig. 2.48. Free energy change for contact adsorption.

We shall have to take two kinds of work into account. For example, there will be the electrostatic work which will be done in promoting the ions from the outer Helmholtz plane to the inner Helmholtz plane (see fig. 2.48). This will be given by an equation of the type field times distance. The field will be $q_M/\varepsilon\varepsilon_0$. The charge is e, and so the force is $q_M e/\varepsilon\varepsilon_0$. The 'force times distance', therefore is

$$W_{\text{el}} = \frac{q_M e(x_2 - x_1)}{\varepsilon_r \varepsilon_0} \tag{2.28}$$

where x_2 and x_1, are the positions of the outer and inner Helmholtz planes.

We must also account for the electrostatic interaction between the ions which are adsorbing and thus (being of like sign) repelling each other. There is a good deal of algebra in the calculation. One finally obtains a relation for the work done which is of the form

$$W_{\text{interact}} = A\theta^{3/2} - B\theta^{5/2}, \tag{2.29}$$

where A and B are known constants, and θ is the coverage with contact adsorbed ions. If one knows, thus, the basic interaction laws and the work done in promoting the ions from the outer Helmholtz plane into the inner Helmholtz plane, one can use the Maxwell–Boltzmann law and write:

$$\frac{n_{IHP}}{n_{OHP}} = \exp(-\Delta G^\circ/RT), \tag{2.30}$$

where the n_{IHP} is the number of ions in the inner Helmholtz plane, which are under contact adsorption conditions, and n_{OHP} is the number of ions in the outer Helmholtz plane.

The final equation given by the BDM isotherm is:

$$n_{CA} = (1-\theta)\frac{N_0 2r_i}{1000} a_i \exp\left[-\frac{\Delta G^\circ{}_c}{RT} + \frac{q_M e(x_1 - x_2)}{\varepsilon_r \varepsilon_0 kT} - \frac{e^2 r_i^2 \pi^{7/2} n_{CA}{}^{3/2}}{4\varepsilon_r \varepsilon_0 kT}\left(1 - \frac{3}{4}\frac{\pi^3}{15} r_i^2 n_{CA}\right)\right]. \tag{2.31}$$

Here n_{CA} is the number per square metre of contact adsorbed ions, a_i is the activity of the solution, r_i is the radius of the ion, N_0 is the Avogadro constant. The ΔG_c° symbol is the standard free energy of interaction (chemical interaction) of an individual ion undergoing contact adsorption, without taking into account the effect of its interaction with the other ions, i.e., it is the standard free energy of adsorption when the coverage, θ, tends to 0. The other two terms in the exponent correspond to W_{el} and $W_{\text{interaction}}$.

Wroblowa and Kovac showed that equation (2.31) can be expressed when $q_M = 0$ (p.z.c.), in the form:

$$\log a_\pm - \log \frac{\theta}{1-\theta} = C + B\theta^{3/2} \tag{2.32}$$

where

$$B = -\frac{\pi^{7/2}e^2r_i^2}{2.3\,.\,4\varepsilon_r\varepsilon_0 kT}\left(\frac{q_{\max}N}{F}\right)^{3/2} \tag{2.33}$$

and

$$C = \frac{\Delta G_c{}^\circ}{2\,.\,3RT} - \log\left(\frac{2r_iF}{1000q_{\max}}\right). \tag{2.34}$$

Equation (2.32) should represent the straight line if $\log a_\pm - \log\theta/(1-\theta)$ is plotted against $\theta^{3/2}$. The gradient of the line gives B, while the intercept at $\theta = 0$ gives C. Since B can be calculated from equation (2.34) this provides a good test for the theory. Besides that, the intercept of the experimental straight line gives the numerical value for C.

By using the experimentally obtained C and known numerical values for other factors in equation (2.32), the $\Delta G_c{}^\circ$, free energy of adsorption at zero coverage ($\theta = 0$), can be estimated. Figure 2.49 and Table 2.4 show the agreement obtained by testing the BDM isotherm with eqn. (2.32).

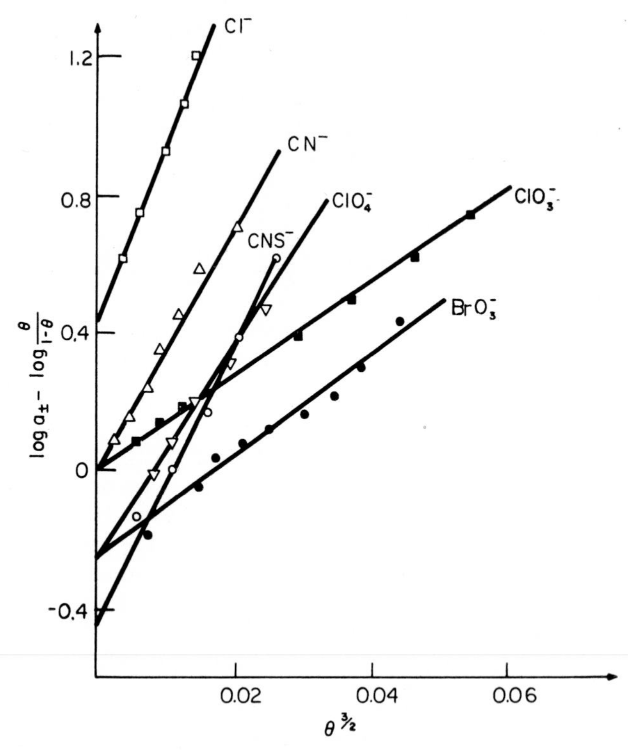

Fig. 2.49. A test of the BDM isotherm. Points: experimental values. Lines: calculated values.

Table 2.4. Experimental and calculated values based on the BDM model of the double layer at $q_M = 0$

Ion	Slope B Experimental	Calculated	Intercept C	Energy of adsorption $-\Delta G_c^\circ$ kJ mol^{-1}
Cl^-	52	43	0·42	6·49
ClO_3^-	14	13	0·01	6·65
ClO_4^-	36	32	−0·26	7·99
BrO_3^-	15	16	−0·25	8·20
CN^-	36	40	0	8·37
CNS^-	34	49	−0·45	11·13

What the figure and table show is that the BDM isotherm gives fair agreement between theory and experiment, and that one can accept it for the present as a working model. The double layer following from the BDM model is shown in fig. 2.50. Of course, it contains many approximations and crudities.

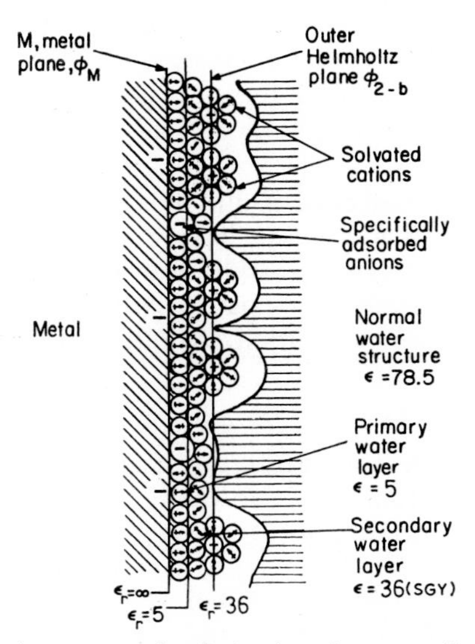

Fig. 2.50. Double layer at metal–solution interface according to BDM theory.

We come, thus, to the borderline of the present situation in work on the model for the double layer, and to arguments beyond the scope of the present work.

The Adsorption of Molecules at Interfaces

Why go further with the treatment of the double layer?

It might be thought that, at least for a book of this size and scope, we have done enough. But what about the corrosion chemist who wants to know something about how organic corrosion inhibitors behave? These inhibitors are generally *molecules*, not ions; and we must be able to explain why *they* adsorb, so that he can do some predicting and understand the variation of the efficacy of inhibitors with potential, for example.

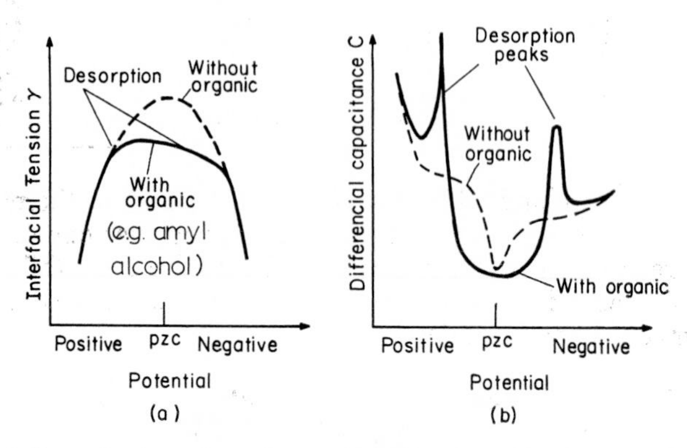

Fig. 2.51. Effect of adsorption of organic molecules: (*a*) electrocapillary curve; (*b*) capacitance–potential curve.

The adsorption of molecules is different from the adsorption of ions. The ionic adsorption picture is largely one of electrostatic charge balance, although this may be carried out in rather complicated ways. The adsorption of molecules, particularly 'pure molecules', those which do not form ions in solution, is quite different.

What facts must we know about the adsorption of molecules on electrodes?

We can distinguish two kinds of adsorption. One is 'molecular adsorption', the situation where an entity A comes up to an electrode and sits upon it as a molecule. It may, indeed, undergo a reaction to form, say, carbon dioxide later on in a reaction sequence involving a number of organic radicals; but most of what is actually on the electrode consists of *molecules*, undissociated and unchanged.

However, there is another kind of adsorption, 'adsorption with dissociation'. Here the molecule dissociates as it crosses the double layer, and often undergoes a reaction which involves electron transfer. Thus, in the case of propane, the first step is

$$C_3H_{8\,\text{solution}} \rightarrow C_3H_{7\,\text{adsorbed}} + H^+ + e.$$

Whether one calls such a situation the 'adsorption of propane', or an electrode reaction undergone by propane, is a matter of choice. This section discusses 'molecular adsorption' (adsorption without dissociation).

The coverage of an electrode by adsorbed molecules often depends on the electrode potential in a parabolic way.

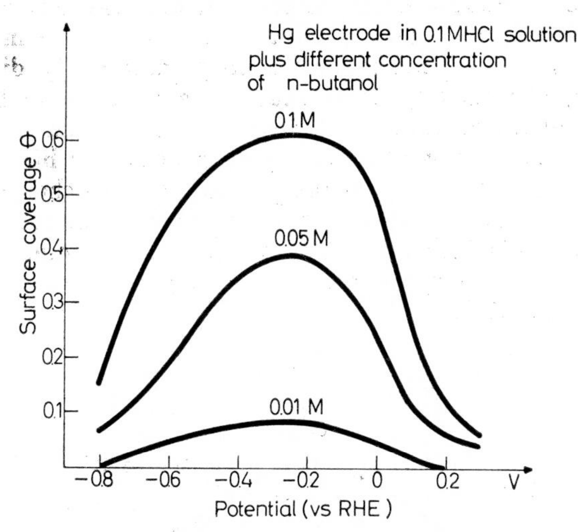

Fig. 2.52. Adsorption of butanol on mercury as a function of potential and concentration.

A model can be developed in terms of competitive adsorption on electrodes between organic molecules and water

At an electrode having a negative surface charge, q_M, the water dipoles will all tend to stand with their positive (hydrogens) ends in contact with the metal. If it has a positive charge, they will tend to

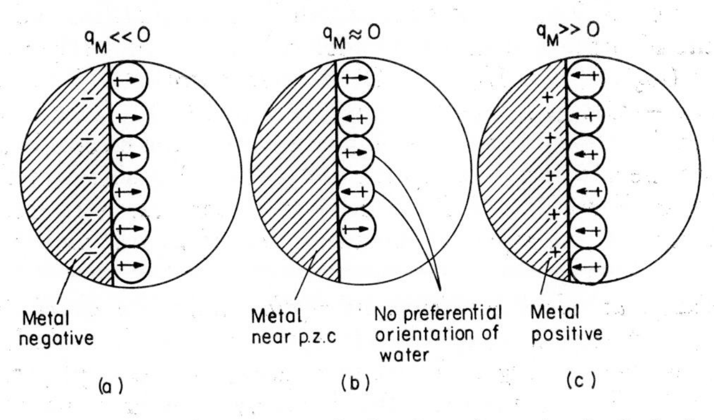

Fig. 2.53. Orientation of water dipoles depends on the electrode charge.

stand with their negative (oxygen) ends on the metal. Either way, water molecules are attracted when the size of the charge (whatever its sign) is large.

'In the middle', when the electrode potential is somewhere near zero, the water molecules will be least held. Really, as there is no charge on the electrode, the water dipoles are not held electrochemically at all. Therefore, the potential of zero charge for the metal is the potential at which organic molecules may most easily displace the water. Also, qualitatively, there must be a relationship between θ, the coverage of the electrode with water molecules, and the potential. Thus, θ reaches its maximum at highly negative or highly positive potentials. It is a minimum at the potential of zero charge when the water molecules are least held, and the organic molecules have the most chance of displacing adsorbed water and becoming themselves adsorbed. Qualitatively, we are approaching the desired parabolic relationship (fig. 2.54).

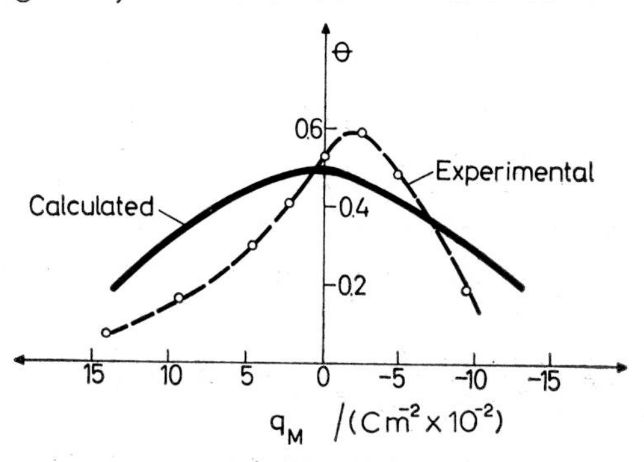

Fig. 2.54. Comparison between double layer theory and experiment for butanol on mercury electrode.

Possibly conditions at the surface will be such that, instead of only getting the adsorption of an organic molecule, there will be the discharge of H_3O^+ ($H_3O^+ + e \rightarrow H_{ads} + H_2O$) to give adsorbed H; or that of H_2O ($H_2O \rightarrow OH_{ads} + H^+ + e$) to give adsorbed OH. The adsorption of these radicals would cause secondary effects at the electrode surface, decreasing the adsorption of organic molecules. Russian investigators, in particular, Frumkin and Petrii, have in recent years stressed this H and OH competition aspect of the adsorption of organic molecules.

The charge at which maximum adsorption occurs on an electrode.—There is, in theory, a maximum adsorption of organic radicals at the potential of zero charge. In simple cases, for example, aliphatic alcohols adsorbing on mercury, this is *nearly* what happens, although there is a displacement by about 0·02 Cm^{-2} in the negative direction (see fig. 2.55).

Organic molecule–electrode interactions and their effects on organic adsorption.—We have so far considered only the effect of the dipole behaviour of water molecules and said nothing about the role of the interaction of the organic molecule with the electrode. There are systems where this is a reasonable approximation. Suppose that we have an alcohol, and that it is adsorbed upon the electrode with its CH_3 'head' in contact with the metal, while its OH 'feet' are out in the solution. The dipole moment of an alcohol molecule resides in the OH group, and when the molecule is adsorbed, this OH end may be some 10 Å away from the metal, and thus respond little to changes in charge on the electrode (for at this distance the field of the double layer in the solution is very small).

But in many more cases the interaction of the *organic molecule* with the electric field of the electrode *is* significant. This aspect of organic adsorption is that stressed in an earlier, less modelistic, attempt by Frumkin and Damaskin to interpret organic adsorption in terms of the change of energy of the double layer, as adsorbing organics change the dielectric constant and hence the capacitance (energy $= \frac{1}{2} CV^2$).

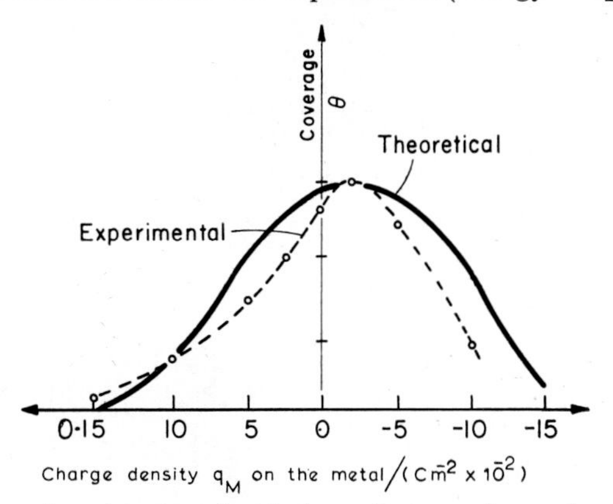

Fig. 2.55. Comparison between double layer theory and experiment whilst taking into account the interaction of butanol molecule with the metal.

The theory outlined above for molecular adsorption in terms of water molecules can also be applied when the interaction of the organic molecule with the electric field is also taken into account.

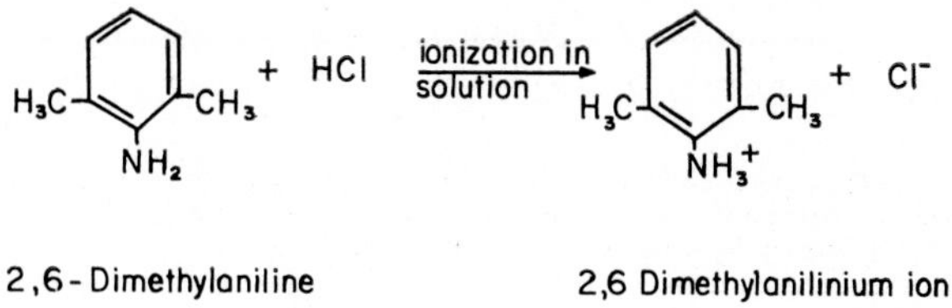

H_3C–$C_6H_3(NH_2)$–CH_3 + HCl $\xrightarrow[\text{solution}]{\text{ionization in}}$ H_3C–$C_6H_3(NH_3^+)$–CH_3 + Cl^-

2,6-Dimethylaniline — 2,6 Dimethylanilinium ion

Fig. 2.56. Organic bases dissociate in electrolytic solutions producing organic cations.

Strong chemical interactions at the electrode gives unexpected results. For example, 2,6-dimethyl aniline is a substance often used in corrosion inhibition. In acid solution, it forms the 2,6-dimethyl anilinium ion, and here there is very little variation of organic adsorption with potential. The parabola which would be expected if the molecules only were being adsorbed is not found; and the sharp decrease in coverage expected when the electrode becomes positive does not appear. In

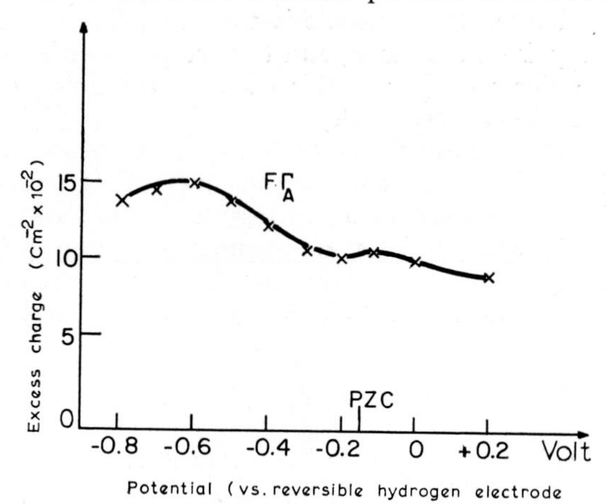

Fig. 2.57. The variation of adsorption of 2,6-dimethyl anilinium ion as a function of potential. Note the very small variation of coverage with potential.

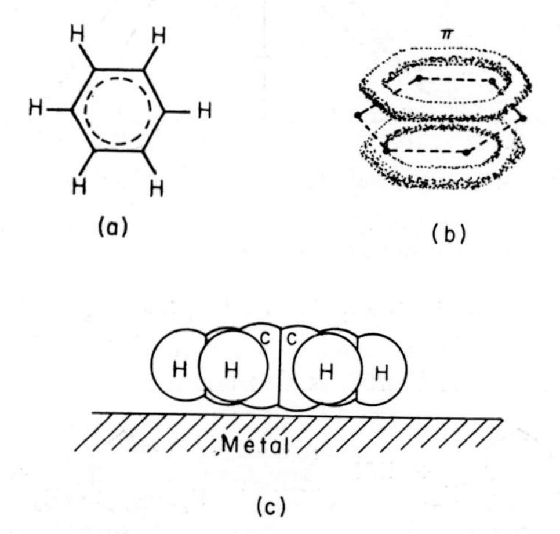

Fig. 2.58. Adsorption of benzene. The benzene ring (*a*) has a resonance structure due to a π-resonance molecular orbital (*b*); when adsorbed in the flat position (*c*) the π electrons can interact with the metal.

fact, the coverage is relatively independent of the potential, as is shown in fig. 2.58. The explanation is that the positive anilinium ion is more attracted when the electrode becomes more negative; but when the electrode tries to repel the ion, as the metal becomes positive, chemical bonding between the metal of the electrode and the organic molecule reduce the repulsion. This bonding has been proved to be interaction of the metal with the π bonds of the benzene. If one substitutes hexahydrobenzene (which has not got these π bonds), no adsorption takes place (Gurbachov, Blomgren).

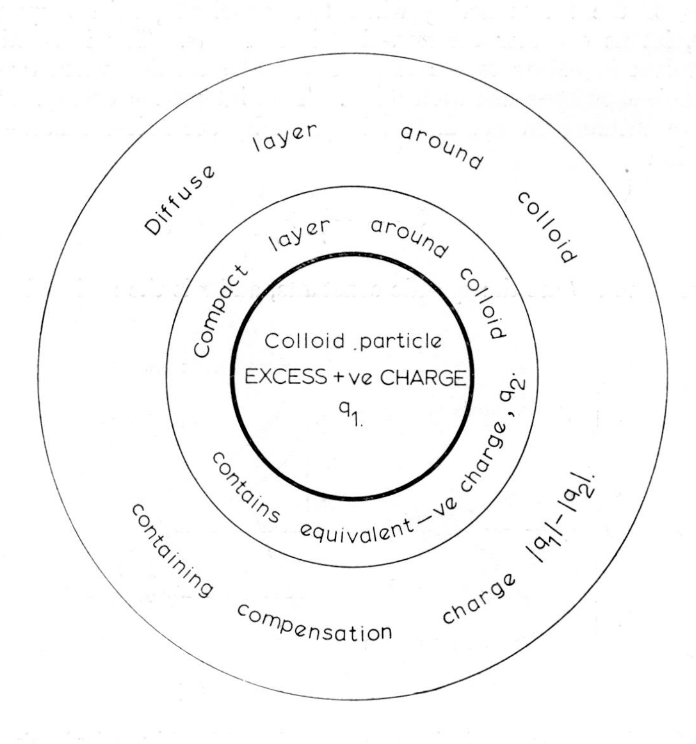

Fig. 2.59. Colloidal particle with the surrounding charge cloud.

The Double Layer Around Colloidal Particles

We have so far studied the double layers at metal–solution interfaces, all *plane* interfaces. Small particles do not present such planes.

Consider a solid particle of colloidal dimensions, let us say about 10^{-6} m, carrying an excess charge. A double layer of particles with charge of opposite sign to that on the particle then forms about the particle. In most colloidal situations, the solution is very dilute and most of the charge on the solution side is upon the *diffuse* double layer (just as in concentrated solutions, the excess ions of one sign (or charge) concentrate near the electrode, and are quite like the 'line of charges on a condenser plate' in Helmholtz's view).

Why do colloidal particles remain stable and not coagulate?

Life depends upon the stability of colloids. In blood, the *absence* of thrombus formation and clotting depends upon the mutual repulsion between colloidal particles when they approach each other.

The reason for the stability of colloids can be we understand in terms of the forces acting when two colloidal particles approach. First, let us consider the non-electrical aspects. The interaction is equivalent in nature to the van der Waals' attraction when two rare gas molecules approach each other. This interaction energy, a function of distance in fig. 2.60 *a*, is given by the Mie–Lennard–Jones equation

$$U_r = -\frac{A}{r^6}+\frac{B}{r^{12}} \qquad (2.34$$

where A and B are the specific constants, and r is the radial distance.

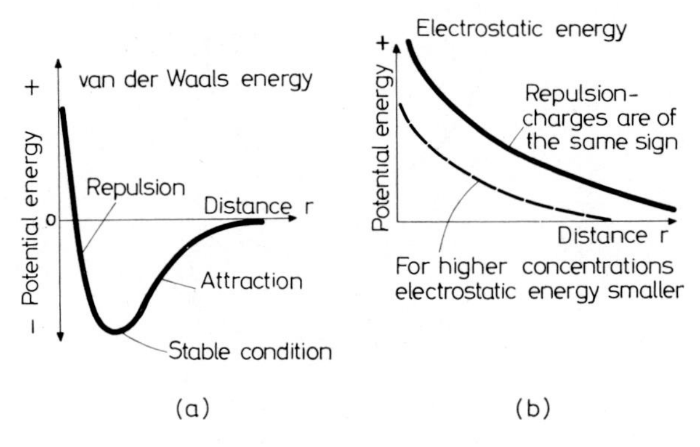

Fig. 2.60. Interaction energies between colloidal particles, (*a*) van der Waals energy, (*b*) electrostatic energy.

Thus, neglecting at first the electrical considerations, there is stability which is reached when the energy is a minimum, which occurs at a certain separation of the two particles.

Now each colloidal particle is surrounded by a double layer. In two dimensions, these double layers can be regarded as 'rings of charge' around each particle. When the particles approach there is electrostatic repulsion between the rings of charge. The electrostatic repulsion energy is given by (cf. 2.23):

$$U_{\text{el.st.}} = Ze\,\phi_{2-b}\exp(-\kappa r) \qquad (2.35)$$

(where Z is the number of elementary charges e) and is plotted in fig. 2.60 *b*.

Taking the van der Waals and the electrostatic effects together, the net-potential-energy distance curve is given in fig. 2.61.

The energy minimum now never occurs in the negative potential energy region. *There is no part of the energy–distance curve where the two colloidal particles could come together and coagulate.* This is a way of saying that the electrostatic charge arising from double layer interactions between particles is the origin of the colloid's stability.

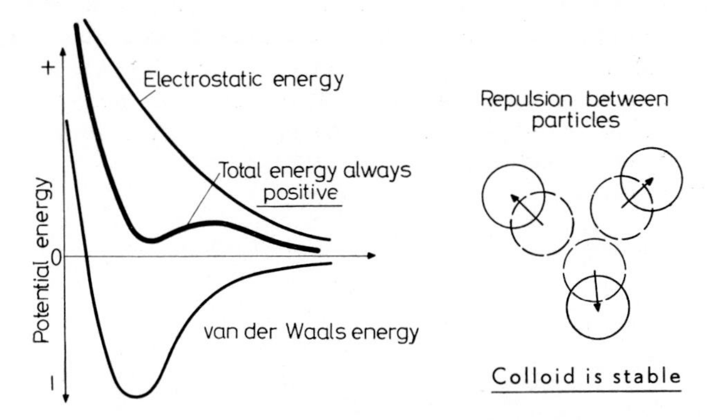

Fig. 2.61. Energy–distance relation when the colloid is stable.

It is interesting to note, however, that our knowledge of the double layer allows us to see situations under which we could *provoke* colloidal particles to flocculate and/or clot. Thus, suppose we add more ions to

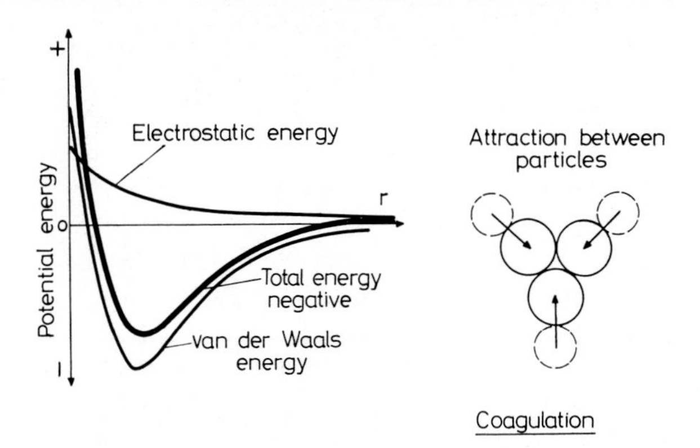

Fig. 2.62. Energy–distance relation when the colloid is unstable.

the solution. The factor κ in the equation above is concentration-dependent. κ *increases* with *increase* of concentration. Hence, ϕ falls more rapidly for the colloid in the more concentrated solution. Thus, the double layer around the colloid becomes compressed, and two particles can come near to each other without repulsion predominating. There is another way to decrease the stability of colloidal systems, namely, by adding contact-adsorbing ions which will populate the I.H.P. and thus the value of ϕ_{2-b} in equation (2.35) will be reduced without significantly changing the concentration of the bulk electrolyte. This latter case is shown in fig. 2.62.

This short introduction to the theory of the stability of colloids also leads us towards the biological realm. The stability of the various types of colloidal particles in blood depends in each case upon the properties of the double layer; but this stability depends on the salt content (and anion adsorbability) of the solution surrounding the particles. This principle applies also to many other important biological materials: electrical double layers play a very important part in biological systems.

CHAPTER 3

charge transfer

Introduction

WE have said that electrochemical science is the study of the consequences of charge transfer at interfaces. Thus, when we pass hydrogen gas over one electrode and oxygen gas over another, have the electrons transfer *from* hydrogen and *to* oxygen, and then get a current through an external circuit between the electrodes, the *central act* is the transfer of electrons at the electrodes (fig. 3.1). If we want to find out why cars decay and tankers split in two, then we have to know why iron atoms dissolve in moisture films and transfer charges to the metal they leave behind. If we want to find out how electrical energy is stored in the nickel–cadmium battery (fig. 3.2), then one of the things we have to do is to find out how nickel (III) oxide gets reduced to nickel (II) hydroxide when electric charges are added to it.

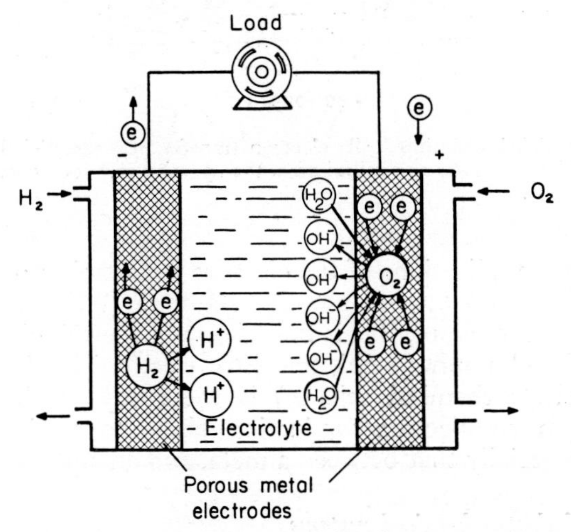

Fig. 3.1. An H_2–O_2 fuel cell; electron transfer between reactants hydrogen and oxygen and the electrodes.

Many important practical aspects of the surrounding world depend upon the transfer of electrons at interfaces. The way we use oxygen in metabolism, the making of photographic images on plates, the synthesis of nylon, the fumeless production of power, the electrical storage of atom-derived energy, the winning of metals, the power for space vehicles, bio-energetics, the growth of bones, and aspects of rheology. All these depend on the interphasial transfer of electrons, and on the electric fields that exist across interphases. A new term, electrodics, has been coined for the study of these two related events. But still the best term is one which indicates the breadth of the study: electrochemical science.

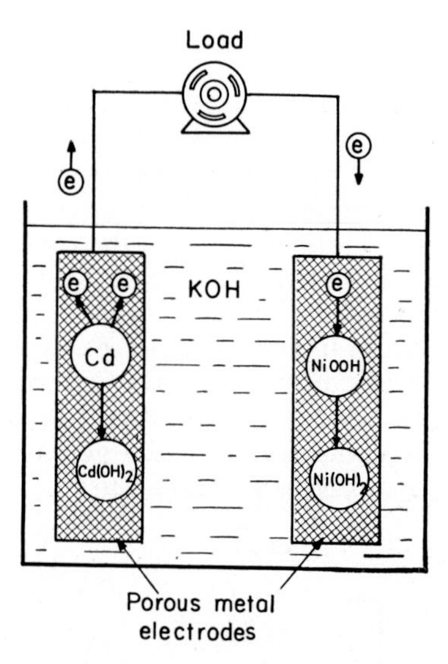

Fig. 3.2. The nickel–cadmium cell; electron transfer between nickel (III) oxide at the positive electrode and cadmium at the negative electrode enables the battery to discharge.

Many of the applications of the electron are simply processes which transfer an electron from one phase to another. When the two phases are a solid and a vacuum, this is the science of thermionics; when they are one solid and another solid, transistor electronics. The science of *electrodics* (electrochemical science) is the study of the transfer of electrons from an electron-conducting phase to an ion-conducting phase, and especially that between a metal and an aqueous solution.

Three uses of electrochemical systems

We talk about the transfer of electrons from one solid phase to *one* solution, or vice versa, but this is to some extent an abstraction. It is only possible to study such events by means of instruments in complete circuits. Actual electrochemical stituations always involve *two* electrodes, one of which is relatively more electron-bearing than the other. Among 'electrochemical cells', we can distinguish three possible types of system.

(1) It may be a *driven* system. This means that the overall electrode reaction in the cell (the sum of that at each electrode) will not be one which would take place spontaneously. Hydrogen and oxygen combine spontaneously to give water, but water does not decompose spontaneously to give hydrogen and oxygen. However, in an electrochemical cell, *if we have a driving force caused by an outside power source*, we can split water up into hydrogen and oxygen. This, then, is the first kind of electrochemical device. Such a device may be called a 'substance producer'. One puts energy in and makes a non-spontaneous reaction give rise to new substances (fig. 3.3 *a*).

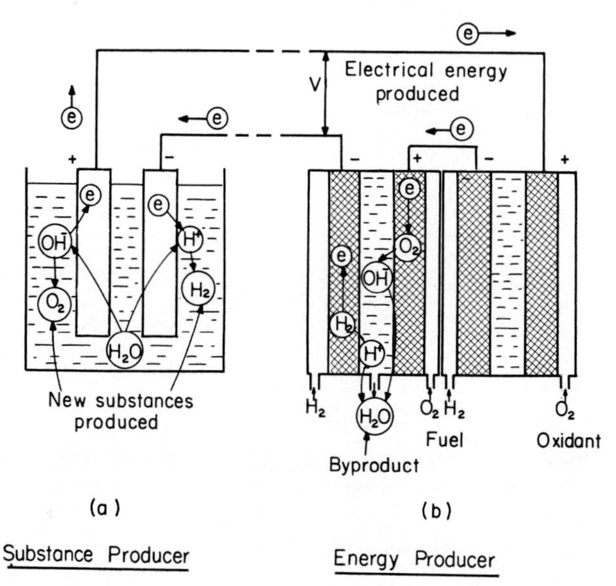

Fig. 3.3. (*a*) *Substance producer.* A water-electrolysis cell producing H_2 and O_2 when energized externally. The overall reaction is not spontaneous. (*b*) *Energy producer.* Spontaneous reactions of H_2 and O_2 at the electrodes produce water and *electrical energy*. Water may be considered as a by-product.

(2) The alternative to a substance producer is a *driving* system, in which the reaction is one which takes place spontaneously. With hydrogen in contact with one electrode and oxygen in contact with another, hydrogen and oxygen interchange electrons with their electrodes (fig. 3.3 *b*) and water is spontaneously produced, giving electrical energy as a by-product. Such a cell may be called an 'energy producer'.

Both the cell driven by an outside power source (called here the substance producer) and the self-driving cell (called here the energy producer) do produce new substances. But the energy producer does this *spontaneously*. Looked at from the point of view of electrochemical syntheses, the electrical energy furnished is a pleasant bonus. Looked at from the point of view of energy conversion, the substances produced may be a useful by-product.

(3) There is a third electrochemical 'device', an example of what one might call the eternal cussedness of things, when the equivalent of the spontaneously driving electrochemical cell also takes place in a way which is unpleasant and unproductive. Spontaneous electrochemical micro-cells can consume materials to produce others that nobody wants, and energy that nobody can use. We refer to this situation as corrosion, fig. 3.4. The corrosion couple is, in effect, a fuel cell in which the two electrode reactions take place on different sites of the same kind of metal.

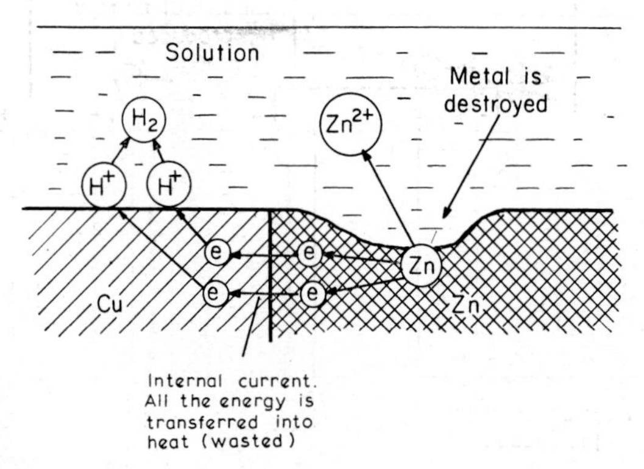

Fig. 3.4. In the copper–zinc micro-couple, zinc dissolves (corrodes) with evolution of hydrogen. The internal electron current converts energy only into heat.

The Velocity of Electrochemical Reactions

Consider a *specific* electrochemical reaction, say the transfer of charge from an electrode to a silver ion in solution. Let us also not dwell too much on details; but see whether we can make an approximate formula for the dependence of the rate of passage of electrons upon potential, which we shall refine in physical detail later on in the chapter.

Thus, the event we are considering is the transfer of a silver ion to the electrode. When it reaches there, it will be a silver atom; interphasial charge transfer will have occurred. The ion will have moved from the position it initially had in the double layer in the solution. In the double layer itself (see p. 62), the silver ion will be hydrated; and so its distance from the metal will be of the order of the diameter of a water molecule attached to the electrode, plus the radius of the hydrated silver ion itself. As the radius of the water molecule is about 1·4 Å, the whole thing will add up to $2 \times 1{\cdot}4 + 1{\cdot}4 + r_{Ag^+}$, or 5–6 Å.

The situation can be divided into two parts. As the silver ion stretches forward to reach the electrode, in one of the vibrations which the ion is constantly executing with respect to its neighbouring water molecules, the energy concerned in this vibration (+ the energy of an electron in the metal) can be regarded as *climbing* an energy barrier. At some point between the original position of the ion on the solution side of the double layer, and the atom on the electrode itself, there is a maximum value of the potential energy (which varies with distance), and the silver *atom* will relax into a vibrational state in which it oscillates with respect to the electrode substrate (fig. 3.5). Somewhere (perhaps near to half way, one might guess) between the start of its motion in the double layer and the end of its motion on the surface of the metal, the silver ion receives the electron from the metal, and becomes the atom.

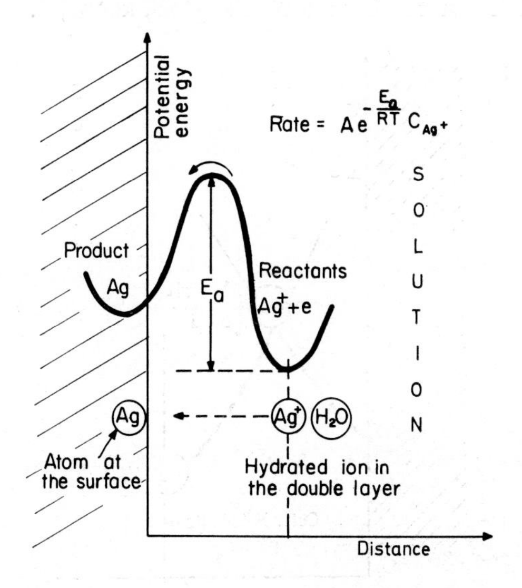

Fig. 3.5. Illustrating electron transfer kinetics.

Suppose that some special state exists between the electrode and the solution such that there is no charge on the electrode; this is at *the potential of zero charge* (see p. 43). Then electron transfer may occur without any push from a potential difference. It is, in this special case, just like a chemical reaction. For this reason, we could write, in this state, that:

$$v_{\text{react}} = kc_{\text{Ag}^+}, \tag{3.1}$$

and this would be the theoretical velocity of the silver-ion neutralization reaction when there is zero excess charge on the metal, and zero field due to the electrode.

We now bring in an excess charge and electric field. Looked at from the point of view of electrostatics, with the electrode negative and the silver ion positive, the electric field will favour the ion going towards the electrode. Now, in ordinary chemical kinetics, when there is no electrochemical component, the rate constant k of a reaction bears a relation to the height E_a of the energy barrier (fig. 3.5) which it has to surmount, given by the following equation, which refers to *molar* quantities:

$$k = A \,.\, \exp(-E_a/RT). \tag{3.2}$$

(Here E_a is in J mol^{-1} and R is the gas constant.) Hence, if we are going to have an electrical component involved in the transfer of the silver ion, then we are going to need an additional energy term as well as E_a, and the rate constant will become now an *electrochemical rate constant*, which can be denoted by the greek kappa, κ.

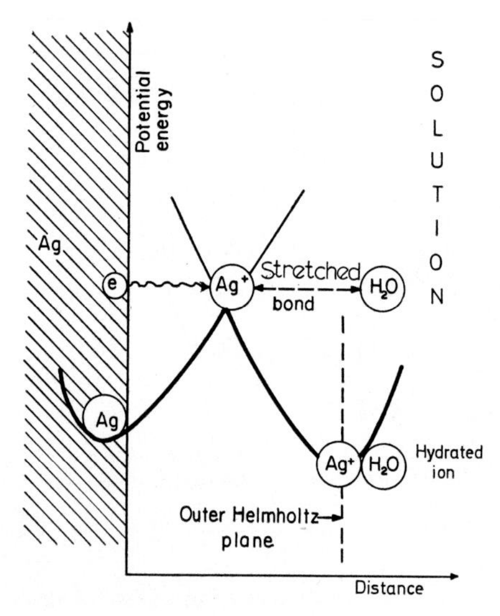

Fig. 3.6. Potential energy diagram for hydrated Ag^+ ion in the double layer and Ag atom at the surface. Ag ions are neutralized by electrons when the bond is stretched so much that the energy of the ion exceeds that corresponding to the top of the energy barrier.

Carrying on with the idea that the potential of the electrode is attracting the silver ion, and remembering that, in electrostatics, the energy associated with the passage of a charge through a potential difference† is: potential × charge, we have:

$$\kappa = A \exp(-(E_a + f(VF))/RT), \tag{3.3}$$

† The potential difference involved is the potential difference between the metal and the outer Helmholtz plane (through the centres of hydrated metal ions in the double layer), $\phi_M - \phi_{2-b}$ (see fig. 2.30, p. 49). Since, except in very dilute solutions, the change of this potential difference is equal to the change of the experimentally measured change of the electrode potential V (see p. 35), in the further text V is used for the sake of simplicity.

where $f(VF)$ is some function of the electrical energy concerned in the passage of the ion across the double layer. On the very simple approach which we are using here, then $f(VF)$ will be something near to $\frac{1}{2}(VF)$. For, the total amount of electrical energy involved when one mole of electrons (total charge F) moves under the potential difference, V, across the double layer would be VF. But we are only interested in the amount of energy which will help the ion to get to the point at which it will pass over the top of its energy hill. If the energy barrier is symmetrical (as drawn in fig. 3.7) then we should just have that $f(VF) = \frac{1}{2}VF$.

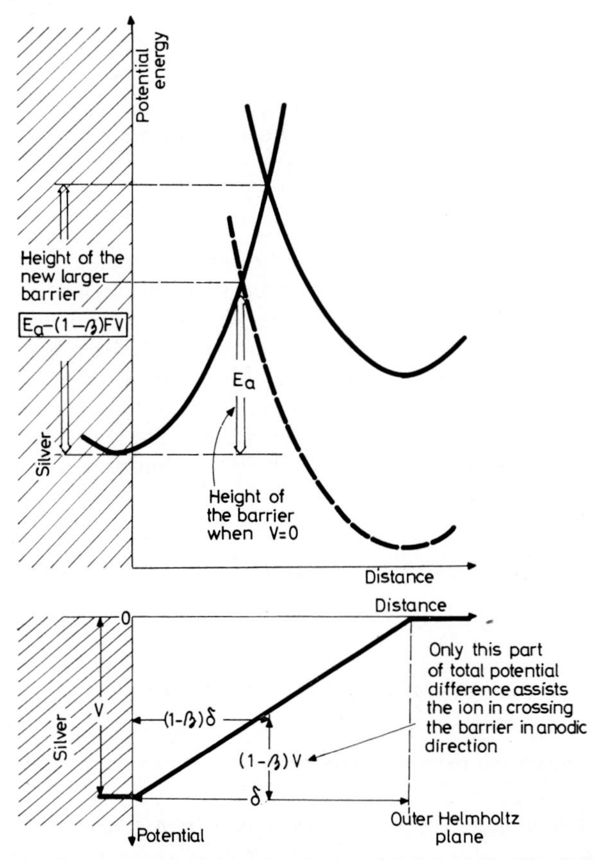

Fig. 3.7. Potential energy profile for Ag atom and Ag^+ ions for dissolution reaction. (Broken line—no field across the double layer; full line—the potential difference is V and negative.) The negative potential difference V decreases the rate, but only $(1-\beta)FV$ is effective. The height of the barrier is increased by $-(1-\beta)FV$.

But it might be better to write β instead of $\frac{1}{2}$, where β is a factor *somewhere near* to $\frac{1}{2}$ (to allow for a lack of symmetry). Thereafter, we may write the expression for the *forward* reaction, with electrochemical rate constant κ_-† as

$$\kappa_- = k_- \exp(-\beta VF/RT) \tag{3.4}$$

where $k_- = A \exp(-E_a/RT)$, is the *chemical* rate constant for the reaction in the same direction.

$$\text{electrochemical rate constant} = \text{chemical rate constant} \times \exp(-\beta VF/RT). \tag{3.5}$$

Finally, we obtain an equation for the electrochemical reaction rate in the cathodic direction, which is:

$$v_- = \kappa_- c_i = k_- \exp(-\beta VF/RT)c_i \tag{3.6}$$

Our argument has been oversimplified, as we shall see, when we present it more precisely. The *result* of the complicated, real, argument is essentially the same as that given here.

Current density and reaction velocity

What we have derived above is the reaction velocity; that means the quantity of silver which gets transferred to a unit area of the substrate in unit time. We could leave things at that, and go on working in reaction velocity terms, and then our units would be most likely to be moles per square metre per second. However, it is more normal to convert to the electrical units of amperes per square metre, since it is the current which is experimentally measured. The conversion is simple, for one mole of electronic charge is 96 500 coulomb; and one ampere is a current of one coulomb per second.

Thus

$$i = nFv_{\text{react}}, \quad \text{if } n \text{ moles of electrons are required to complete one act of the reaction.} \tag{3.7}$$

Hence, from eqn. (3.6),

$$i = nFk_- \, . \exp(-\beta VF/RT)c_i. \tag{3.8}$$

The *current density*, i, is the measured current I (in A) divided by electrode area S (in m^2); $i = I/S$.

Electrons flow in both directions, both to and from a metal

In the foregoing simple argument, we have assumed that the electron is travelling from the electrode to the solution. It is just as likely, at least if we don't tie the conditions down more, that the electrons will

† The subscript indicates the direction of the reaction in which ions from solution react with electrons supplied by the electrode, getting reduced. Often it is called the *cathodic* direction. The opposite direction will be indicated by subscript + and referred to as the *anodic* direction.

travel in the other direction, from the solution to the metal (fig. 3.8 *b*). So we must ask how equation (3.3) for κ is altered for the case $Ag \rightarrow Ag^{+} + e$. If excess negative charge on the electrode *increases* the electron transfer *from* the electrode *to* the solution, it must *decrease* the rate of electron transfer *from* the solution *to* the electrode. This means that any tendency which the silver atoms have to dissolve into the

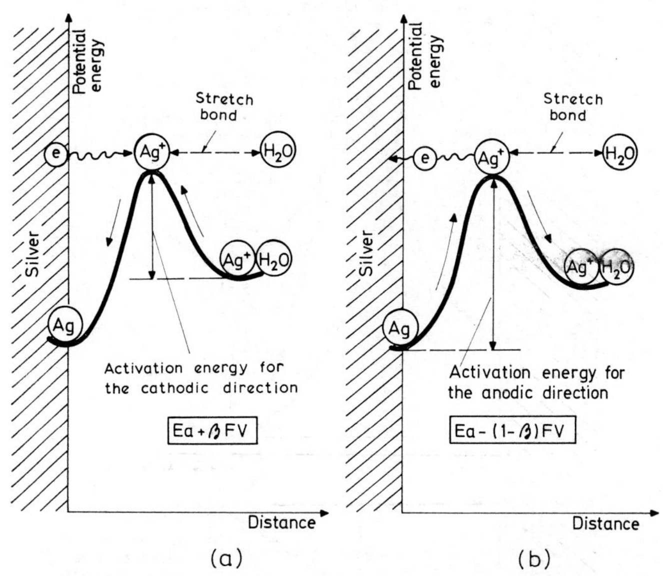

Fig. 3.8. (*a*) For the deposition reaction the Ag^{+} ion is assisted by the βV part of the negative potential difference, V. (*b*) For the dissolution reaction the Ag atom has to surmount the barrier which is enlarged by $(1-\beta)FV$.

solution as ions, will be frustrated by the presence of excess *negative* charge on the electrodes, which will tend to attract them back again. The rate of the reaction $Ag \rightarrow Ag^{+} + e$ will be given by an equation of the type

$$v_{+} = \kappa_{+} \cdot c_{\mathrm{Ag}}. \qquad (3.9)$$

It is obviously this κ (κ_{+}) that we have got to worry about.

In the case where the electrons travel *from* the electrode *to* the ion in the solution, the chemical rate constant is multiplied by $\exp(-\beta VF/RT)$ (eqn. (3.4)).

For the other direction, the energy charge is opposite in sign, so that the index is 'plus' instead of 'minus', and instead of $\exp(-\beta VF/RT)$, we shall write $\exp(+xVF/RT)$. What is the 'x'? Before, it was β, and this represents the fraction of the distance, δ, between the position of the nearest ions to which electrons flow and the electrode (fig. 3.8), which is to be traversed by the silver ion travelling from the solution to the electrode, before it comes to the height of its energy barrier. For the other direction, then, it seems reasonable

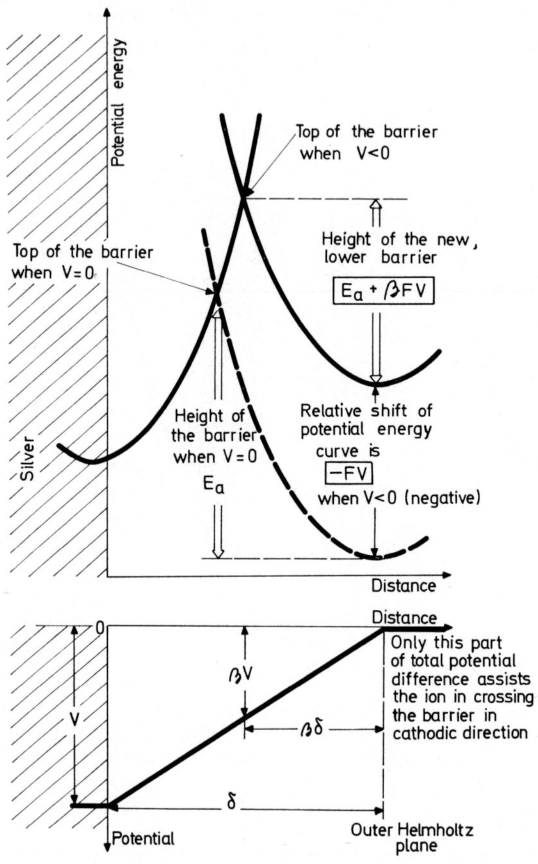

Fig. 3.9. Potential energy profile for Ag atom and Ag^+ ions for deposition reaction. (Broken line—no field across the double layer; full line—the potential difference is V and negative.) The negative potential difference V assists the reaction but only part of it, βV, is effective in helping the ion to reach the barrier top.

to write $1-\beta$, if the fraction is β in one direction, it must be $1-\beta$ in the other direction (fig. 3.9). Hence, $x = 1-\beta$, and consequently, the electrochemical rate constant will be

$$\kappa_+ = k_+ \exp(+(1-\beta)VF/RT). \tag{3.10}$$

Thus, for electron emission from an electrode to an ion in solution (cathodic direction), the equation for rate as a function of potential is

$$v_- = k_- c_i \exp(-\beta VF/RT), \tag{3.11}$$

and the reaction rate gets larger as V gets *more* negative.

But, for electron acceptance by the electrode at the anode, the equation for the dependence of rate upon potential is†

$$v_+ = k_+ \exp [(1-\beta)VF/RT] \qquad (3.12)$$

and the electrode potential becoming more *positive* creates an *increase* of dissolution current density

$$i_+ = nFk_+ \exp [(1-\beta)FV/RT]. \qquad (3.13)$$

We can illustrate this with some figures for silver dissolving into 0·1 M $AgNO_3$ solution.

At +0·74 V, the dissolution rate, expressed as current density, is about 10^2 A m^{-2}, i.e.,

$$i_{0\cdot74} = nFk_+ \exp [(1-\beta)F \times 0\cdot74/RT] = 100 \text{ A m}^{-2}.$$

If we make the potential more positive by 0·24 V, the new potential is now 0·74+0·24 = 0·98 V, and the new current density will be:

$$\begin{aligned} i_{0\cdot98} &= nFk_+ \exp [(1-\beta)F \times 0\cdot98/RT] \\ &= nFk_+ \exp [(1-\beta)F \times 0\cdot74/RT] \times \exp [(1-\beta)F \times 0\cdot24/RT] \\ &= i_{0\cdot74} \exp [(1-\beta)F \times 0\cdot24/RT]. \end{aligned}$$

Taking F = 96 500 C mol^{-1}, R = 8·317 J K^{-1} mol^{-1}, and T = 298 K, β = 0·5 and $i_{0\cdot74}$ = 100 A m^{-2}

$$\begin{aligned} i_{0\cdot98} &= 10^2 \times \exp (0\cdot5 \times 96\,500 \times 0.24/8\cdot317 \times 298) \\ &= 100 \,.\, 10^2 = 10^4 \text{ A m}^{-2}. \end{aligned}$$

Thus, the dissolution rate is *increased* by 100 times when the potential is made more positive by 0·24 V.

Correspondingly, if we decrease V by 0·24 V from the original +0·74 V, the new potential is now 0·74−0·24 = 0·5 V, and the current density at 0·5 V is:

$$\begin{aligned} i_{0\cdot5} &= nFk_+ \exp [(1-\beta)F(0\cdot74-0\cdot24)/RT] \\ &= nFk_+ \exp [(1-\beta)F \times 0\cdot74/RT] \times \exp [-(1-\beta)F \times 0\cdot24/RT] \\ &= i_{0\cdot74} \exp [-(1-\beta)F \times 0\cdot24/RT]. \end{aligned}$$

Taking the numerical values for the constants as before, we obtain

$$\begin{aligned} i_{0\cdot5} &= i_{0\cdot74} \exp (-0\cdot5 \times 96\,500 \times 0\cdot24/8\cdot317 \times 298) \\ &= 10^2 \times 10^{-2} = 1\cdot0 \text{ A m}^{-2}. \end{aligned}$$

† There is an implicit concentration term in equations (3.12) and (3.13) but it is a constant and hence suppressed in the equation. This is because the whole electrode surface is a source of atoms for the action $M \rightarrow M^+ + e$.

In this case, the 0·24 V change of potential in the negative direction, *decreases* the dissolution rate 100 times.

The equation (3.13) is illustrated also by fig. 3.10. Figure 3.10 *a* shows the exponential relation between the current density i_+ and potential V. Figure 3.10 *b* illustrates the linear relationship between the potential and the logarithm of current density.

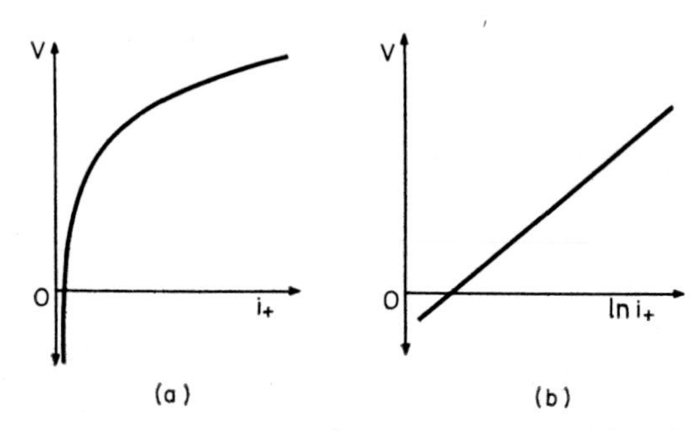

Fig. 3.10. The exponential relationship between potential and current density. (*a*) V against i, (*b*) V against ln i.

If all the potential independent terms in equation (3.13) are separated from those which depend on potential and called K, eqn. (3.13) can be written as:

$$i_+ = K_1 \, . \exp\,[(1-\beta)FV/RT]. \qquad (3.14)$$

Take logarithms (to base e) of both sides of the equation and rearranging,

$$V = K_2 + \frac{RT}{(1-\beta)F} \ln i_+. \qquad (3.15)$$

This equation gives a straight line for V plotted against ln i_+, with a slope of $RT/(1-\beta)F$ (fig. 3.10 *b*). Such plots of potential against log i are sometimes called Tafel lines.

Thus, to summarize the content of the present section, we have verified and repeated what we had already hinted at in our chapter on the double layer (p. 27). Very tiny amounts of charge—we talked about 10^{-6} moles of charge per square metre as typical—can give rise to changes of tenths of volts in the potential across the double layer; and such potential changes give several orders of magnitude change in the rate of electrochemical reactions. Such changes can be decreases or increased. Further, they do not need to be carried out slowly and laboriously, as, for example, with changing a reaction rate by change of temperature in traditional chemistry. They can be brought about in an instant by adjusting a switch.

Overpotential

Consider the expressions (3.11) and (3.12) derived in the last section. The first gives the rate at which electrons leave the metal and become transferred to silver ions in solution, producing silver atoms. The second is the rate at which electrons leave the silver metal, producing silver ions in solution.

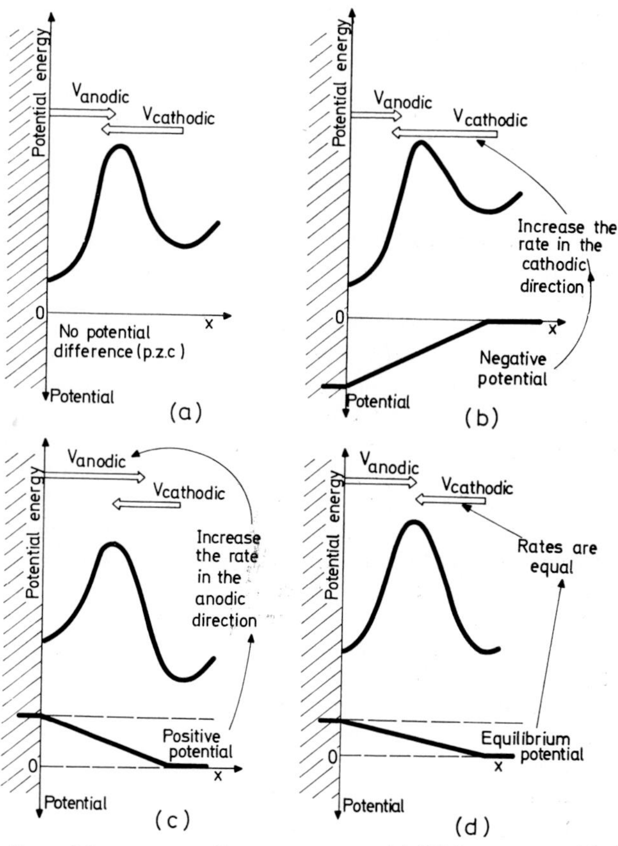

Fig. 3.11. Potential–energy vs. distance curves. (*a*) With no potential difference. (*b*) When a negative potential is applied. (*c*) When a positive potential is applied. (*d*) At the equilibrium potential, the rates of anodic and cathodic reactions are equal.

A sensible name for electrochemical reactions in which electrons leave a solid substrate and transfer themselves to substances in solution would clearly be 'electronation'; and the obvious word for the corresponding reaction—the atoms going to ions—would be, 'de-electronation'. But there happen to be two already established terms. Electronation is called '*cathodic reaction*', and de-electronation is called '*anodic reaction*'.

Let us come back now to the two fundamental reactions, the cathodic and anodic reactions we have been considering. If by making the electrode more electron-filled, we make the cathodic reactions which it can provoke go faster—and if by making it less electron-filled, we can make the corresponding anodic reactions faster—it is clear that, if we take a given electrode reaction, there must be a potential at which the cathodic and anodic reactions take place at the same speed.

But cathodic and anodic reactions are the two different directions in which the same act of transfer can occur. In the cathodic reaction:

$$M^{+}_{(soln)} + e_{(M)} \rightarrow M.$$

In the anodic reaction:

$$M \rightarrow M^{+}_{(soln)} + e_{(M)}.$$

Hence, if the potential just has that particular value at which cathodic and anodic reactions take place at equal rates, we must be at *the state of equilibrium*.

This potential of zero *net* rate should clearly receive a name.

We already have one special potential, the potential of zero charge (Chapter 2). It would be nice to be able to report that this was the potential at which the electron-donating and the electron-accepting properties of an electrode were also equal, but alas, this is not so. An equilibrium potential involves not only the properties of the electrode material but also the properties of the ions in solution. One electrode material, e.g., gold, can enter into a large number of electrode reactions, each involving different ions in solution, and for each of these it would have a different potential at which the reaction is in equilibrium. What then, shall we call this potential of equal electronation and *de-electronation* rates, this *equilibrium potential*? We may call it what it actually is, the equilibrium potential, V_e. Although we would suggest that 'equilibrium potential' is the sensible term, the name 'reversible potential' is often used.

Now that we understand 'equilibrium' or 'reversible' potential, let us see whether we need to define another potential to deal with the situation when the electronation and de-electronation rates are *not* equal and opposite. Thus, if we represent the cathodic current density by i_- and the anodic current density by i_+, then when the potential $V = V_e$, we have that $i_- = i_+$. When the potential is more negative than the equilibrium potential, we have that $i_- > i_+$. There will be a net flow of electrons across the interface from solid to solution. Correspondingly, when $i_+ > i_-$, electrons will flow from the solution into some outer circuit. Thus, the equilibrium potential, is not only the potential of no net current flow; it is also the value of the potential in passing through which the net current reverses its direction.

When the potential of the electrode becomes *more negative* than that which corresponds to equilibrium for the given reaction, there is a net emission of electrons to the solution, a net electronating, cathodic, current flow. But if we make the electrode *more positive* than the equilibrium value, then there is a de-electronating, anodic, current (fig. 3.12).

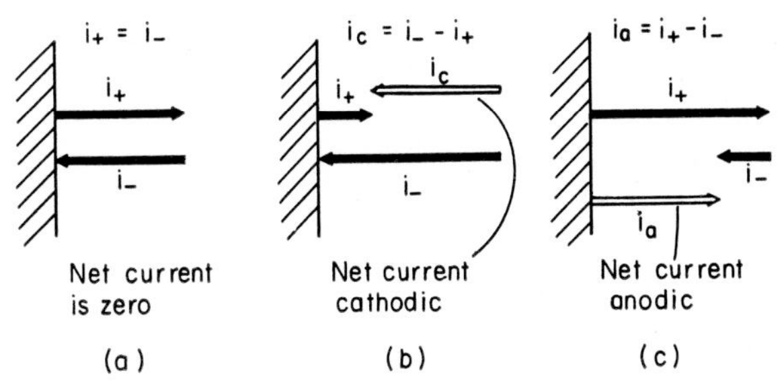

Fig. 3.12. Net current density and individual current densities: (*a*) for equilibrium (no net current); (*b*) net current cathodic; (*c*) net current anodic.

Thus, if the electrode potential V, is more negative (the electrode more electron filled) than that of the equilibrium potential,

$$\vec{i}_- > \vec{i}_+.$$

Then, the observed current in an outer circuit of a practical device for measuring electrode kinetics (fig. 3.14) will be such that the net electron flow is *into* the electrode (the middle one of fig. 3.14) from some electron source outside the cell. The current is cathodic, and the current density i_c calculated from the readings of an ammeter in the circuit is:

$$i_c = \vec{i}_- - \vec{i}_+.$$

Conversely, if the electrode potential, V, is more positive (*less* electron filled) than that of the equilibrium (reversible) potential,

$$\vec{i}_+ > \vec{i}_-,$$

and these will be a net flow of electrons *out* of the electrode to the circuit. The current is 'anodic' and the current-density i_a calculated from the circuit current is

$$i_a = \vec{i}_+ - \vec{i}_-.$$

Enough has already been said to make out the shape of the relation between the net current-density and the electrode potential. At $V = V_{\text{equil}}$ (or V_{rev}), $i = 0$. At V more negative than V_{equil}, the flow of electrons from the electrode to the ions on the solution side of the double layer will increase. At V more positive than V_{equil}, the flow of electrons from ions in solution to the electrode will increase.

From equations (3.11) and (3.12 (which give only i_+ and i_-, the individual anodic and cathodic current densities, not the *net* ones, $i_+ - i_-$ or $i_- - i_+$, we can see that something of an exponential dependence of current density on potential would be expected (fig. 3.13).

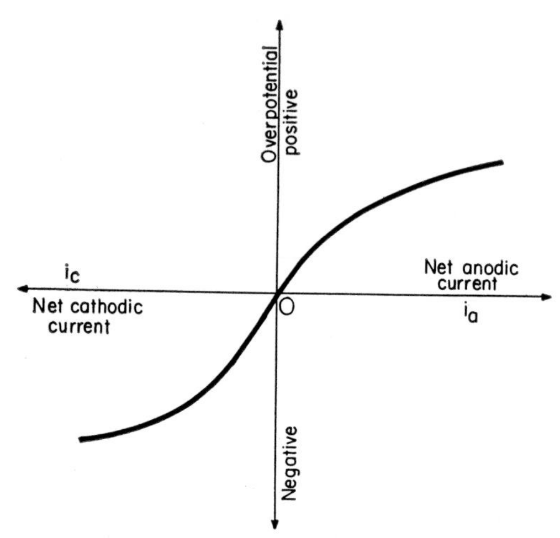

Fig. 3.13. An early prediction of the form of the net current–potential relation. The ordinate is the overpotential, namely the amount by which the potential differs from equilibrium.

We clearly need to specify and to define a potential which refers to *how far away from the equilibrium or reversible potential we are.* (We might say: How much *irreversibility* is there?) Figure 3.13 shows that it is the size of this 'departure-from-the-equilibrium' potential, and its sign, which will tell us whether indeed we are going to have a net cathodic current or a net anodic current, and how much that current is.†

The 'how-far-we-are-away-from-the-equilibrium-potential' potential is called the "OVERPOTENTIAL" of the electrode reaction.

The overpotential (literally named!) is the *extra* potential which one must apply to an electrode reaction to make it occur at a certain net velocity. If the overpotential is zero, the cathodic and anodic partial electrode reactions *are still occurring*; but they are occurring at equal and opposite rates in both directions, and therefore there is no *net* current to be observed by an ammeter in the circuit between the two electrodes of a cell.

When the net reaction rate is zero, the overpotential is zero, and the electrode is at its reversible, or equilibrium, position.

† Electrochemical scientists often abbreviate current density and refer to current. But it is always current per unit area which is meant.

If the overpotential is negative, there will be a net emission of electrons from electrode to solution. If the overpotential is positive there will be a net acceptance by the electrode of electrons from the solution.

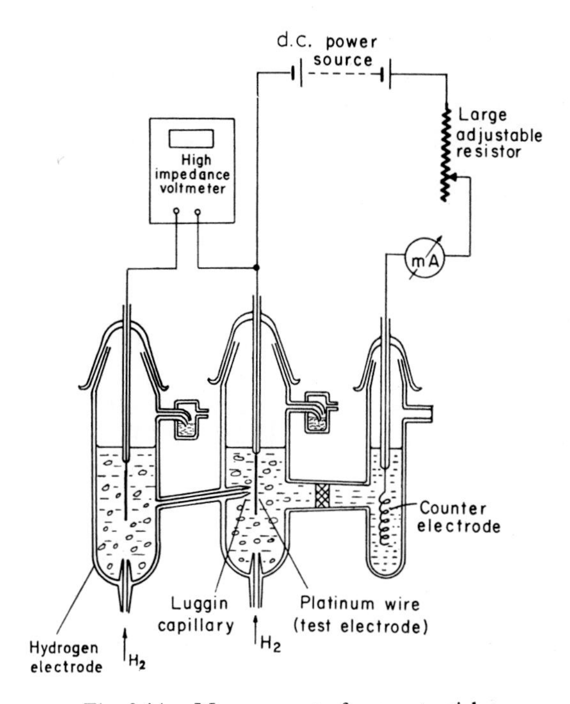

Fig. 3.14. Measurement of overpotential.

In the next section, we shall relate the net current to the overpotential.

The velocity of an electrode reaction as a function of overpotential

We define the overpotential as the difference between the actual electrode potential V, and the equilibrium potential, V_{equil} or V_{rev} (V_{e} or V_r). Thus,

$$\eta = V - V_{\text{e}}. \tag{3.16}$$

Depending on the values of V and V_{e}, η can be positive (anodic) or negative (cathodic). Alternatively, we could say that the actual electrode potential is the sum of the equilibrium potential, which is a fixed quantity for a given solution and electrode reaction, and the overpotential, which can be changed by changing the electrical potential applied in an external circuit.

$$V = V_{\text{e}} + \eta. \tag{3.17}$$

Now, we can go back to the equations (3.13) and (3.8) for the individual anodic and cathodic rates, or current densities,† and replace V with $V_e + \eta$.

$$i_+ = nFk_+ \exp[(1-\beta)FV/RT]$$
$$= nFk_+ \exp[(1-\beta)FV_e/RT] \exp[(1-\beta)F\eta/RT]. \quad (3.18)$$

$$i_- = nFc_i k_- \exp(-\beta FV/RT)$$
$$= nFc_i k_- \exp(-\beta FV_e/RT) \exp(-\beta F\eta/RT). \quad (3.19)$$

All the terms in front of that containing the overpotential η, also represent a current density‡, but this is the current density at the equilibrium potential V_e; when $i_- = i_+$ (fig. 3.12 *a*), and so

$$nFk_+ \exp[(1-\beta)FV_e/RT] = nFc_i k_- \exp(-\beta FV_e/RT) = i_0. \quad (3.20)$$

Here, i_0 is known as *the exchange current density*. It is a characteristic constant for each particular electrode system—that is, the assembly of metal electrode and the solution of given concentration, composition and temperature. Equations (3.18) and (3.19) can be written in a simpler form §,

$$i_+ = i_0 \exp[(1-\beta)F\eta/RT] \quad (3.21)$$

and

$$i_- = i_0 \exp(-\beta F\eta/RT). \quad (3.22)$$

Since the net current density is

$$i = i_+ - i_- \quad (3.23)$$

then after introducing (3.21) and (3.22) in (3.23), and taking the common i_0 out

$$i = i_0\{\exp[(1-\beta)F\eta/RT] - \exp(-\beta F\eta/RT)\}. \quad (3.24)$$

This is the Butler–Volmer equation relating the net current density of the electrochemical reaction to the overpotential. It will be shown

† Current density and reaction rate per unit area are exactly equivalent. The former is simply the electrochemical equivalent of the latter. This has already been discussed on p. 6, where it was shown that $i/nF = v_{reac}$.

‡ We must be clear about *net* and *partial* current densities. There are always two partial current densities, a cathodic, i_-; and an anodic, i_+. There is always a *net* current density, which is the *difference* of i_+ and i_- or i_- and i_+. The net current density is taken as positive, so that, if η is positive, $i_+ > i_-$, and $i_a = i_+ - i_-$; if η is negative, $i_- > i_+$, so $i_c = i_- - i_+$. At $\eta = 0$, $i_c = i_a = 0$ and $i_+ = i_-$.

§ In the example given on page 89, when the effect of the change of potential was calculated, it was the exchange current density $i_0 = 100 \text{ A m}^{-2}$ which was in effect used for the current density at $V = 0{\cdot}74$, since $+0{\cdot}74$ V is $V_{equil.}$ for $Ag-Ag^+$ electrode in 0·1 M $AgNO_3$.

later (p. 99), that in special cases it can be written approximately in even simpler forms.

A closer look at overpotential

We have shown earlier (see p. 81) that one can consider two types of electrode reaction. In one type, in the overall electrochemical cell the reaction has to be *driven*, by forcing it to work, using an outside source of potential. Here, the overpotential is the *extra* potential which has to be applied to the electrode concerned so that the reaction may take place at the desired velocity. For example, we might be measuring the potential of an electrode of platinum in a cell driven by an external battery by connecting this platinum electrode electrically to another at which zero current flows. Further, in this 'reference electrode' (cf. fig. 3.14 and also fig. 2.12), we pass hydrogen from some external supply, and keep the H_2 in the electrode at a constant pressure, usually simply 1 atmosphere. Then, if no current passes across the central test electrode of fig. 3.14, when hydrogen gas is bubbling on these two, both the 'test' and the reference electrode, are at $i = 0$ and equilibrium conditions exist. The potential difference between them is zero. We now make the overpotential more negative, cathodic, by $-0{\cdot}1$ volt by adjusting the resistor in the circuit so that the potential with respect to the reference electrode is $-0{\cdot}1$ volt. We find, *now*, that hydrogen is evolved from the platinum test electrode at a rate of about 100 amp m^{-2}.

Similarly, one can consider the same electrode as a part of a driving cell when the overall reaction is a spontaneous one, e.g., in a H_2–Br_2 cell. Then, the overpotential is, in a sense, what the reaction demands if it is to go at a given rate. Thus, if we ionize hydrogen on an electrode, and the potential at this electrode when there is no net rate of ionization of hydrogen is 0 volt with respect to another hydrogen electrode (the reference electrode of fig. 3.14), then if it is going to dissolve at a rate of about 100 amp m^{-2}, the overpotential should be about 0·1 V positive, anodic, in respect to the reference electrode.

This kind of measurement can be done in the same set-up shown in fig. 3.14, if the solution around the platinum *counter* electrode is replaced by a solution containing, e.g., bromine in an aqueous solution, say, of HBr. This electrode will behave as a bromine electrode, and has a reversible potential about 1·1 V more positive than the hydrogen electrode. If the power source is taken out of the circuit, the resistor will serve as a load for the H_2–Br_2 cell. By adjusting the resistor, the current through the cell, i.e., the rate of the overall reaction ($H_2 + Br_2 \rightarrow 2HBr$), can be controlled. Instead of the Br_2 electrode any other electrode with more *positive* potential than a H_2 electrode (cf. Table 5.3) can be used (e.g., oxygen, chlorine, silver, copper, etc.).

It should be pointed out, however, that by allowing the cell to behave spontaneously, and thus produce current, instead of driving it, it is only the *direction* of the current, i.e., the direction of the net reaction which is reversed. Instead of evolving H_2 ($2H^+ + 2e \rightarrow H_2$) we are ionizing molecular hydrogen ($H_2 \rightarrow 2H^+ + 2e$). The net hydrogen electrode reaction is anodic (de-electronation) and the overpotential positive.

In studying processes at one electrode, it is usual to do the measurements in the set-up shown in fig. 3.14. The current through the test electrode can be made to go in either direction, i.e., net cathodic or net anodic, by changing the polarity of the power source. By doing this, the direction of the electrode reaction is reversed, and the electrode reaction can be made to function as: $H_2 \rightarrow 2H^+ + 2e$; or as $2H^+ + 2e \rightarrow H_2$. In studying the reaction at the test electrode, what is happening at the counter electrode is of no importance, it does not effect the value of the overpotential on the test electrode or the current density at it.

Overpotential and physics.—It can be shown that the overpotential for the production of a definite reaction rate at a metal surface is in fact the shift of the Fermi level in the metal from the value which it had when the electrode reaction was taking place at an equal speed in both directions, i.e., at the equilibrium potential.

Overpotential and philosophy.—Overpotential may be seen as an example of the principle that one cannot get something for nothing. It is *not* possible for an electrochemical reaction to take place *at a significant rate* under the conditions at which thermodynamics says it may occur. If it is to occur at a detectable rate, there has to be an overpotential; this is the electrochemical analogue of the pressure *in excess of the equilibrium pressure* that is needed to drive a thermal reaction at a finite rate. A spontaneous electrochemical reaction cannot take place at finite velocity unless it rejects some of the energy which it could otherwise convert directly. It must 'pay' for happening at a given *rate* of conversion by rejecting some of the energy released in the reaction, in the resulting overpotential. The faster the reaction goes, the greater the rejected energy and the greater the overpotential at the electrodes.

Special cases of the current–potential relation

Let us go back to the Butler–Volmer equation (fig. 3.15):

$$i = i_0\{\exp[(1-\beta)F\eta/RT] - \exp(-\beta F\eta/RT)\}. \qquad (3.24)$$

Figure 3.15 also illustrates the equations (3.8) and (3.13), i.e., the effect of overpotential at the individual, cathodic and anodic partial reaction rates (broken lines). For a positive overpotential the anodic process wins, giving a net *anodic* current while for the negative overpotentials the *cathodic* process wins giving a net *cathodic* current.

Three particular cases can be considered, when applying Butler–Volmer equation: (i) for large values of η; (ii) for small values of η, and (iii) for $\eta = 0$.

(i) *Large* η

In equation (3.24), we have the difference of two exponential terms. If η is positive, an increase of η would increase exponentially the numerical value of the first term, and at the same time decrease the value of the second term. It is easy to show that, if $\eta = 0{\cdot}052$ V the

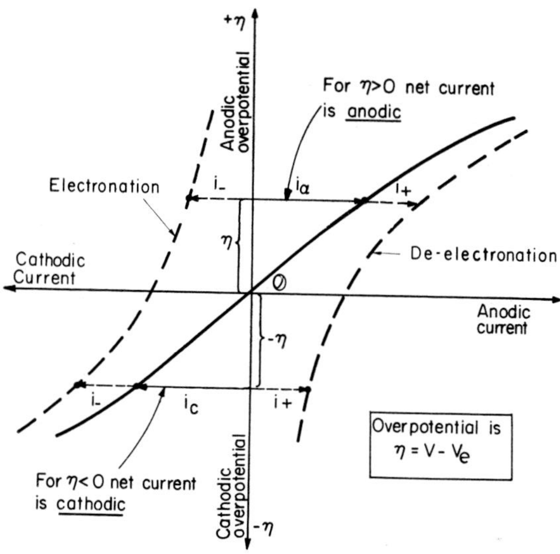

Fig. 3.15. Overpotential–current density diagram for an electrode reaction. Broken lines, electronation and de-electronation processes. Full line, the net current density.

first term in equation (3.24) becomes equal to $e = 2{\cdot}71$, while the second term is nearly ten times smaller, i.e., $1/e = 0{\cdot}36$. If the overpotential is more positive than about 0·052 V the second term becomes increasingly smaller and, therefore, can be neglected. Therefore, for large positive η, equation (3.24) reduces to a simpler equation:

$$i = i_0 \exp[(1-\beta)F\eta/RT]. \tag{3.25}$$

The same argument is valid for large negative overpotentials, i.e., those more negative than 0·052 V. When the first exponential term becomes negligible, a similar equation is obtained:

$$i = -i_0 \exp(-\beta F\eta/RT). \tag{3.26}$$

The meaning of these two equations is very simple. For overpotentials greater than about 50 mV, the effect of the reaction going in a direction opposite to the main one for the sign of the overpotential concerned, is negligible. It is only when η is less than about 0·05 V from the equilibrium potential, that the opposite process affects the net current, significantly and the complete Butler–Volmer equation (3.24) should be used.

One can take the logarithms of both sides of equation (3.25) (or (3.26))

$$\ln i = \ln i_0 + \frac{(1-\beta)F\,\eta}{RT} \tag{3.27}$$

and solve it explicitly for η

$$\eta = -\frac{RT}{(1-\beta)F}\ln i_0 + \frac{RT}{(1-\beta)F}\ln i. \tag{3.28}$$

Since only η and i are variables for a given electrode system the equation can be written as

$$\eta = a + b\ln i, \tag{3.29}$$

a linear relationship (fig. 3.16 *b*).

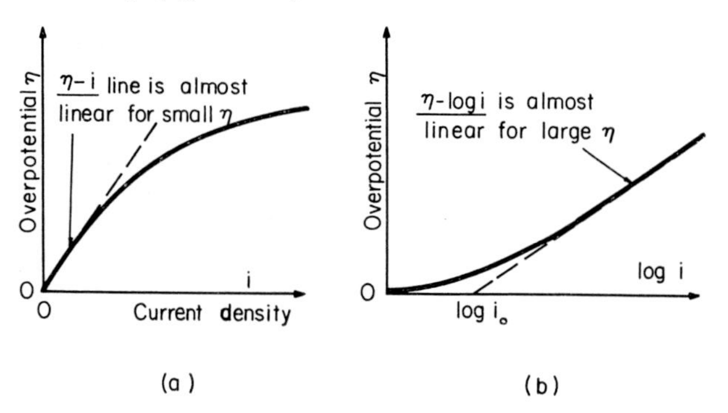

Fig. 3.16. (*a*) For small overpotentials, the η–i curve is practically linear. (*b*) For large overpotentials, the η–log i curve is practically linear. Extrapolation to $\eta = 0$ provides log i_0.

The equation (3.29) derived above is the Tafel equation (p. 90). Tafel established the relationship more than 65 years ago, but it was considered for a long time as a kind of peculiarity of the hydrogen evolution reaction instead of as the basic relation applying to all charge-transfer electrode reactions.

A plot of experimental results in η–log i coordinates usually furnishes two important pieces of information (full line in fig. 3.17 *b*):

Here the graph becomes a straight Tafel line. The gradient of this line is sometimes of interest in elucidating the molecular mechanism of the electrode reaction. (This point will be elaborated on in more detail on p. 116.) Since for $\eta = 0$, $i = i_0$, one can obtain the direct *exchange current density*, i_0, which is, as said before, the characteristic parameter of the electrode reaction.

(ii) *Small* η

For overpotentials smaller than 5 mV, the Butler–Volmer equation (eqn. (3.24)) can be simplified by expanding the exponential and taking only the first two terms†. Then, instead of the equation (3.24) one can write

$$i = i_0\left[\left(1+\frac{(1-\beta)F}{RT}\eta\right)-\left(1-\frac{\beta F}{RT}\eta\right)\right]. \tag{3.30}$$

After the rearrangement, one obtains:

$$i = \frac{i_0 F}{RT}\eta \tag{3.31}$$

or

$$\eta = \frac{RT}{i_0 F}i. \tag{3.32}$$

For small overpotentials ($\eta < 5$ mV) the relation between overpotential and current density is linear. In η–i coordinates this is a straight line with the gradient RT/i_0F, as shown by broken line in fig. 3.17 *a*.

Since R and F are constants, and T is also independent of the electrode system, the value of the gradient is determined by the exchange current density, i_0. This is also one of the experimental ways of determining i_0 for electrodes under investigation.

By analogy with Ohm's Law ('$V = RI$') (3.32) the gradient of the η–i line can be understood as the equivalent resistance per unit area, R_E, of the charge-transfer process on the electrode

$$R_E = \frac{RT}{i_0 F}. \tag{3.33}$$

Since the exchange current density, i_0 and the resistance per unit area R_E are inversely proportional (eqn. (3.33)), the larger i_0 is the smaller will be R_E. So, in order to carry out an electrochemical reaction in which the resistance of the interface is *small*, one has to have a *large* i_0. The effect of the electrode material and the relation of i_0 to the electrode material will be discussed in Chapter 5 (Electrocatalysis). In some cases, as in corrosion (e.g., the sudden failure of the side of a ship by stress corrosion cracking), a large i_0 might mean a disaster. One of the ways to reduce corrosion rate is to decrease the exchange

† $$e^x = 1+x+\frac{x^2}{2!}+\frac{x^3}{3!}\ldots \simeq 1+x \quad \textit{if } x \textit{ is small.}$$

$$e^{-x} = 1-x+\frac{x^2}{2!}-\frac{x^3}{3!}\ldots \simeq 1-x \quad \textit{if } x \textit{ is small.}$$

current density, i_0, for one or both of the coupled electrochemical processes which form the basis of corrosion.

At overpotentials above some 10 mV, the equivalent resistance of the electrochemical reaction, R_E, is not independent of potential as given by equation (3.33) (see fig. 3.16 *a*. The gradient, (R_E) is decreasing with increase of η). It is usually the value of R_E at the equilibrium potential V_e (or at $\eta = 0$) which is measured experimentally.

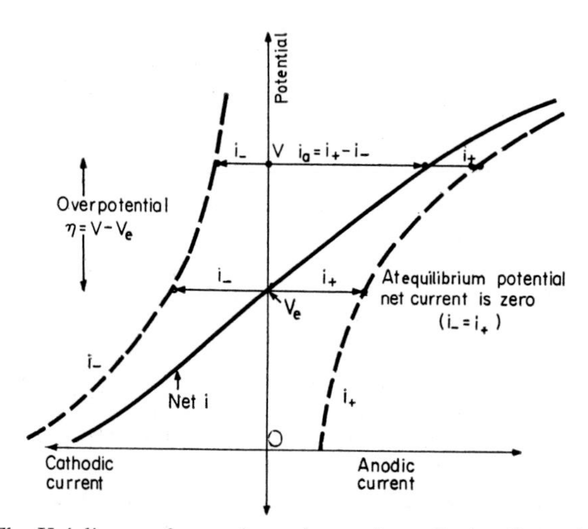

Fig. 3.17. The V–i diagram for an electrode reaction. Broken lines, the net current density.

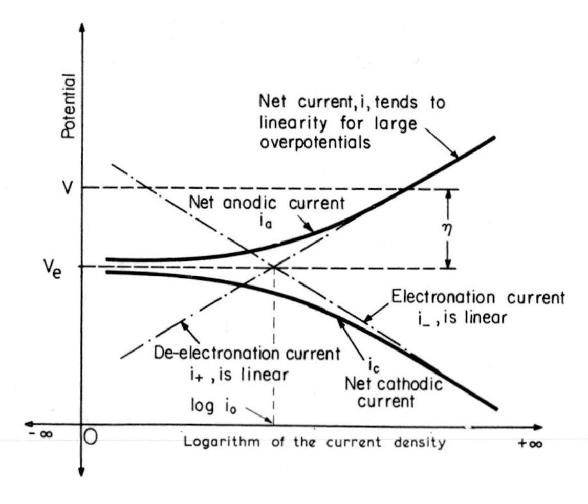

Fig. 3.18. The V–ln i diagram for an electrode reaction. Full lines, net cathodic and anodic current densities. Broken lines, electronation and de-electronation current densities.

Everything we have said about a net anodic reaction (with *positive* overpotential) is correspondingly applicable for a net cathodic reaction (with negative overpotential). Both cases are illustrated in more detail in fig. 3.17 but this time in V–i coordinates, and in fig. 3.18 in V–$\log i$ coordinates.

(iii) $\eta = 0$

When the overpotential is zero, the electrode is at its equilibrium potential, V_e. The net current, i, is zero, since the cathodic and anodic current densities are equal ($i_+ = i_-$). Then we can write again the equation (3.20)

$$nFk_+ \exp[(1-\beta)FV_e/RT] = nFc_i k_- \exp[-\beta FV_e/RT]. \quad (3.20)$$

We can take logarithms of both sides:

$$\ln k_+ + \frac{(1-\beta)F}{RT} V_e = \ln c_i + \ln k_- - \frac{\beta F}{RT} V_e \quad (3.34)$$

and rearrange the equation to give:

$$V_e = \frac{RT}{F} \ln \frac{k_-}{k_+} + \frac{RT}{F} \ln c_i. \quad (3.35)$$

The first term on the right hand side of this equation contains the two constants, k_- and k_+ and we can introduce a new constant, V_e. Then:

$$V_e = V_e^\circ + \frac{RT}{F} \ln c_i. \quad (3.36)$$

The equation (3.36) is Nernst's equation (1.3) applied to the equilibrium between a metal and the metal's ions in solution, i.e., to $M^+ + e \rightleftarrows M$, V_e° being the standard electrode potential when the concentration of ions in the solution is unity ($c_i = 1$).† Thermodynamically, equilibrium potentials and Nernst's equation are obviously applicable only to the very special situation, in which there *is* thermodynamic equilibrium; it usually does not exist at a metal–solution interface.

† For a general electrode reaction, e.g.,

$$aA + bB + ne \rightleftharpoons pP + qQ.$$

The equilibrium potential can be calculated by using a more general form of Nernst's equation

$$V_e = V_e^\circ + \frac{RT}{nF} \ln \frac{C_A{}^a \,.\, C_B{}^b}{C_P{}^p \,.\, C_Q{}^q}. \quad (3.36\ a)$$

Note that the denominator refers to the reduced state of the electrochemical reaction (right hand side).

The quantum mechanical nature of all electrode reactions

There is no hint of quantum mechanics in what we have said so far about electrochemical reactions. Up to now, it has been a matter of the particle, typified by a hydrated silver ion on p. 88, approaching the electrode, and then hopping through an energy barrier, receiving its electron on the way somehow, and arriving as an atom on the electrode.

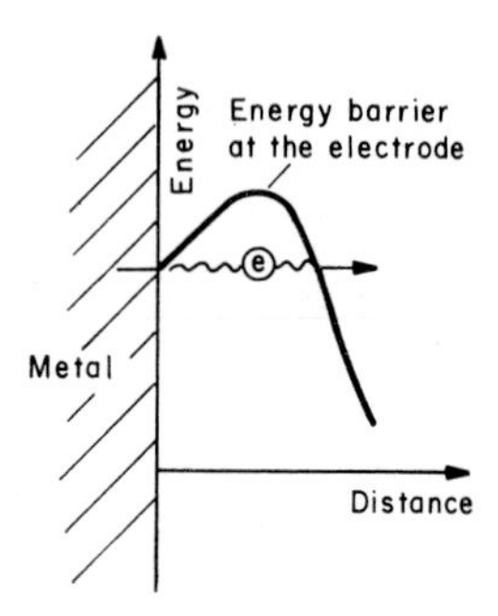

Fig. 3.19. Energy barrier for the escape of electron from an electrode surface. Electrons can tunnel through the barrier, even though the probability of doing this is small.

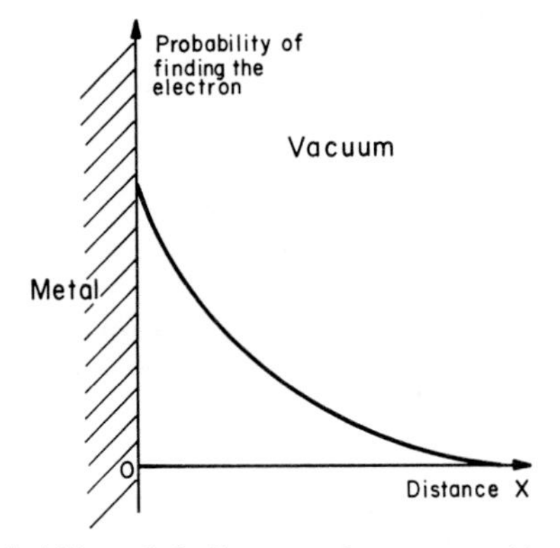

Fig. 3.20. How probability of finding an electron outside a metal in a vacuum decreases with distance from the metal surface.

It is the 'somehow' which brings in the quantum mechanics. We have kept our eyes shut about the electron, assuming, vaguely, that it 'got to the ion at the summit of the barrier' without having a more detailed or explicit model. We must now think about how the electron got there. We can do this equally well by considering either a cathodic reaction, or an anodic reaction. The first thing we would naturally do would be to calculate its emission rate by a classical (non-quantum-mechanical) method, assuming that the average thermal energy of an electron in the metal is sufficient to make some of them spill out of the energy states in which they are held in the metal and therefore get to the ions in the double layer. Such a calculation indicates a negligible rate of electron emission, somewhere in the region of 10^{-16} A/m^{-2}, for a typical electrode reaction, whereas in real cases the current densities are at least 10^{10} times greater. Thus, we are faced with a great 'no', there is *no possibility of obtaining sufficient electrons from the metal for electrode reactions to occur.* But, they do occur. How, then, does an electron get out from a metal to the ion?

The problem is not dissimilar to that of radioactive α-decay. Radioactive substances *do* decay; particles (He nuclei), do leave the nucleus although from a classical standpoint they are not supposed to—they ought never to be able to acquire sufficient energy to enable them to jump over the top of the energy barrier of the nucleus and escape. But they do escape.

The answer in each case is that the particles do not leap the energy barrier at all. For they also possess wave properties which enable them, in effect, to tunnel through an electric field which is a barrier with less than a certain energy. The tunnelling effect, strange though it seems, is a central part of quantum mechanics.†

The reader is referred to other works for this explanation of quantum-mechanical tunnelling which is a highly mathematical affair. But we can show here that the reason underlying the tunnelling is something that Heisenberg's Principle of Uncertainty would lead us to expect. Because of the impossibility of knowing the precise position of a particle which has a definite velocity, we cannot pin down precisely the position of an electron. With this idea as a basis, we can calculate the possibility of an electron's being 'anywhere'. In fact, the calculation shows that the probability of an electron's being very far away (say a micrometre, 10^{-6} m) from a point at which it would be expected classically is so small as to be negligible. However, there are quite real probabilities that an electron which classically would be 'in the surface of' a metal can be, in terms of quantum mechanics, many ångströms outside the surface of the metal.

This, then, is the picture that we have of how electrons escape from the interior of metals to take part in an electrochemical reaction. The electrons *tunnel* out of their energy levels within the metal and find their way to ions in the solution, in a quantum mechanical way. One can say that electrochemical reactions are 'entirely quantal' in character. This has the following meaning: in ordinary reactions, those not involving radioactive decay or electron transfer at interfaces, reactions take place roughly according to classical theory. The (more correct) quantum mechanical treatment turns out to imply only a small correction

† We recommend Sir Nevill Mott's *Elementary Quantum Mechanics* published by Wykeham Publications Ltd in this series.

term, which with heavier particles is often quite negligible. Electrode reactions always involve electrons and are, therefore, always *entirely* quantal.

Acceptor states in solution

But now we come to a dilemma. In our calculations for the relation of current to potential, we did not use any quantum mechanical reasoning. Were these equations wrong? This question can only be answered convincingly by a full quantum-mechanical analysis which is outside the scope of this book. However, we can give a qualitative answer. When electrons tunnel out from a metal to the particles in the solution, they do not do so without having to fulfil certain energy conditions. One of these is that the *quantized electronic states* of the particles in contact with the electrode in solution must be exactly equal

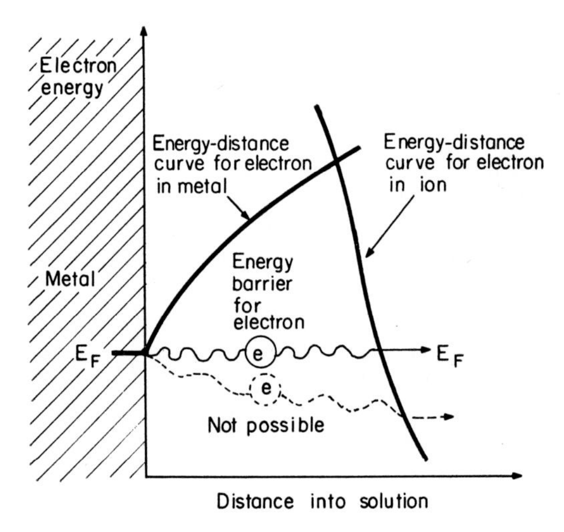

Fig. 3.21. Electrons can tunnel through the barrier only if the energy levels happen to be equal at both sides.

in energy to the energy of the electron in the metal. For, otherwise, energy will be lost or gained in the transfer; radiation would occur; and that is not observed. This means that an electron in an energy state, E_F, in the metal (fig. 3.21) must go to an electronic state in the molecule which is exactly E_F. Now, it is possible to show that such states do exist for the particles in the solution, but they involve *vibrationally excited* states. For example, in the reaction $H_3O^+ + e \rightarrow H_{ads} + H_2O$, it is imagined that the H–O bonds which receive electrons are in excited vibrational states. The degree to which this excitation energy exceeds the ground state of the reaction is a contribution to the energy of activation. From the physical point of view, the quantum mechanical aspect is absolutely necessary. Why? *If it were not for quantum mechanical tunnelling, no electrochemical reaction could occur at all, for no electrons would be able to escape from the metal!* From the point of view of the numerical answer, however, a simple version of the quantum mechanical treatment and the classical calculations agree. That is why our simple deduction of the current–potential relation (see eqn. (3.8)) happens to give the right answer!

But how do we know that electrons do tunnel easily from and to a metal to and from the ions in solutions which are adjacent to the electrode? This brings us rather to a limit of knowledge at present.

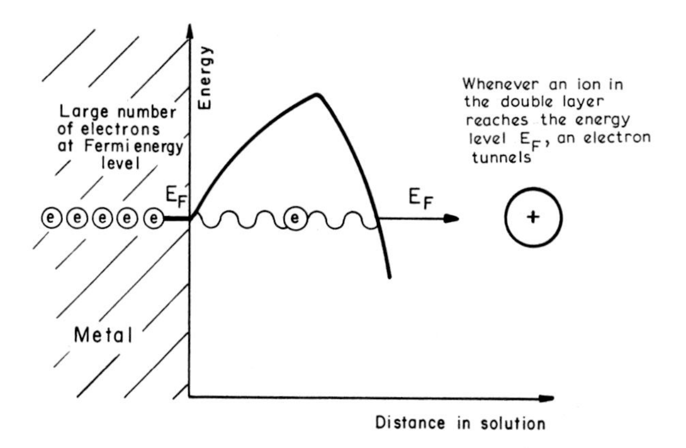

Fig. 3.22. In 'adiabatic' transfer, electrons tunnel whenever the ion reaches the energy level corresponding to the Fermi-level electron energy, E_F.

It seems, as far as we know at present, that transfer is 'adiabatic'. This means that electrons are always easily available whenever the appropriate quantum state turns up for them in solution; and that the rate of successful transfers does depend only on the number of particles on the solution side of the metal–solution interface which exist in appropriate quantum states to offer electrons a berth at the right price—an energy state in the appropriate quantum level (fig. 3.22). If that were not so (if the electron tunnelling itself were the bottleneck), then the way in which the rate of electron transfer would depend upon the potential difference across the interphase would not be that given by the probability of occurrence of excited states in the solutions. In fact, it *is* so given experimentally.

Is there any advantage, then, in looking at electrode reactions in this new, quantum mechanical way? The answer is that we cannot look at them in any other way, because the classical picture gives an impossibly small number of electrons emitted from the surface of a metal; according to this, then electrochemical reactions could never take place! However, some people may say, 'But is quantum mechanics more useful?' The answer is that if one is thinking along the right path, one is more likely to make sensible predictions, and produce more useful science and engineering, than if one is thinking in terms of the wrong model.

A New Kind of Chemical Reaction?

We saw on p. 3 that corrosion takes place by one metal atom giving up an electron to the substrate, and that this electron then wanders around in the metal surface until it finds a proton which it can discharge (figs. 3.4 and 1.3). Corrosion can also be looked at as a chemical reaction. Thus, for iron, the reaction would be

$$Fe + 2H^{+} \rightarrow Fe^{2+} + H_2, \qquad (3.37)$$

and this involves two distinct electrochemical processes:

$$Fe \rightarrow Fe^{2+} + 2e \qquad (3.38)$$

and

$$2H^{+} + 2e \rightarrow H_2. \qquad (3.39)$$

A characteristic feature of this reaction is that the particles which take part in the reaction (the iron atoms and the hydrogen ions) *do not have to come into contact.* We usually think of 'chemical reactions' as occurring essentially by collision, and that the molecules must be near one another, come into momentary contact, exchange energy, make and break bonds, and then go off again as new particles. The mechanism of corrosion suggests that perhaps there is another *kind* of chemical reaction which occurs in the same way as corrosion.

It would be an overall reaction consisting of *two partial electrochemical reactions*, one involving electron acceptance by particles in solution, and the other involving electron acceptance by the substrate electrode.

Such a mode of reaction seems to have been proved in a few cases. One of these is the chemical reaction by which titanium is generally produced (see fig. 3.23). Molten magnesium is injected (in the form of droplets) into a molten salt containing a dissolved halide of titanium. At each droplet, the metal dissolves electrochemically:

$$2Mg \rightarrow 2Mg^{2+} + 4e. \qquad (3.40)$$

The excess electrons formed by this dissolution then migrate to other sites on the surface of the drop and transfer to Ti^{4+} ions:

$$Ti^{4+} + 4e \rightarrow Ti. \tag{3.41}$$

We do not yet know how common this type of electrochemical mechanism may be. But it is interesting to note that in the case of some reactions which occur on surfaces, and which are now termed 'chemical' (where it is implicitly assumed that the particles collide on the substrate), the reaction rate is lowered if the electrical conductivity of the substrate is reduced: just what one would expect if the mechanism of such 'chemical' reactions were electrochemical.

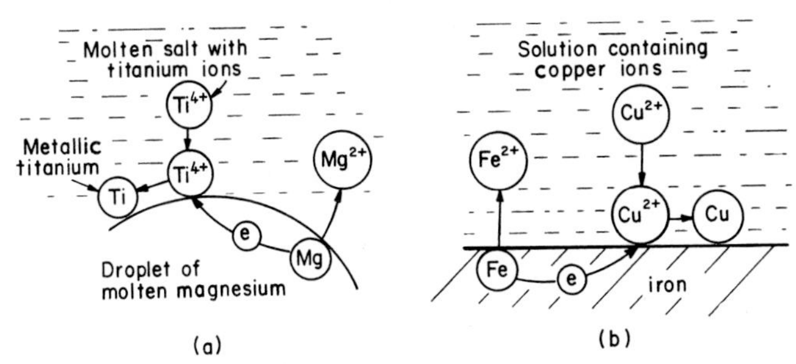

Fig. 3.23. Electrochemical mechanism of processes used (*a*) for titanium production, and (*b*) for extraction of copper from copper-mine waters. Note that the magnesium and the iron are in fact 'corroding'.

We must not imagine that reactions of this type need a recognizable 'electrode' on which to take place. They can occur on any substrate, so long as it conducts. Nor is it necessary to have a conductivity equal to that of a metal in the substrate. Oxide semiconductors, for example, would do. Electronic conductivity recently has been observed in some biological materials (see p. 252), and the presence of interfacial electrochemical mechanisms in biophysical situations awaits investigation.

As can be seen from fig. 3.23, there is no collision between the particles which react by this electrochemical mechanism. There is collision with the substrate *but no collision between the reactants*. Now such *reactant–reactant* collision is the essence of *chemical* reactions. It just isn't known as yet whether the electrochemical (and it could be called corrosional or fuel-cell) approach to chemical surface reactions will turn out to be something occasional or the most likely mechanism of *most* surface reactions.

Multi-step Reactions

Hitherto all the considerations of electrochemical reactions in this book have assumed that the reaction $M^{+} + e \rightarrow M$ is the only sort of electrode reaction which takes place. This is not the case; it has been assumed to be so hitherto for simplicity. There are some reactions which take place in this simple way; and, indeed, there are even more simple electrochemical reactions in which *only* a charge transfer occurs —reactions, for example, of the type $Fe^{2+} \rightarrow Fe^{3+} + e$. However, in practice, the majority of electrode reactions do not take place in a single electron transfer step, but, like other chemical reactions, have several consecutive steps.

One illustration of this and a reaction which has received far more attention than any other electrochemical reaction, is the cathodic reaction of hydroxonium ion deposition followed by the evolution of hydrogen gas. This reaction is the result of the electronation of protons in solution. Thus, the overall reaction is $2H^+ + 2e \rightarrow H_2$. This is by no means the whole story, for the reaction goes in steps. One path for this reaction, sometimes called the hydrogen atom combination path, goes in this way: A proton comes† to the cathode and reacts with an electron, giving an adsorbed hydrogen atom. A number of adsorbed hydrogen atoms diffuse across the surface and meet each other, so that they may combine to hydrogen molecules. The reaction may be represented as

$$H^+ + e \longrightarrow H_{ads} \tag{3.42}$$

$$H_{ads} + H_{ads} \rightleftarrows H_2. \tag{3.43}$$

This is a simple example of a two-step reaction. Most multi-step reactions are more complicated. An example of medium complexity is that of the oxidation of propane. The probable first two steps for the overall reaction

$$C_3H_8 + 6H_2O = 3CO_2 + 20H^+ + 20e \tag{3.44}$$

are

(1) $$C_3H_8 = (C_3H_7)_{ads} + H^+ + e \tag{3.45}$$

and

(2) $$(C_3H_7)_{ads} \longrightarrow (C_2H_4)_{ads} + (CH_3)_{ads}. \tag{3.46}$$

Those following are unknown, but there may be several more steps.

Several interesting questions must be asked about these multi-step reactions. What contribution to the rate does the charge transfer step make? If there is more than one charge transfer step, do they all have the same effect upon the rate? Does one of the partial reactions, be it a charge transfer reaction or not, affect the rate more than the others? If a non-charge transfer reaction is the most important in determining the rate of the reaction, what sort of effect does potential

† In water solution protons (or hydrogen ions) are always linked to a water molecule forming the hydroxonium ion H_3O^+. For the sake of simplicity we write H^+ instead of H_3O^+.

have on the reaction? These questions lead us to another of the ideas which play an important role in the post-Nernstian electrochemistry: the rate-determining step.

The Rate-determining Step

We must first discuss the idea of the *rate-determining step* (r.d.s.).

Consider the hydrogen evolution reaction. Let us take the case in which the rate of discharge of protons to form hydrogen atoms is much slower than the rate of combination of hydrogen atoms. Then we can imagine that whenever a proton gets across the double layer from the solution (fig. 3.24), it immediately combines with another hydrogen atom which is waiting for it. Under these conditions, the rate of the

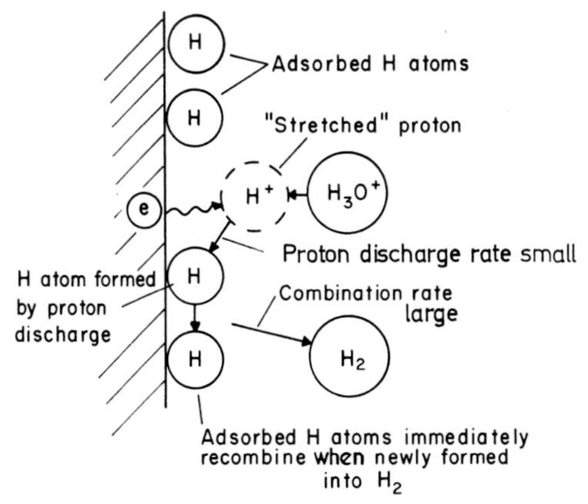

Fig. 3.24. Stages of H_2 evolution reaction when proton discharge is the rate-determining step.

overall production of hydrogen will be controlled by the *rate of the discharge of protons*. This discharge of protons is the 'rate-determining step' for the over-all reaction $2H^+ + 2e \rightarrow H_2$.

Few hydrogen atoms will be present on the surface of the electrode during the reaction, because directly they are made available by proton discharge they form hydrogen molecules and leave the surface.

But what about the other possibility, that the rate of proton discharge will be very fast, and that of the combination reaction rather slow? Here the protons are easily available from the solution, stream across to the electrode, but find difficulty in getting off the surface. A high concentration of hydrogen will build up on the surface before hydrogen combination, the rate of which is proportional to $\theta_H{}^2$, will catch up with proton discharge. If the fraction of the surface covered with hydrogen is θ_H, we can say that, for the second case, $\theta_H \gg 0$, while in the first case, with proton discharge rate-determining, $\theta_H \simeq 0$. In this second case, the combination of hydrogen atoms is the rate-determining process for the over-all reaction.

We may generalize and say that, in a multi-step reaction, one of the partial reactions is rate-controlling for the whole sequence. The whole sequence must travel at the net rate of this rate-determining step.

One matter which must be cleared up here concerns the meaning of the words 'slow' and 'fast' in relation to rate-determining steps. It is often said that the rate-determining step (r.d.s.) is 'slow' and the other reactions are 'fast'. For example, in the sequence of equations (3.42) and (3.43) above, the proton discharge has been said to be 'slow' in the first example (see fig. 3.25).

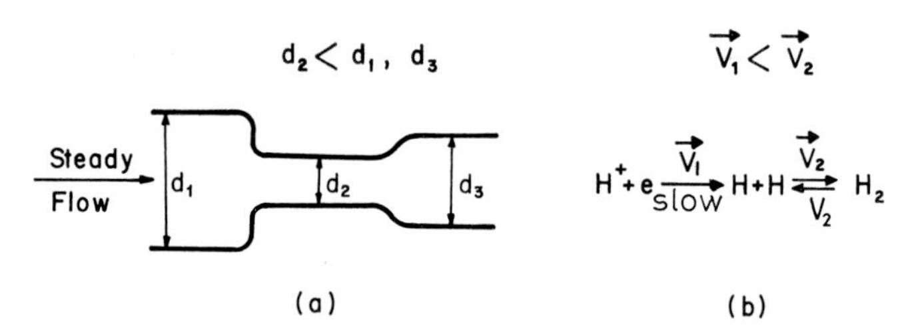

Fig. 3.25. (*a*) Fluid flow is controlled by the smallest diameter of the tube. (*b*) The rate of hydrogen evolution is controlled by the partial reaction which has the lower rate.

Now, the terms 'slow' and 'fast' here refer to those consecutive reaction steps of the overall reaction, which in one direction have smaller or larger individual reaction rates respectively. If proton discharge ($H^+ + e \rightarrow H_{ads}$) has reaction rate $\mathbf{v}_1$ in the cathodic direction, and combination reaction ($2H_{ads} \rightarrow H_2$) reaction rate $\mathbf{v}_2$ in the same direction, the first step is 'slow', i.e., rate determining, if $\mathbf{v}_1 < \mathbf{v}_2$.

However, if the over-all reaction $2H^+ + 2e \rightarrow H_2$ is proceeding at a *steady rate*, there is no possibility that one individual reaction step, e.g., $2H_{ads} \rightarrow H_2$ can go faster than the preceding step. All the steps in a consecutive sequence must go at the same *net* rate when the reaction is 'in a steady state', i.e., when it is not accelerating or decelerating in rate. However, *one* of the partial reactions will control what this net rate is.

The idea of a rate-determining step in a consecutive sequence is quite a general one. In any series of operations there is one step which controls the whole of the sequence. A trivial example is that on a journey from Los Angeles to New York the speed of the air flight determines the time for the journey; but if the distance travelled by air is sufficiently short, the rate of arrival from home to home may well be determined by the trip to the airport. (Particularly if the lack of application of electrochemical power sources to transportation is being illustrated by the presence of the smoggy state in Los Angeles.)

A better example is that of a stream of cars going from town A to town B. The traffic is heavy in the direction of A to B until the drivers find that there is a bridge broken down, and that only one traffic lane is open. Passage across this bridge may then become the rate-determining step for the arrival of cars at town B. It is common-sense to expect that, on learning the conditions and that the overall journey would now take perhaps five times as long as had been planned, a number of drivers would turn back. We shall return to this idea of a reverse direction of some surface reactions *before* the rate-determining or 'bottleneck' step when we talk about the 'pseudo-equilibrium' below.

Our remarks here on rate-determining steps are rough and ready ones; the idea does not always apply in this simple way. It would be expected to apply if the number of steps in the sequence is fairly small. But suppose we have a complicated reaction—a biological reaction, for example—in which there are twenty or thirty consecutive steps. It can be shown that to be effectively *rate-determining*, a step must have an energy of activation (E_a in eqn. (3.2)) higher by at least 10 kJ mol^{-1} than that of the steps before and after it. The energy-of-activation range over which chemical reactions take place is usually less than 100 kJ mol^{-1}, so that if we have thirty steps, it is quite probable that many steps will have an energy of activation which will not differ by 10 kJ mol^{-1} from those of surrounding steps, whereupon (for such lengthy and complex reactions) the rate-determining step is harder to identify (but see p. 118).

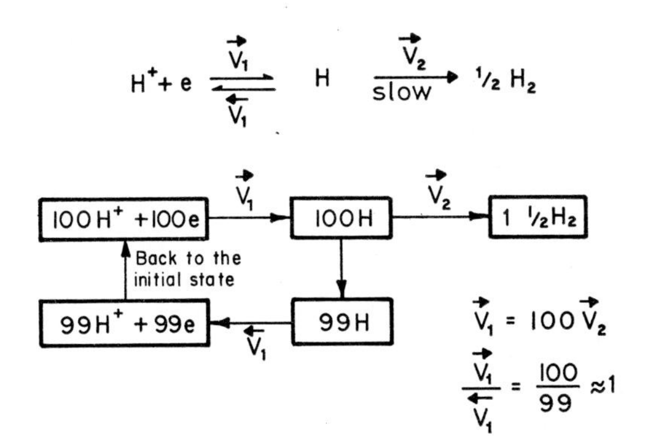

Fig. 3.26. Illustration of pseudo-equilibrium.

Pseudo-equilibrium

The effect illustrated by our bridge–traffic analogy does happen in molecular reactions. Suppose that we have a very slow reaction for the combination of hydrogen atoms to make hydrogen molecules in the cathodic hydrogen evolution reaction. The protons discharge easily, but the atoms do not combine readily. What happens? Instead of remaining stuck upon the surface while θ_H rises to 1, the hydrogen atoms may re-dissolve. Thus, if the rate of proton discharge is, say, 10^{20} protons m^{-2} s^{-1}, but the rate of combination of hydrogen atoms on the surface is only 10^{18} atoms m^{-2} s^{-1}, then there must be a back reaction (hydrogen atom dissolution to form protons) which occurs at $0{\cdot}99 \,.\, 10^{20}$, the net rate being, then, $(1-0{\cdot}99) \,.\, 10^{20} \approx 10^{18}$ in the forward ($H^+ \rightarrow \frac{1}{2}H_2$) direction. Or, in general,

$$\begin{bmatrix}\text{forward rate}\\ \text{of reaction}\end{bmatrix} - \begin{bmatrix}\text{backward rate of}\\ \text{this reaction}\end{bmatrix} = \begin{bmatrix}\text{net forward rate}\\ \text{of the overall reaction}\end{bmatrix}.$$

If the reaction rate in the forward direction is almost equal to the rate in the backward direction, we have what is called a *pseudo-equilibrium*, and it is common to say that the non-rate-determining partial reactions before the rate-determining step are in pseudo-equilibrium (fig. 3.26).

Why the rate-determining step is important in an electrochemical reaction

The importance of knowing the rate-determining step in a reaction is, of course, that it is the one which determines not only the *rate* of the overall reaction but also all its characteristics, e.g., how much the rate will change if the potential changes, or how much faster it will take place if the substrate electrode material is changed, etc.

Knowledge of the rate-determining step, where this can be obtained, should give rise to a practical advantage: the possibility of *predicting* what kind of substrate will give the highest rate constant for the overall reaction, i.e., will catalyse it best. Catalysts, as will be seen in Chapter 5, affect reaction rates in a way which is entirely dependent upon the mechanism of the reaction (fig. 5.3). If we are ever, then, to get out of our stage of guessing and empirically groping our way with catalysts, and arrive at a more intelligent way of selecting them, we certainly will have to know the rate-determining step of the reaction concerned.

Determination of a rate-determining step

There is a whole subsection of the science of electrochemical kinetics associated with the determination of the rate-determining step, and many separate methods may be used. One of these, which *occasionally* yields unique information concerning rate-determining steps, is the connection between the current and the potential, i.e., the evaluation of the derivative $d\eta/d \log i$, the variation of the current density, i, of an electrode reaction as the overpotential is changed. It is found that, according to the assumptions made with respect to which reaction step in a given path is rate-determining, this derivative differs characteristically. In reaction sequences in which this difference is clear and indicative (i.e., two hypothetical rate-determining steps do not give the same value of the derivative), the experimental evaluation of $d\eta/d \log i$ then leads one to a distinction between the two steps.

However, the situation is more often complicated by a number of rate-determining steps having the same $d\eta/d \log i$ associated with them, so that other methods must be used to obtain indication of the true rate-determining reaction step.

This situation of two different derivatives for different rate-determining steps can easily be shown for the hydrogen evolution reaction.

Let us consider the overall reaction path for H_2 evolution given by two reaction steps

$$H^+ + e \rightarrow H_{ads} \tag{3.42}$$

$$H_{ads} + H_{ads} \rightarrow H_2. \tag{3.43}$$

We can assume that two distinct cases might arise: (*a*) the first step, proton discharge, being the rate-determining step, and (*b*) the second step, combination of atomic hydrogen, being the rate-determining step. Let us see the consequences.

(*a*) *Proton-discharge as the rate-determining step*

If the proton discharge is the rate-determining step the relation between the overpotential and current density is as for the single electron transfer step elaborated previously on p. 99, and is given by equation (3.26)

$$i = i_0 \exp(-\beta F\eta/RT). \tag{3.26}$$

By taking logarithms of both sides and rearranging, one obtains

$$\eta = \frac{RT}{\beta F} \ln i_0 - \frac{RT}{\beta F} \ln i. \tag{3.47}$$

This is again an equation of the Tafel's type, with gradient

$$\frac{d\eta}{d \ln i} = -\frac{RT}{\beta F} = -\frac{2RT}{F}, \tag{3.48}$$

if $\beta = 0{\cdot}5$. To obtain the derivative $d\eta/d \log i$, which is more practical, one has to use the conversion factor 2·3; $d\eta/d \log i = 2{\cdot}3\, d\eta/d \ln i$.

Therefore, if the proton-discharge is the rate-determining step, the slope of the linear part of the experimental curve should be

$$-2{\cdot}3 \frac{2RT}{F} = -0{\cdot}120 \text{ V}.$$

So the overpotential should become more negative by 0·120 V for a tenfold increase of current density (the logarithm change of unity).

(*b*) *Combination of* H_{ads} *as the rate-determining step*

If the second step, combination of adsorbed H atoms at the surface, is rate-determining, one might at first expect that the rate of the reaction should not depend on overpotential, since it is a simple chemical reaction. And since it is rate-determining, the rate of the overall reaction should be proportional to the square of the concentration of H_{ads}. (Since this is a surface reaction we shall use instead the surface coverage, θ_H)

$$\text{Rate} = k \cdot \theta^2_H. \tag{3.49}$$

When we assumed that this second step is rate-determining, we assumed simultaneously that the first, proton discharge step, is much faster, and therefore in a pseudo-equilibrium:

$$H^+ + e \rightleftarrows H_{ads} \tag{3.50}$$

i.e., the rates (cathodic and anodic current densities) in forward and backward directions for this, first step, are practically equal. The consequence will be that the surface coverage θ_H will depend on the overpotential, increasing when the overpotential becomes more negative. If this is true, the overpotential must, indirectly, affect the rate of the second step, and therefore the rate of the overall reaction. By how much? To find out, we have to find how the potential is related to surface coverage θ_H, and use this relation, $\theta_H = f(V)$, in equation (3.49).

If reaction (3.50) can be treated as reversible we can apply the Nernst equation (eqn. (3.36)) which, if we take θ_H as proportional to the concentration of H_{ads}, is:

$$V = V^\circ + \frac{RT}{F} \ln \frac{c_{H^+}}{\theta_H}, \tag{3.51}$$

c_{H^+} being the H^+ ion concentration in solution.

Rearranging, and taking the antilogarithm,

$$\theta_H = c_{H^+} \exp(-F(V - V^\circ)/RT). \tag{3.52}$$

Taking into account that $V = V_e + \eta$, and that V_e, V° and c_{H^+} are constants, independent of overpotential, the equation can be reduced to a simple form:

$$\theta_H = K \exp(-F\eta/RT). \tag{3.53}$$

The surface coverage θ_H is exponentially dependent on overpotential, increasing with the increase of overpotential. (Cathodic overpotential is negative. Therefore, the exponent is positive.)

If we put θ_H from equation (3.53) into (3.49) and take into account that two electrons have been exchanged we obtain for the overall current:

$$i = 2\,.\,F\,.\,k\,.\,(K \exp[-F\eta/RT])^2 = K_1 \exp(-2F\eta/RT). \quad (3.54)$$

K_1 is the new constant containing all other constants. If we take the logarithms of the both sides and solve for η we obtain:

$$\eta = \frac{RT}{2F} \ln K_1 - \frac{RT}{2F} \ln i. \quad (3.55)$$

This is again an equation of the Tafel type with gradient

$$\frac{d\eta}{d \ln i} = -\frac{RT}{2F}. \quad (3.56)$$

If common logarithms are used the slope would be:

$$-2{\cdot}3\,\frac{RT}{2F} = -0{\cdot}030 \text{ V}.$$

In this case, for the combination reaction as rate-determining the expected gradient is quite different—four times smaller (fig. 3.27). Therefore, as the numerical value of the slope in the linear region of η–$\log i$ curve depends on the position of the rate-determining step in the reaction sequence, the experimental determination of $d\eta/d \log i$

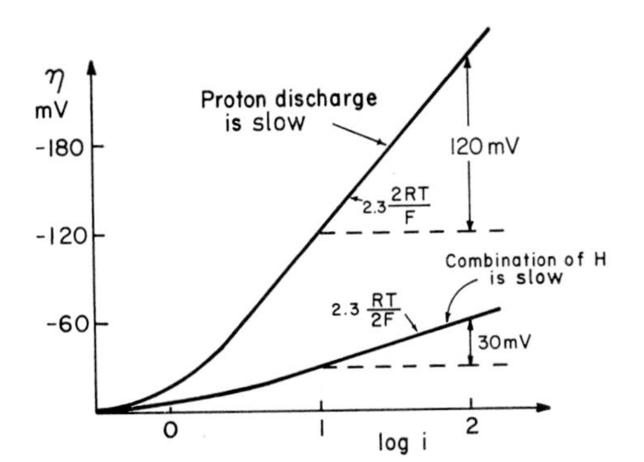

Fig. 3.27. Plot of η against $\log i$ for H_2 evolution reaction when proton discharge and combination of H atoms are rate-determining steps.

can be a valuable tool in the analysis of the reaction mechanism. However, we have to point out that in most cases different rate-determining steps can give the *same* slope. In this, more frequently met, case, additional parameters are necessary for the complete analysis. Many of these involve the interpretation of transient measurements, as described below. These sometimes give information on mechanism studies as sure and clear as that illustrated above for measurements in the steady state. More often, transient (or 'sweep') studies give information on surface radicals, and this, then, indirectly helps in mechanism studies.

Transient Currents and Potentials

Up to now, we have not considered the possibility that the potential at an electrode, and therefore the reaction rate occurring at it, might be altered with time. However, there certainly must be a beginning to a reaction, and it is wrong to think that when we switch on a certain overpotential the reaction 'immediately' attains the steady reaction rate corresponding to that overpotential. Study of what is happening while the steady state is being attained is informative. It can, for example, give an indication of the rate-determining reaction step, or a determination of θ, etc.

Thus, if we have ions in contact with an electrode which has an equilibrium potential of, let us say, +0·5 V, then, until the electrode has reached 0·5 V no net electrochemical reaction will occur. However, we are implicitly assuming that the electrons, when they go into, or are withdrawn from, an electrode (so that its potential changes), immediately transfer to ions in solution. But we have forgotten the electrode itself, i.e., the metal of the electrode, independent of the solution. We must recall that it has capacitor properties (Chapter 2), and that it needs electrons to charge it up, or to discharge it, so that it takes time to reach or leave a given overpotential.†

When we connect up our electrode to an outer circuit, there is an appreciable time after the connection has been made before the electrode attains a certain potential (fig. 3.28 *a*). This time is needed for the electrons to change the potential of the electrode to that at which an electrode reaction will take place at a given rate. Often these times are very small, for example 100 microseconds; but they may sometimes be lengthened, by using small currents, to as much as one second.

There are many ways of studying transients at electrodes. Here is a cross-over point between electronics and electrodics. Advanced electronic circuitry—where the knowledge is many years ahead of the

† Why do we sometimes use the word 'potential' and sometimes 'overpotential' when we refer to the electrical state of a metal in solution? The overpotential which is necessary for a reaction to occur at a given rate (see eqns. (3.25) and (3.26)) is very simply related to the potential:

$$\eta = V_{(i)} - V_e,$$

where $V_{(i)}$ is the necessary potential of the electrode to make the current density, i. Hence, it does not matter too much whether we refer to $V_{(i)}$ or to η, because they differ only by the equilibrium potential, V_e, which is constant in a given solution for a given reaction. However, it is better to refer to the electrical state of the electrode in terms of overpotential, because of the fact that it says more in a shorter time. Thus, $\eta = 0$ means no net reaction (cf. eqn. (3.24)), η as negative means a cathodic reaction, η as positive an anodic reaction, and so on.

knowledge of electrochemistry needed to apply it to electrode reaction—can be utilized to put an electrode through a great variety of manoeuvres. For example, we can put on a square-wave current pulse as in fig. 3.28 *a*, square wave potential pulse, as in fig. 3.28 *b*, or a triangular pulse, as in fig. 3.28 *c*, etc. On the whole, there are three main regimes which

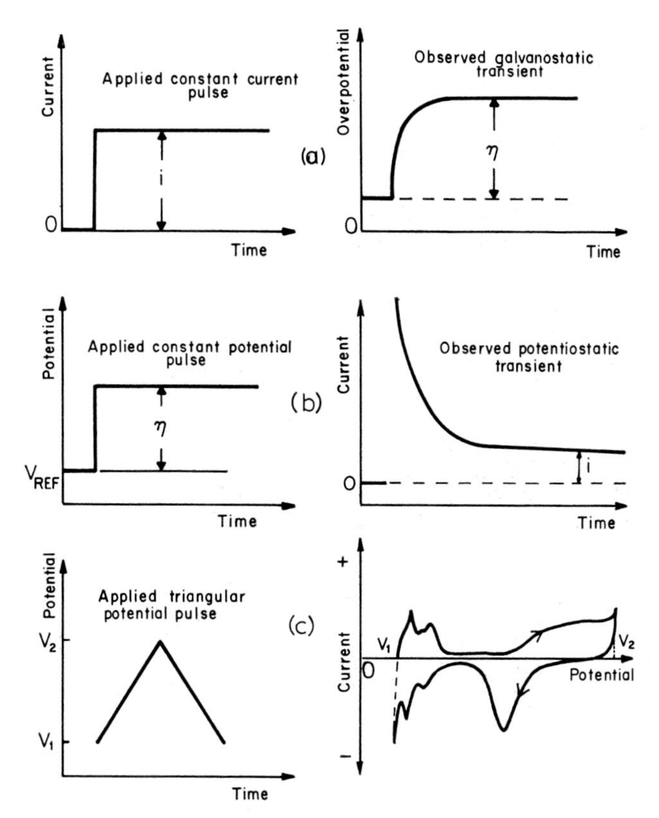

Fig. 3.28. Some ways of studying electrode reactions. (*a*) *Galvanostatic.* A constant current pulse is applied, giving a change of potential with time. (*b*) *Potentiostatic.* A constant potential pulse is applied, giving a change of current with time. (*c*) *Potentio-dynamic.* A linearly changing potential is applied, and the change of current with potential (proportional to time) is observed.

we usually use in studying electrode reactions. We can switch on a constant current exceedingly quickly (say, in 10^{-9} s) and watch the variation of potential from, say, 10^{-8} s onwards, recording the potential variations on a cathode-ray oscilloscope (fig. 3.28 *a*). Or we can switch on a constant potential in a time which, for electronic reasons, is somewhat longer—for example, 10^{-5} s—and watch the resulting current at some later time, say, 10^{-4} s (fig. 3.28 *b*). Finally, it is possible to subject the electrode–solution interface to a constantly changing potential, and watch the more complicated changes of current which take place under these circumstances (fig. 3.28 *c*). Let us try to understand the happenings in one of these transient methods.

Happenings during a constant-current transient pulse

Let us suppose that we have a mercury electrode, and that it is in contact with a sulphuric acid solution. At a given moment we will subject the electrode to a large and constant current, say of value $10\ \mathrm{A\ m^{-2}}$. We record the change of potential by photographing the trace which records it on a cathode ray oscillograph (fig. 6.13). The circuitry is as shown in fig. 3.29.

Now at first, when the electrons come into the electrode (from a cathodic pulse), they find nothing to do except charge up the electrode with electrons. The reason we say 'they find nothing to do but . . .'

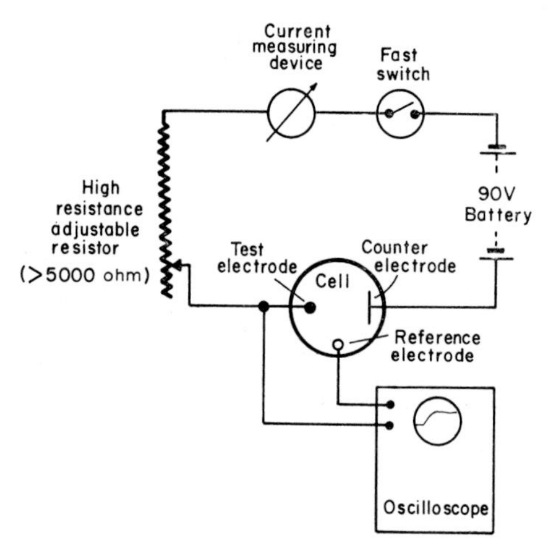

Fig. 3.29. Circuit for galvanostatic transient. A large resistor in series with the cell keeps the current practically constant with time whilst the impedance of the electrode changes.

is that they do not, to a significant extent, cross the boundary between the electrode and the solution. This follows from the Butler–Volmer equation. For example, let us suppose that we are considering the cathodic hydrogen evolution reaction on mercury. Then the Butler–Volmer equation is

$$i = i_0\{\exp[(1-\beta)F/RT]\eta_t - \exp(-\beta F/RT)\eta_t\} \qquad (3.57)$$

where η_t represents the overpotential which changes from $\eta_t = 0$ before the constant current pulse was applied to some stationary value after some time has elapsed. What is happening in the transient period? Even though we applied total *constant* current through the cell of 10 A m^{-2}, the hydrogen evolution current i from equation (3.57) will be much smaller than this, at first, and will rise with time, as η_t becomes more negative during the time the electrode is charging up.

Thus, suppose that after some time, we have $\eta_t = -0{\cdot}12$ V. For H_2 evolution on mercury $i_0 \approx 10^{-9}$ A m^{-2}, and for large cathodic overpotentials ($\eta = 0{\cdot}12$ V is a considerable overpotential) the first exponential term in Butler–Volmer equation can be (roughly) neglected (see p. 99). Then, at that moment the corresponding H_2 evolution current density is†, if $\beta = 0{\cdot}5$:

$$i = 10^{-9} \exp\left[\frac{F(0{\cdot}12)}{2RT}\right] = 10^{-9} \times 10 = 10^{-8} \text{ A m}^{-2}.$$

Hence, we are impressing 10 A m^{-2} upon the electrode, but the current which is going across the barrier when the overpotential has only risen to 0·12 V, is only 10^{-8} A m^{-2}, a very small amount. Hence, until the η_t value has been changed by the charging of the electrode to an amount where a significant number of electrons can cross the double layer to neutralize protons in it, the current will largely go to charging the electrode, i.e., to altering its potential in a negative direction.

If the capacitance of the double layer is constant in the potential region concerned, then the simple equation $C = q/V_t$ will apply;‡ and V_t will change linearly with the input of charge (fig. 3.28 *a*). Eventually, the V_t will rise to an amount such that electrons will be able to pass over the double layer and find protons to neutralize in a significant number, and the simple equation above will no longer be applicable, and the $V_t - t$ will no longer be linear. At still higher V_t or η_t, when it becomes so large that by substituting η_t into the Butler–Volmer equation, i, the current equals the external charging current (10 A m^{-2} for this example), all of the latter can be accommodated by passage across the double layer, and the potential of the electrode will no longer change with further injection of electrons from outside. The cathodic hydrogen evolution reaction will now be in the steady state, and the transient character of the potential-time situation will be terminated.

The electrochemical determination of radicals on surfaces

Something has already been said about the fact that different reaction sequences are connected with a difference in concentration of radicals. For example, if the proton discharge reaction is rate-controlling in the hydrogen evolution reaction (p. 115), then there is little concentration

† $2{\cdot}3RT/F = 2{\cdot}3 \times 8{\cdot}317 \times 298/96\,500 \approx 0{\cdot}060$ V.

‡ Since $V = V_e + \eta$, change of η_t is identical to the change of V_t.

of hydrogen atoms on the surface ($\theta_H \ll 0{\cdot}01$), whereas if hydrogen atom combination is rate-determining, then $0{\cdot}1 < \theta_H < 1$. The connection of the θ_H value and the mechanism of hydrogen evolution reaction indicates that the determination of radical concentrations could give detailed reaction paths for this reaction. Often—as in organic reactions—there are many radicals on the surface at the same time, although one of them is usually there at concentrations much higher than those of the other radicals. Knowledge and technique at the present time do not allow us to determine them all, but we can often determine the one which is there in greatest concentration. Here, we shall give only a simple example of radical determination, the determination of the concentration of hydrogen atoms on a noble metal surface by means of constant current pulse.

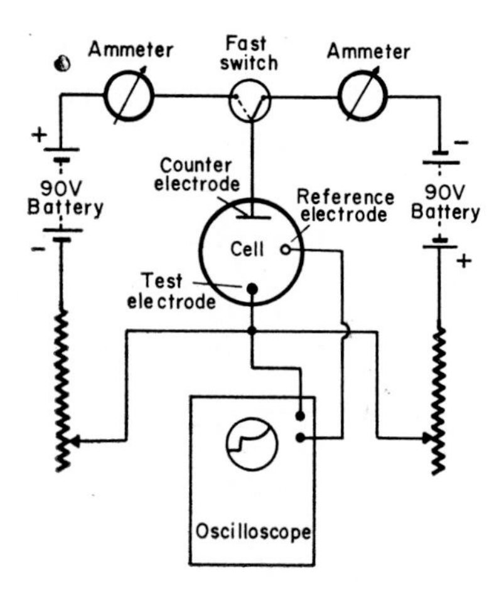

Fig. 3.30. Circuit for θ_H determination. Two galvanostatic circuits are involved. The left one is for cathodic polarization, the right one for anodic pulse.

Let us say that the hydrogen evolution reaction is set going on platinum at 10 A m^{-2}. In the middle of the steady state at this reaction rate, one uses a rapid electronic switch to change the current over from the steady state cathodic one to a highly anodic one. The change over rate must be quick, 10^{-6} second or less, so that during the time of change-over of the current the concentration of hydrogen atoms on the surface, characteristic of the cathodic reaction, does not have time to change significantly. One then observes the change of potential with time on a cathode-ray oscillograph, and it has the shape shown in fig. 3.31. The part A to B simply represents the change of the potential due to the change in charge in the electrode from that corresponding to the excess of electrons corresponding to the cathodic situation to a deficiency of electrons corresponding to the anodic situation, in which the hydrogen atoms dissolve off, following the reaction $H \rightarrow H^{+} + e$. The electrons thus given back to the electrode in this reaction will be the ones used up by the current. While this reaction is occurring, the potential will remain almost constant. So the number of electrons in the electrode is constant, for the hydrogen ionization reaction is feeding them into the electrode as fast as the circuit is taking them away; and the electrode potential will change only if the concentration of electrons in the electrode changes.

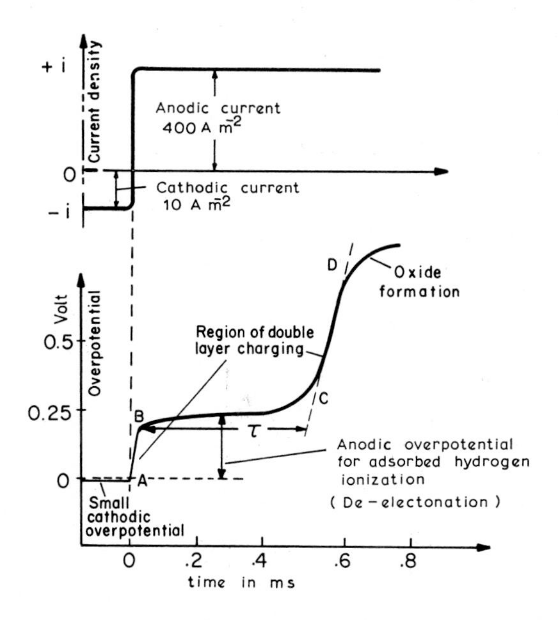

Fig. 3.31. A typical galvanostatic transient observed on the oscilloscope screen (lower diagram), when a constant current pulse is applied to a platinum electrode (upper diagram).

Eventually, when the hydrogen atoms are dissolved off, the electrode potential will change again, as shown from C to D in the figure; the electrons in the metal are being pulled out to the external circuit, and there are now no hydrogen atoms to supply electrons to the electrode.

Hence, the line B to C in the figure corresponds to the region in which the hydrogen atoms are being ionized, and it is reasonable to assume here that there is no other reaction occurring. We know that there is a constant current upon the surface which is, during the time interval τ, used only for H_{ads} ionization. The charge passed during this time is

$$q = i \times \tau = 400 \text{ A m}^{-2} \times 0{\cdot}5 \times 10^{-3} \text{ s} = 2 \text{ C m}^{-2}.$$

If we take the charge on the electron† to be $q_e = 1{\cdot}59 \times 10^{-19}$ coulombs and each H_{ads} releases one electron, the total number of H_{ads} involved should be:

$$\text{number of } H_{ads} = \frac{q}{q_e} = \frac{2}{1{\cdot}6 \times 10^{-19}} = 1{\cdot}25 \times 10^{19} \text{ } H_{ads} \text{ m}^{-2}.$$

Using the lattice parameter for platinum (distance between two neighbouring Pt atoms = 3·942 Å) obtained by X-ray measurements, one can calculate the number of Pt atoms at the flat surface. It comes out that for the closed packed structure, the number of Pt atoms at the surface is $1{\cdot}5 \times 10^{19}$ Pt atoms m^{-2}. Assuming that each H bonds to one Pt atom, the coverage of the surface, θ_H will be

$$\theta_H = \frac{\text{number of } H_{ads}}{\text{number of Pt atoms}} = \frac{1{\cdot}25 \times 10^{19}}{1{\cdot}5 \times 10^{19}} = 0{\cdot}83.$$

It comes out that the surface coverage is $\theta_H = 0{\cdot}83$ the platinum surface is nearly completely covered with adsorbed atomic hydrogen.

A Revolution in Electrochemistry

Enough has been said to show that a revolution has taken place in the old electrochemistry, which has become a new science. The present book is being written in 1972, and developments which led to the New Electrochemistry were just being contemplated in 1950. At that time, it was unusual for electrochemists to use the exponential relation between current and overpotential. Electrochemistry was still thermodynamically frozen. People had not yet developed the connection between the rates of electrochemical reactions and the solid state physics of the substrates, or the quantum mechanics of the transfer of electrons across the double layer.

The new electrochemistry contrasts in four important ways with the thermodynamically-oriented electrochemistry of the pre-1950 era.

1. It is molecular–kinetic and microscopic in concept; and theory is progressing by the application of solid state physics and quantum mechanics.

2. It contributes broadly to the sciences, wherever there is a solid–solution interface across which electrons pass (even if the solution part of the interface is in fact a moisture film), and is the basis of progress

† Electron charge = Faraday constant/Avogadro constant = $96\,500/6{\cdot}03 \times 10^{23}$ = $1{\cdot}59 \times 10^{-19}$ coulombs.

in corrosion, syntheses, energy conversion and storage, extractions from wastes, much metallurgy, much biophysics, and potentially, most anti-pollutive chemistry.

3. It suggests a fundamentally new kind of chemical reaction.

4. It provides the basis for a revolutionary change in technology from a fossil-fuel based, polluting economy to a hydrogen-based economy, which can make the planet habitable for the forseeable future.

CHAPTER 4

transport processes and the action of electrochemical cells

The Logistic Situation at an Electrode

LET us consider a silver nitrate solution, 0·1 M. Suppose that the current density is *very* low, so low that the silver ions will always be there in abundance, and we shall not have to worry about the effect of any lack of supply upon the current–potential relationship. Things will be as we have assumed them to be in Chapter 3.

However, it is clear that if we make the potential more and more negative, demanding ever more and more ions from the solution to be incorporated into the crystal lattice of the substrate as atoms, we shall reach a current density at which the supply of silver ions in solution will simply *not* be able to keep up with the increasing demand of the electrode for silver. This is so in any logistic situation—the demand can become so high that the supply of goods becomes rate-determining in fulfilling the demand.

In fig. 4.1 the happenings at the electrode are compared with the happenings near a dam. The flow of water can be regulated by adjusting the height or the opening of the dam. The flow of ions (current) can be regulated by adjusting the electrode potentials. If the dam height is below a certain level (or if it is completely removed) the flow of water will depend only on the rate of supply of water by the river. Similarly, if the potential of the electrode is such that all the ions reaching the electrode react immediately at the electrode surface (the electrode easily 'swallows' them), the rate of the reaction (i.e., the current) will be determined by the supply of ions from the bulk of solution, i.e., by diffusion.

It is easy to see what happens in a cathodic situation, with the electrode becoming increasingly negative with respect to its equilibrium potential. But what is the situation when the potential is moved in the other direction, departing from the equilibrium potential towards the *positive* side, the anodic side, and the silver is dissolving? Here there will be virtually an infinite source of supply, the whole piece of metal that makes up the electrode. There will be no catastrophic situation in which the supply of silver runs out and some great change has to occur. There can be, at the most, a great excess of silver ions in the vicinity of the silver metal, perhaps unable to diffuse away quickly enough to maintain equilibrium, which will cause a change; but nothing dramatic, nothing to cause any calamitous change in events, as will be shown below to occur at a cathode.

However, it would be ridiculous to say: 'Cathodic reactions can get into logistic difficulties; but with anodic reactions, nothing of this kind occurs.' For, one can have anodic reactions in which ions have to be transported from the solution of the electrode—for example, the negative chlorine ion being neutralized evolves on platinum when this is at a potential positive enough to oxidize Cl^- to Cl_2 and eventually there may,

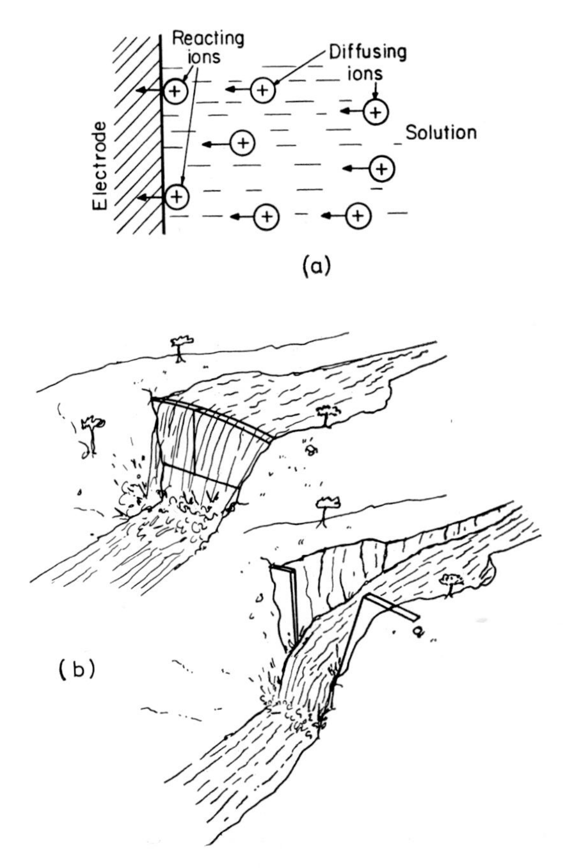

Fig. 4.1. Analogy between the metal–solution interphase (*a*) and water flow over a dam (*b*). The flow is controlled by the potential barrier or the height of the dam. If the barriers are removed, the flow depends on the ion diffusion rate, or water supplied by the river.

therefore, be the same kind of difficulty in logistics as with positive silver cations coming up to a cathodic electrode. The difficulty can become important *whenever an ion is diffusing to an electrode*, whether that electrode is then going to inject electrons into the ion—as in the cathodic reaction with silver (positive) ions—or whether the ion is going to give electrons, as in an anodic reaction, such as that in which the chlorine (negative) ion arrives at a platinum surface and pushes across an electron for it to accept.

Transport in Solution

There are three types of transport in electrolytic solutions, two of them easily understood, the third being an only partially solved problem.

(1) *Diffusion.*—Diffusion is the process that tends to smooth out concentration gradients. A difference in concentration can be caused when an electrode takes ions out of the solution by electron transfer

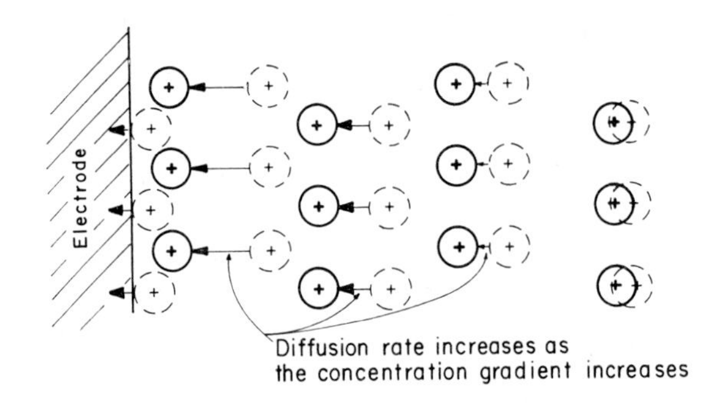

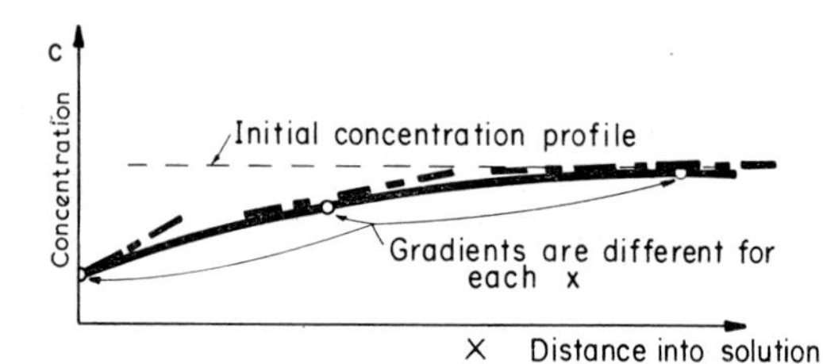

Fig. 4.2. If the rate of the electrochemical reaction is larger than the rate of diffusion, the concentration gradient builds up. *Upper part:* illustrating the initial position of ions, before switching on (dotted circles), and some time after (full circles); the number of ions in the space close to the electrode is reduced. *Lower part:* initial concentration profile (horizontal broken line) and concentration profile after some time (full line).

and makes the concentration of ions near the electrode small compared with the concentration a few thousand ångströms farther out into the liquid. When this happens, there will be a movement of ions in towards the interface to fill up the gap. This is diffusion (fig. 4.2).

(2) *Ionic transport.*—Ionic transport is another type of transport we can easily understand. The electric field exerts an electrostatic force on the electric charges of the ions, and drags them towards the

interface. Thus, there is an electric field between the electrodes in the cell, apart from the tremendous field in the small region of the double layer. If we have two electrodes in an externally driven cell and have applied, say, 10 volts between them, and one volt falls across the few ångströms of the double layer region at each electrode, $(10-2) = 8$ volts is the potential drop across the solution between the electrodes (see fig. 4.3). The potential gradient will act upon the ions to push the positive ions towards the negative electrode and the negative ions towards the positive electrode.† If the concentration of ions reacting at the electrode is small compared to the concentration of other ions in the solution, as is very often the case in electrochemical cells, the effect of ionic migration is negligible compared to diffusion.

(3) *Convection.*—The third type of transport, the one where the mathematical theory is still blurred, is convection. There are two kinds of convection, forced and natural, and the conditions of the liquid

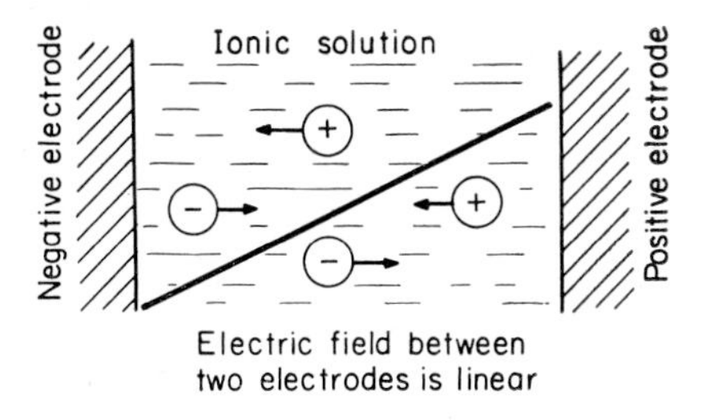

Fig. 4.3. The field in the solution between the two electrodes is linear. Due to this field the ions migrate.

in which the convection occurs may be either turbulent or non-turbulent. Forced convection is easiest to understand. It is the condition which arises when we stir a solution. In the simplest case, suppose we assume a paddle is rotating in the electrolyte in such a way that it constantly pushes the solution from some middle part of the cell, where the ions are in no sense exhausted by their removal onto the electrode, towards the cathode. All questions of theory aside, it is correct to think of the paddle as 'pushing' ions in the solution towards the electrode, giving them a shove, and hence increasing the number which can reach the electrode in unit time. Forced convection is carried out in electrochemical cells by paddles, by propellers, by rotating the electrode, bubbling gases near it to stir the solution, sending in ultrasonic radiation (which greatly agitates the molecules of the solution), and so forth (cf. fig. 4.4).

† Note that in a self-driving cell the direction of current is opposite to that in the driven cell. Therefore, the field in the solution is also opposite. Then, the *positive ions*, cations, are moving toward a *positive* electrode (acting in this case as *cathode*). Negative ions move in the opposite direction.

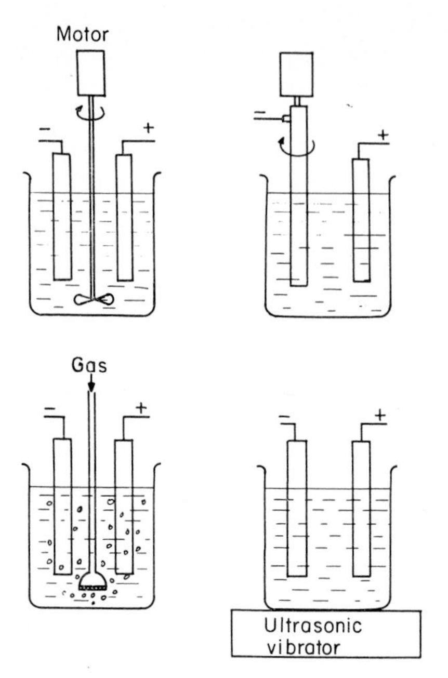

Fig. 4.4. Various ways of stirring.

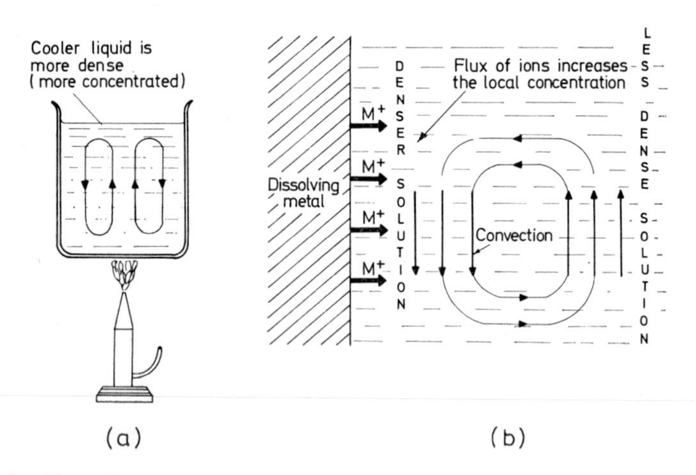

Fig. 4.5. Natural convection (*a*) in heating; (*b*) in electrochemical reactions, where the local build-up of more concentrated (more dense) solution at the electrode produces a local increase in density which causes convection.

Then, there is natural convection. This occurs whether we stir the solution intentionally or not, owing to the fact that when ions are deposited on the electrode, they cause a reduction in the density of the solution, just as the most vital point—at the electrode–solution interface. This density change causes an influx of ions from the surrounding part of the solution towards the electrode, independently of that caused by diffusion. The diffusional part occurs because of changes in *concentrations* of the ions. The convectional part occurs because there are gravitational changes which make the solution, as a liquid, move towards the electrode, and bring ions with it in the process.

We come now to turbulence and non-turbulence. The theory of convection towards electrodes, and the increase in the maximum rate of transport towards the electrode (the 'limiting current'), has been worked out by Levich and also by Arvia; but their equations only apply when the situation is not turbulent. When the stirring is so great that the flowing liquid has broken up into turbulent eddies—the flow is no longer honey-like—then we have to fall back on engineering approximations, empirical factors and dimensional analysis, to cope with phenomena at present too difficult for us to make into molecular models, ripe for a mathematical treatment.

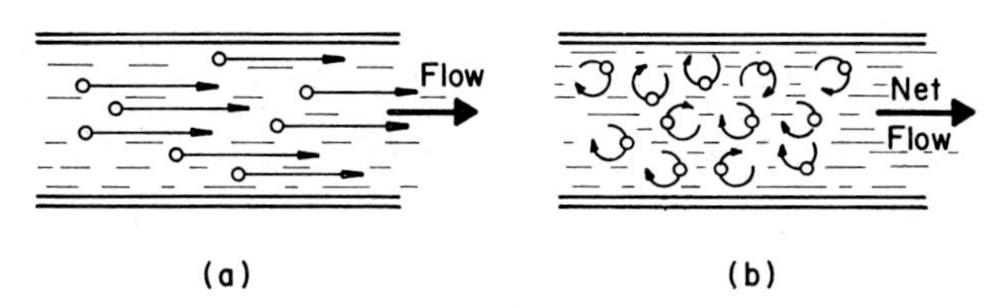

Fig. 4.6. Two types of liquid flow through a tube (*a*) non-turbulent, laminar flow, (*b*) turbulent flow.

The attitude that we shall take in this chapter will be that we understand diffusion and can handle it with assurance. But when we come to convection, whether turbulent or not, we have to use empiricisms and artifices to deal with it. This is not quite the modern situation, because, as stated above, for non-turbulent conditions there is a theory of convection. However, its mathematics is too difficult to present here; and, as we shall see, we can deal with the transport of ions to the electrode under convective stirring fairly well without it.

Fick's first law of diffusion

This is an empirical law. The flux of material, $\mathrm{d}Q/\mathrm{d}t$, which passes per second across one unit area is proportional to the concentration gradient at the crossing plane. The mathematical expression is

$$-\frac{\mathrm{d}\underset{\sim}{Q}}{\mathrm{d}t} = D\,\frac{\mathrm{d}c}{\mathrm{d}x}. \qquad (4.1)$$

D, the constant of proportionality, is called the diffusion coefficient. Since $\mathrm{d}c/\mathrm{d}x$ is in mol m^{-4}, $\mathrm{d}Q/\mathrm{d}t$ is in mol m^{-2} s^{-1}, clearly correct for the *rate* of diffusion of particles to an electrode; the diffusion coefficient is in m^2 s^{-1}.

Another way of writing Fick's law would be

$$-\frac{\mathrm{d}Q}{\mathrm{d}t} = D\frac{c_b - c_e}{\delta}, \tag{4.2}$$

where c_b is the concentration of the cation in the bulk; c_e is its concentration *at* the electrode, and δ is the distance over which the concentration change occurs.

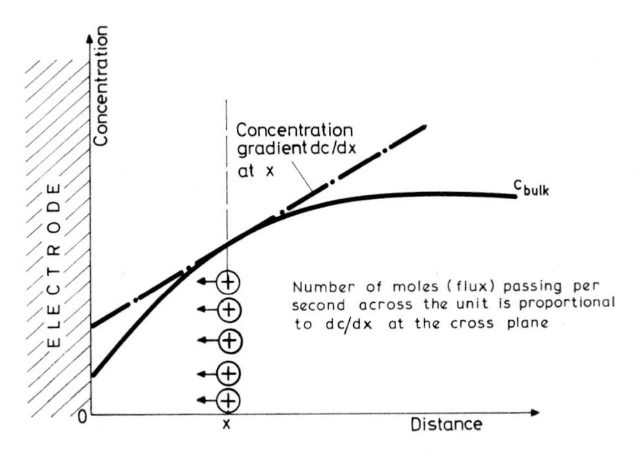

Fig. 4.7. Illustration of Fick's first law. The concentration decreases near the electrode. The concentration gradient also becomes more +ve as the electrode is approached.

In reality, the figure is as shown in fig. 4.8. When we first switch the current on, the distance over which the concentration changes is small. As time passes, the region over which this change extends increases. And *while pure diffusion is the only thing influencing the transport*, the distance over which the concentration change extends just goes on increasing.

The shape of the concentration–distance gradient is as shown in fig. 4.8, at the best, *quasi* linear near the electrode.

This is too complicated for simple treatment. Nernst (with his student, Merriam) suggested the approximation that it is all linear. If so, we get the situation shown in fig. 4.9.

With this Nernst–Merriam diffusion layer, as it is called, we can write Fick's law, so that, $\mathrm{d}c/\mathrm{d}x$ becomes then $(c_b - c_e)/\delta$. The degree of validity of the equation depends upon how far off the Nernst–Merriam linear model of the concentration–distance model is from reality.

Now, our definitions of c_b and c_e are clear enough, but what about our definition of δ? It is not much help for us to say 'δ is the thickness of the Nernst–Merriam layer', because it only begs the question: how thick is that?

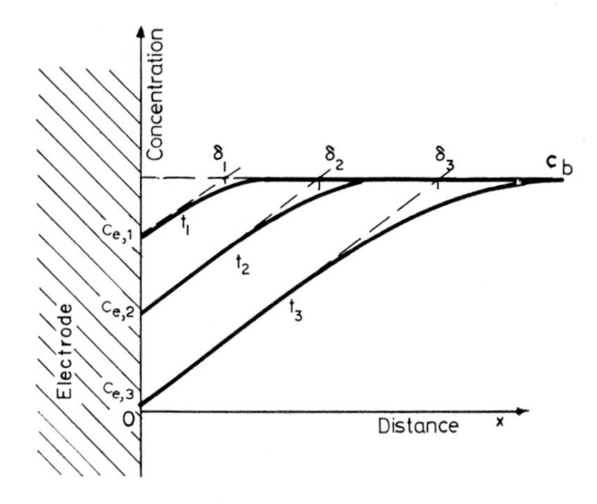

Fig. 4.8. The concentration profile and thickness of the diffusion layer change with time.

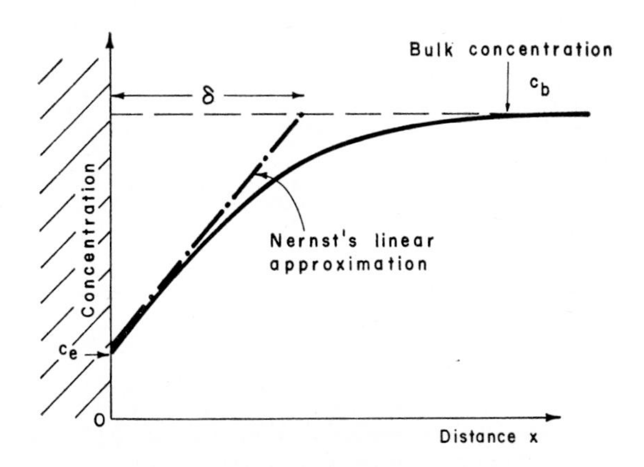

Fig. 4.9. The Nernst–Merriam approximation.

Thinking out δ in the Nernst–Merriam diffusion layer

To start with, we can assume that pure diffusion is the only thing occurring (no convection, stirring, electrical migration, etc.). Then, it is possible by a little more complicated calculation to obtain the following equation for δ:

$$\delta_t = \sqrt{\pi D t}, \tag{4.3}$$

where D is the diffusion coefficient (numerically, usually in the region of 10^{-9} m² s⁻¹), and t the time after switching on the current. Thus, δ_t varies with time, just as it seemed to be doing from fig. 4.8. With $D = 10^{-9}$ m² s⁻¹, $t = 10^{-3}$ s, and $\pi = 3{\cdot}14$, then δ_t is $1{\cdot}77 \times 10^{-6}$ m. Correspondingly, if $t = 1$ s, δ_t is $5{\cdot}5 \times 10^{-5}$ m.

This is satisfactory, but what about longer times? What happens after one hour? It is easy to show that, from equation. (4.3), δ_t after one hour would be about 1 cm, and after 100 hours, about 10 cm. Now, the confines of the experimental vessel can often show that δ_t never gets to values as high as this.

In addition, from Fick's law (eqn. (4.2)) we know that the amount of ions per second reaching one square metre of the electrode is

$$-\frac{\mathrm{d}Q}{\mathrm{d}t} = D\frac{c_b - c_e}{\delta}. \tag{4.4}$$

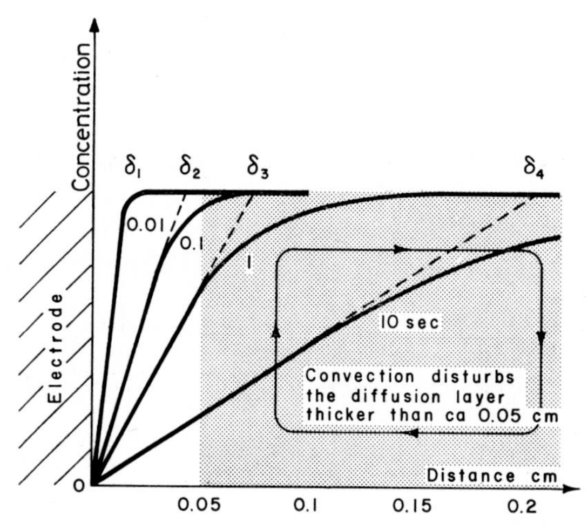

Fig. 4.10. At a sufficiently large cathodic current, the surface concentration is nearly zero, while δ changes with time. If only diffusion were involved, the concentration profile would change approximately as shown by the full lines. But due to convection, it does not increase any more after about 1 second. Convection comes in and reduces the extent of the concentration gradient.

Figure 4.8 shows that c_e tends to zero as the current increases. This looks all right, for we can clearly go on increasing the current density at the electrode until it just promptly removes every ion arriving at it, i.e., until $c_e = 0$. The maximum value of the rate is hence given by equation (4.2) with $c_e = 0$, i.e.,

$$\frac{\mathrm{d}Q}{\mathrm{d}t} = -D\frac{c_b}{\delta}. \tag{4.5}$$

Now, we can use this maximum rate to compare with what we find experimentally, and we find that δ obeys equation (4.3) only up to about 1 second after switching on the current. In numerical value, it never exceeds about 0·5 mm.

What goes wrong (at higher times) with our diffusion theory-based calculation, equation (4.3), which is in fact, verified at lower times? The answer is, natural convection has come in (see figs. 4.10 and 4.11).

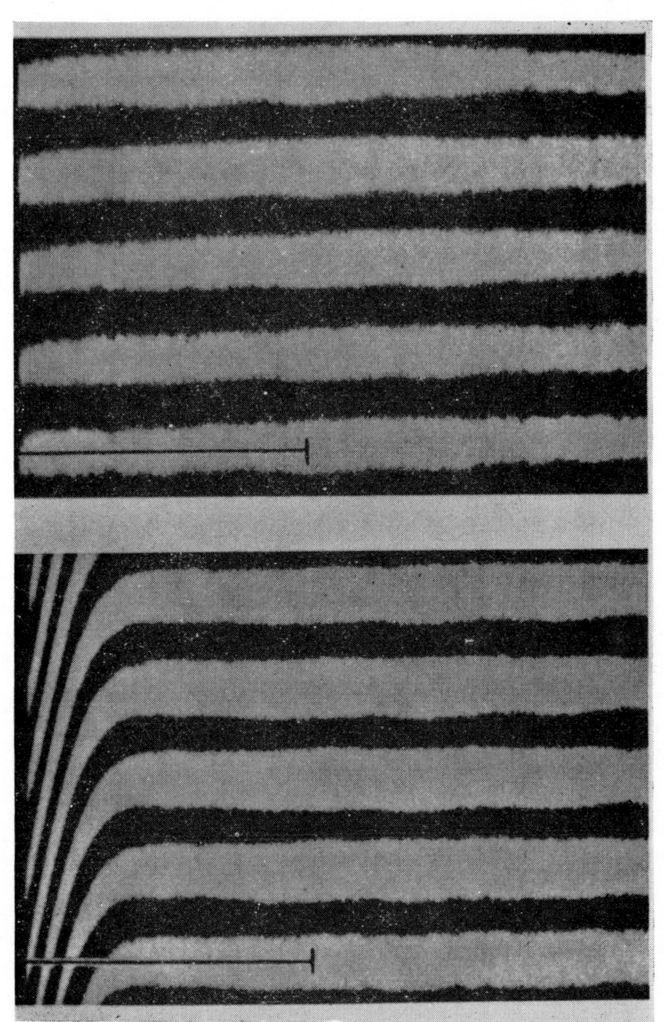

Fig. 4.11. Change in concentration of solution within the diffusion layer can be observed by the interferometric method. The shift of the interference bands is proportional to the change of concentration. The scale line is 1 mm from the electrode surface. Above, no current. Below, with current.

When the time is short enough, the density changes of the solution near the electrode are sufficiently small for there to be negligible natural convection. However, when the time gets large (it depends somewhat on the current density at what time the change occurs), the density alters near the electrode. Natural convection overwhelms diffusion, and equation (4.3) (which assumed only diffusion as the cause of transport to or from an electrode) is no longer applicable.

Thus, so far we have got an equation for δ_t at time up to about 1 s, not very helpful for use in electrochemical experiments for longer times. We need not despair, however, because natural convection gives an empirical answer to the question: What value shall we take for δ, after times which are *not* very small—the kind of times that we are often concerned with in practice? It is that the process of natural convection extinguishes† the growth of δ_t to higher values at longer times, as indicated by equation (4.3), and shows an upper limit of δ at about 0·5 mm (in unstirred solutions). Hence, if we are dealing with unstirred solution, and want to know what value of δ we can use, we have to look at time. If we are dealing with a special short-time condition then, in times up to about 0·1 s, we do use equation (4.3). Thereafter, we assume that natural convection has set up its steady state value of δ which is 0·5 mm. But we must take 0·5 mm with a pinch of salt; it is not some constant of nature which has been argued out, but merely a blanket on a situation we don't want to look at too closely, because it is too difficult for us. Wrapped inside the blanket of $\delta \simeq 0{\cdot}5$ mm (no stirring), are several factors: the rate of removal of ions on to the electrode, the change of density that this provokes, the resulting convective flow, tending to level out a concentration gradient, and the counter-forces of diffusion, trying to build δ up and increase it. In reality, δ may lie between 0·2 mm and 0·7 mm. The theory of transport to electrodes is rather like this: once one departs from the transient condition (when everything is controlled by simple diffusion, and can be treated theoretically) the information is a little imprecise.

The boundary layer under forced convection

We talked about stirring, forced convection, and turbulence. What do we do about them, in seeking a value of δ? Instead of trying to find a complicated expression for δ in terms of hydrodynamical theory, we retreat to experiment and find out how δ decreases with stirring.

Of course, 'stirring' is a vague term, and we must make it more precise, even if we are going to use empirical means. One of the ways of doing this is to use a rotating electrode, whereupon we can state the value of δ at a given rate of rotation so long as we know that value for

† 'Extinguishes' is about the word for it. Thus, according to equation (4.3) the larger the δ the greater would be the density changes in the solution which lie at the basis of natural convection, and hence the greater the δ, the greater the movement of solution to wipe out this concentration gradient.

the electrode. Table 4.1 gives experimental values of δ at various stirring conditions. We can go down to values of δ that are 1–2 orders of magnitude less than the 0·5 mm that is appropriate for unstirred solutions.

Table 4.1. The influence of stirring rate (number of rotations) of a rotating disc electrode on diffusion layer thickness and limiting current density for hydrogen evolution reaction in 0·0005 M H_2SO_4 and 0·1 M KCl. $D_{H^+} = 3{\cdot}83 \times 10^{-9}\ m^2\ s^{-1}$

Number of rotations per second	i_{Lim}/A m^{-2}	δ/m
1	8	$4{\cdot}8 \times 10^{-5}$
4	16	$2{\cdot}4 \times 10^{-5}$
9	24	$1{\cdot}6 \times 10^{-5}$
16	32	$1{\cdot}1 \times 10^{-5}$

δ and its diminution by agitation, etc., is a subject well fitted for heat transfer engineers. There are all sorts of ways they can *decrease* the 'boundary layer thickness', a problem which frequently becomes important in heat transfer.† Anyone interested in further work on the control of δ should consult a book on heat transfer, such as Carslaw and Yeager's 'Conduction of Heat in Solids', Oxford University Press (1947).

The Limiting Current

Looking back at the equation for Fick's first law, written in terms of the Nernst–Merriam diffusion layer, we see that the current may get increasingly large, as the concentration at the electrode gets increasingly small (fig. 4.12). As the call of the electrode for current gets higher and higher, c_e will get smaller and smaller, eventually reaching zero. After this, it is not possible to go higher, and therefore we have reached a *maximum rate of transport* to the electrode, given (from eqn. (4.5)) by:

$$-\frac{dQ}{dt} = \frac{D}{\delta} c_b. \tag{4.6}$$

Let us convert this equation to one for a current density. This is done by utilizing our equation on page 86,

$$-\frac{dQ}{dt} = \frac{i}{nF}, \quad \text{in mol m}^{-2}\,\text{s}^{-1}, \tag{4.7}$$

† Note that the desire all engineers have is to *reduce* δ; few wish to increase it. Thus, it is more usual to have situations in which one wants to get heat from, say, a hot plate to a liquid, to increase the efficacy of heat transfer. In the same way, one usually wants to be able to pass larger currents, not smaller ones, as for example in batteries and fuel cells. In corrosion, this might not be so. For example, the diffusion of oxygen to an interface in corrosion is sometimes rate determining and we would like to *minimize* it.

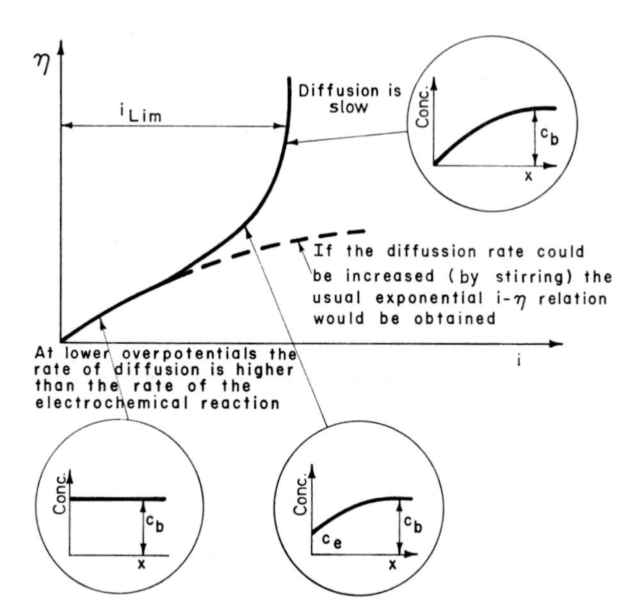

Fig. 4.12. The variation of the current density with the value of c_e at the electrode surface. At low current densities, electron transfer controls the rate. At high current densities, it is diffusion.

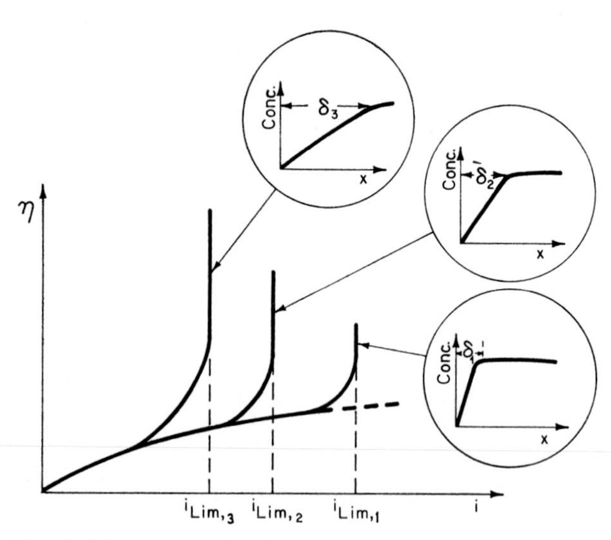

Fig. 4.13. The limiting current density depends on the stirring conditions. Better stirring reduces δ, and therefore increases i_{Lim}.

where i is the current density, F, the Faraday constant and n the number of moles of electrons involved in electrochemical reaction.

It follows from this equation, and our expression of Fick's first law in its limiting, maximal form in equation (4.6), that the maximum possible current density is

$$i_{\text{Lim}} = \frac{nFDc_b}{\delta}. \tag{4.8}$$

This is the limiting current density, and it has enormous importance in practical electrochemistry.

Let us see what sort of values this limiting current density has.

Let us take the same example given in Table 4.1, i.e., hydrogen evolution reaction in 0·0005 M H_2SO_4 + 0·1 M KCl solution. For unstirred solution, $\delta = 5\times10^{-4}$ m and taking $D_{H^+} = 3{\cdot}83\times10^{-9}\ \text{m}^2\,\text{s}^{-1}$, $n = 1$, and $c_b = 1\ \text{mol m}^{-3}$ one can calculate the limiting current density:

$$i_{\text{Lim}} = \frac{nD\,.\,F}{\delta}c_b = \frac{1\times3{\cdot}83\times10^{-9}\,.\,96\,500}{5\times10^{-4}}\times1 = 7{\cdot}4\times10^{-1}\ \text{A m}^{-2}$$

As is obvious from the equation (4.8), i_{Lim} is directly proportional to the bulk concentration, providing that the diffusion layer thickness δ is constant. This direct proportionality between the concentration and limiting current is the basis of most electroanalytical methods.

Thus, we see that in any electrochemical situation there is a maximum beyond which we simply *cannot* go. Hence, if you are asked to make a current of a certain magnitude pass through an electrolytic solution, the first thing to do is to ask what is the concentration of the solution, and calculate back from equation (4.8) whether the demand for current as the electrolytes is logistically possible. If it isn't possible in an *unstirred* solution, one has got a power or two of 10 in hand if one can apply stirring of increasing vigour which decreases δ. After that, a higher current depositing the ion concerned than that indicated as the maximum current density in Fick's equation is *impossible.* Then, the ions simply cannot get there fast enough to acquire all the electrons offered by the electrode.

The effect of transport delays in electrochemical situations upon the potential of the electrode

The last sentence raises the question, what will happen if we use a powerful outside source and keep on raising the current until we pass the limit laid down by Fick's first law? If we are, for example, electrolysing copper sulphate in the presence of excess potassium sulphate, then if we exceed the limiting current for the deposition of copper, the most likely thing that will happen is that *hydrogen* gas will start to be evolved on the cathode. There is always a large reservoir of hydrogen in any *aqueous* solution,† and, therefore, hydrogen ions will take over the current when the supply of copper ions can no longer provide enough receptor states for the electrons, and allow the current to increase still further. Of course, copper ions will continue to be deposited, but at the maximum value of the limiting current for the concentration in the bulk of the solution. Therefore, depending on the total current taken from the power source driving the electrode, the copper current will be a certain fraction,

$$\simeq \frac{i_{\mathrm{Lim,Cu}^{2+}}}{i_{\mathrm{Lim,Cu}^{2+}}+i_{\mathrm{H}^+}},$$

of the total current ($i_{\text{total}} = i_{\mathrm{Lim,Cu}^{2+}}+i_{\mathrm{H}^+}$).

Now, of course, the total current increases as a function of the increase of the overpotential at the electrode, as in the Butler–Volmer equation (eqn. (3.24)). Hence, if we increase the overpotential to higher and higher values, we get a relationship between current and overpotential which, qualitatively, would look as shown in fig. 4.14.

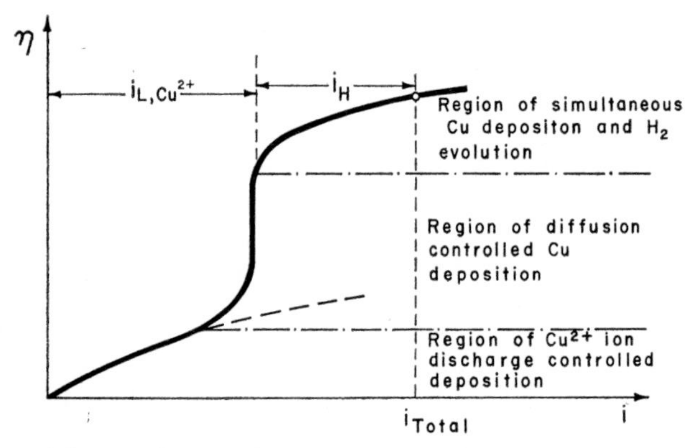

Fig. 4.14. η–i diagram showing change of current with potential as copper deposition is succeeded by hydrogen evolution.

A derivation of the current–potential relation when the only kind of overpotential is that due to diffusion

Our task is to try to see what happens to a current–potential relationship, taking into account diffusion and convection in an electrolyte which we ignored in our elementary treatment in Chapter 3. The first thing to say is rather relieving. Until the current density is about $\frac{1}{10}$ of the limiting diffusion current, we can indeed forget about

† This is because hydrogen can be a receptor for an electrode's electrons not only from

$$H_3O^+ + e \rightarrow H_{ads} + H_2O,$$

but also by

$$H_2O + e \rightarrow H_{ads} + OH^-.$$

the effect of diffusion and convection on the relations between current and electron transfer overpotential that we have dealt with earlier. This means that our Chapter 3 material *is* all right, most of it; but the equations deduced there won't work well if the current rises too near to the limiting diffusion current. What that limiting diffusion current is, one has to calculate for every new situation (how much is the concentration of the ion concerned? what is an appropriate value of δ, 0·5 mm or lower?) from equation (4.8).

To get an equation for the relationship between the overpotential which diffusion causes, and the current density, let us make a simplifying assumption. We will take a situation where the exchange current density is so high that there would be virtually zero overpotential when current passed (cf. eqn. (3.31)). (Overpotential is usually neglected in an electrochemical situation, if it is less than one millivolt.)

Hence, in this fairly contrived situation, we should, in practice, only observe a significant overpotential when the current is switched on, because of diffusion or convection, i.e., 'transport difficulties'.

How can we calculate the relationship between η and i in this case?

If the electrochemical reaction is really reversible, the diffusion overpotential will depend on the difference between bulk concentration c_b and surface concentration c_e, according to the Nernst equation

$$\eta_d = \frac{RT}{nF} \ln \frac{c_e}{c_b}. \tag{4.9}$$

After rearranging, we obtain

$$c_e = c_b \exp (nF/RT)\eta_d. \tag{4.10}$$

By substituting c_e from equation (4.10) into equation (4.2) and taking into account (4.7) we obtain

$$i = \frac{n\,.\,F\,.\,D\,.}{\delta} (c_b - c_b \exp [nF/RT]\eta_d)$$

$$= \frac{nFDc_b}{\delta} (1 - \exp [nF\eta_d/RT]). \tag{4.11}$$

Or, if we recall equation (4.8), we can write

$$i = i_{\text{Lim}}(1 - \exp [nF\eta_d/RT]). \tag{4.12}$$

Hence, in practice, it is seen that the equation yields a diagram of the type in figs. 4.12 and 4.13, i.e., that there is here, at the beginning, zero overpotential due to diffusion, the overpotential mounts up to an order of 50 millivolts and the current density approaches the limiting one in equation (4.12) asymptotically: η_d is negative (cathodic). Therefore, for larger numerical values of η_d, the exponential term in equation (4.12) becomes negligible and the current approaches the limiting current, i_{Lim}.

Hence, one might say something like this, as far as the effect of transport difficulties on the actual cell is concerned: the electrode kinetics are controlled by the electron transfer kinetics of Chapter 3 until one is near enough to the limiting current to make the phenomena sketched in this deduction come into play. When is that? It depends

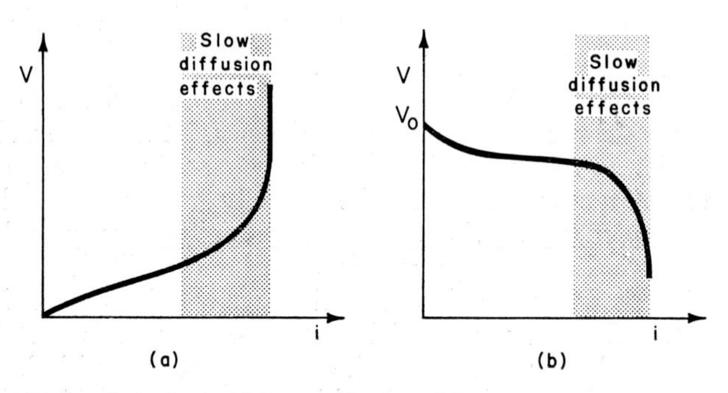

Fig. 4.15. (*a*) In electrolysis (driven cell) slow diffusion increases the cell voltage. (*b*) In batteries (self-driven cell) slow diffusion decreases the useful cell voltage.

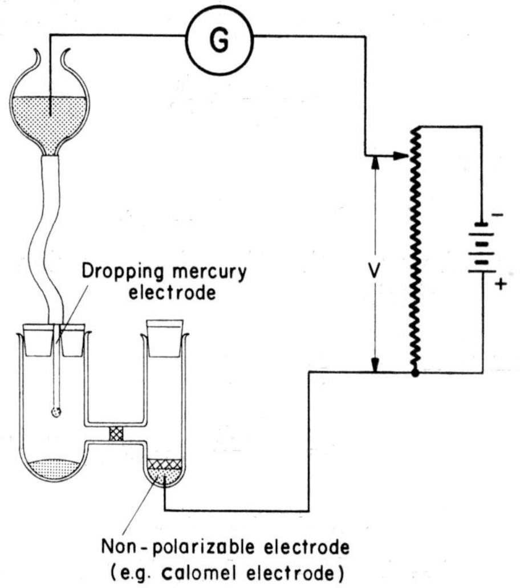

Fig. 4.16. Potentiometer circuit for polarography. The change of the cell voltage V with current is identical with the potential change at the dropping mercury electrode (counter electrode is a non-polarizable one (cf. fig. 2.11)).

on what one calls significant. Let it be 1 mV. Then, the arithmetic of equation (4.12) shows $\eta_d = 10^{-3}$ V at $i/i_{\text{Lim}} \simeq 0{\cdot}05$. If we can accept 2 mV as still negligible, $\frac{1}{10}i_{\text{Lim}}$ is the first time we shall have to bother about an effect of diffusion on overpotential, whereafter, however, it causes a sharp increase in the overpotential of a cell which is being driven, or a sharp decrease in the current of a cell which is driving itself (fig. 4.15).

Polarography

The things which we have been talking about can give rise to an analytical method: polarography. A schematic polarograph circuit is shown in fig. 4.16. The figure which we have qualitatively drawn in fig. 4.14 can in fact be realized in practice as shown in fig. 4.17. Suppose we have several different materials in the solution. They

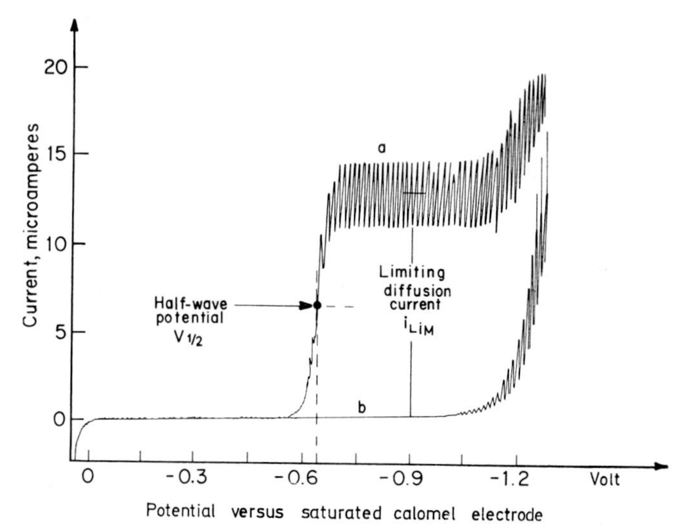

Fig. 4.17. Polarograms (i–V curve) of (a) 1 M HCl solution containing 0·5 mM cadmium ion; and (b) 1 M HCl alone, i_{Lim} is proportional to concentration of cadmium ions. Half-wave potential has a characteristic value. Current oscillation is due to surface area change while dropping. The steep increase of current at very negative potential is due to hydrogen evolution.

will all have their different thermodynamically reversible (or equilibrium) potentials, i.e., the potentials at which they will start to play a part in deposition. Hence, as we make the potential of the electrode more and more negative, they will *begin* to deposit one after the other (see fig. 4.18), each ionic species mounting up to its limiting current density in that solution and then letting the next ionic species come in to carry the extra current, and so on. Hence, a current-potential curve of the type given in fig. 4.18 will be obtained.

If we know what the equilibrium potential is at which they deposit we can tell from the potential preceding each plateau whether that plateau refers to cadmium ions, to zinc ions, or to calcium ions. Then, by plotting a polarogram, fig. 4.17, we can obtain the concentration of the substances present, because each of the limiting currents is related to concentration by equation (4.8).

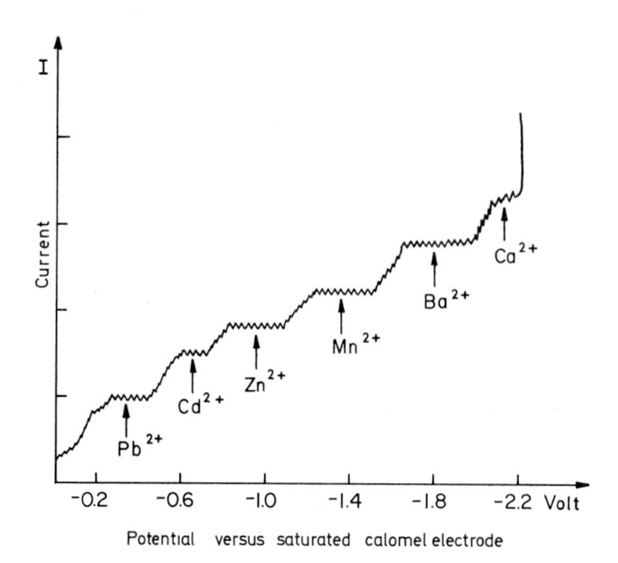

Fig. 4.18. Polarogram for a composite solution. The half-wave potentials are different for different ions. The difference between plateaus of each polarographic wave is the limiting current for the ions concerned.

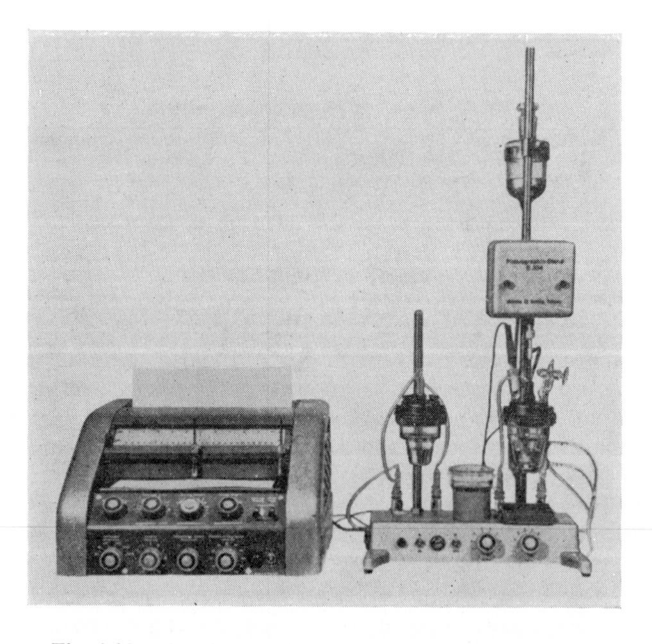

Fig. 4.19. A polarograph as used for fast electroanalysis.

Only two more things need be said here about polarography. One is that the equation for the relation of limiting current, (4.8), is not that actually used in polarography. A more complicated one is needed, with the relevant constants found empirically.† Secondly, one always chooses a mercury electrode, and further, to have this mercury electrode *dropping*. One of the reasons is that the constant reforming of the drops keeps the electrode surface clean of metal deposited a moment before, and thus makes the conditions much *simpler* than if there were a deposit of metal formed on the substrate, as would happen with, for example, electrodes made of solid platinum. The other, is the kinetic reason, the very slow formation of H_2 on mercury. As will be shown in Chapter 5, the exchange current density i_0, for this reaction is about 10^{-8} A m^{-2} (far lower than i_0 for metal deposition, which ranges between 10^{-3} and 10 A m^{-2}). Therefore, if the potential is more negative than the equilibrium hydrogen potential, hydrogen evolution is still negligible, so the metal ion deposition current is what is observed. However, i_0 for H_2 evolution on platinum is about 10 A m^{-2}, and H_2 hydrogen evolution therefore becomes appreciable with very little excess potential over that for the reversible thermodynamic potential. So a platinum electrode *cannot* be used in polarography if the potential region is likely to become more negative than the equilibrium hydrogen potential.

Polarography is an important part of modern analytical chemistry.

Transport Difficulties in Real Electrochemical Systems

At the beginning of this section, we tended to play down the transport-controlled side of electrode kinetics, perhaps following an unintelligent tendency to equate something old with something less good. Transport kinetics is a very important part of real electrochemical science, and the fact that it is less fundamental than electron transfer kinetics with its relation to the energy levels in the substrate, does not make it any the less important to the understanding of currents and interfaces, particularly in a practical engineering sense.

In the laboratory an attempt is often made to get rid of the concentration overpotential effects, for example by rapid agitation of the solution ($\rightarrow \delta$ very small), use of a rotating electrode (fig. 4.20), or working with rapid pulses at short times so that there is no *time* for the diffusional overpotential to build up (cf.p. 134). But in practical electrochemical cells, one cannot usually take such measures, for economic reasons. They have to pass current for prolonged times, days or weeks. The technologist is interested in the production, in mass per unit of area occupied per unit time, of his apparatus; and therefore he wants to work at the highest current densities possible (and, therefore, near

† One cannot actually make much of equation. (4.8) in a direct numerical way because knowledge of δ is not precise. One usually *calibrates* a polarographic electrode, setting $i_{\text{Lim}} = Kc_i$, and thus obtains c_i for unknown solutions.

to i_{Lim}, so that diffusional overpotential may come in (eqn. 4.9)). How he tries to reduce it† is a detailed story in electrochemical engineering.

There are many other cases in electrochemistry where concentration overpotential turns up and is unavoidable. Consider a vital case, the attempts made to make a fuel cell planted in the body which will take glucose from the blood and oxygen from some other part of the body fluids and produce sufficient electric power to run an electric motor to drive a pump to take the place of the heart. Here, the difficulty is that one cannot alter the pH of the body fluids, often near to 6 or 7. Under such circumstances, when one oxidizes glucose in a glucose–air fuel cell, there is a rapid change of the pH near the interface (because the products of the oxidized glucose are H^+ and CO_2), and a good deal of concentration overpotential (cf. eqn. (4.9)) develops. A fuel cell is

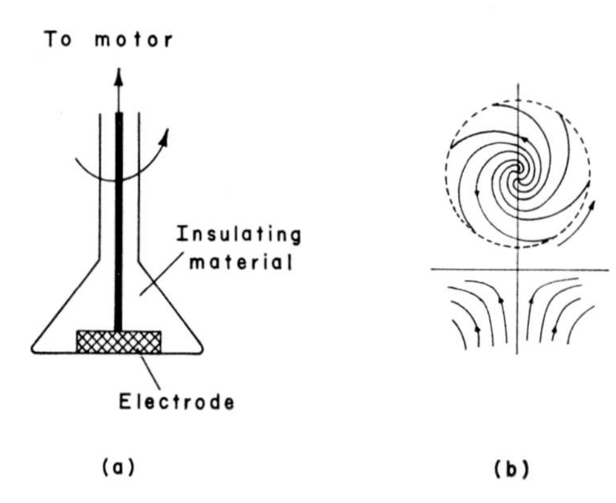

Fig. 4.20. Rotating disc electrode. (*a*) Cross-section; (*b*) side and bottom view of liquid flow patterns at rotating disc-electrode. δ is the same all over the surface and depends on the speed of rotation.

a spontaneously working energy producer, and its power output diminishes as the overpotential at its electrodes increases (see p. 150 for detailed equations). A satisfactory artificial heart, driven electrochemically, would, therefore, be only possible if we could eliminate the concentration change in H^+ produced at the interface.

The functioning of a whole cell

Earlier we said that in Chapter 3 we had left out two important things. One was the implicit assumption that the transport control had been

† He wants to do this for reasons of economy. To run a cell takes electrical power $I \times V$ watts, where V is the *total potential difference* across the cell. Now, the V is the sum of all the potentials in the cell. A diffusional overpotential is an *extra* overpotential, and it will cost more to run the cell than it would do without it. Even worse, if the current exceeds the limiting current for the main process all the extra current over the limiting current is wasted for the subsequent unimportant process (e.g., H_2 codeposition in metal deposition).

looked after—there was nothing to worry about from that. We have now examined to what extent this is true, and shown what we can do to reduce it under circumstances when we approach the limiting current and the diffusional overpotential becomes significant. But we have not answered the accusation that we are dealing with a highly artificial situation, an individual electrode, one hand clapping. We must now say a little about kinetic equations which deal with the whole cell, and which, remarkably enough, were formulated only at the end of the 1960's. Yet it is clearly just those equations which are needed when we wish to find out, for example, whether a corrosion couple will work, or whether a biological situation can be expected to work electrochemically. Whether some electrochemical system will *go* spontaneously is of course to do with a *cell*, and that always has at least two electrodes.

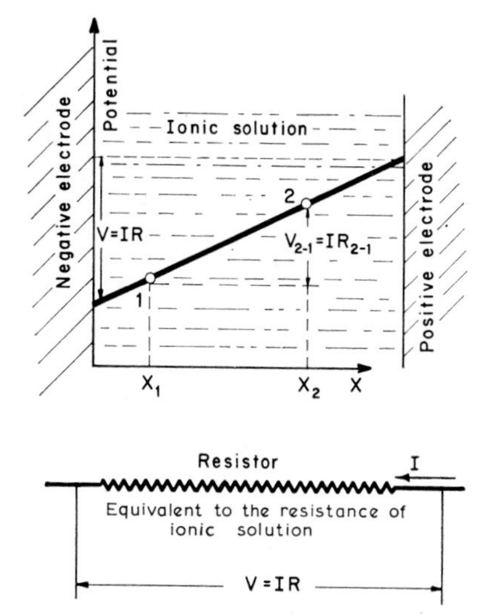

Fig. 4.21. Solutions are ionic conductors, but follow Ohm's law. The voltage drop, V, is linear and depends on current passing and resistance of the solution ($V = IR$).

There is something else which we must take into account and which we have not mentioned yet. This is the *IR* drop, i.e. the 'lost volts' which occurs between the electrodes of a cell, when a current passes round the circuit. Thus, the relations between current and potential *at* the electrode, due to electron transfer (Chapter 3) or due to diffusional delays, are not the only things which we have to consider when a current is actually passing. When a *current* I (not current density here) passes through a resistance R, the ohmic potential drop is IR. If the cell is being *driven* by an outside power source, we have to add IR to the total voltage required at the power source, which then becomes the sum of:

(1) The equilibrium potential of the cathodic electrode;
(2) The charge-transfer overpotential of the cathodic electrode;
(3) Any diffusion (or concentration) polarization developed at the cathodic electrode;
(4) The equilibrium potential of the anodic electrode;
(5) The charge–transfer overpotential at the anodic electrode;
(6) Any diffusion (or concentration) polarization developed at the anodic electrode; and
(7) The *IR* drop in the solution.

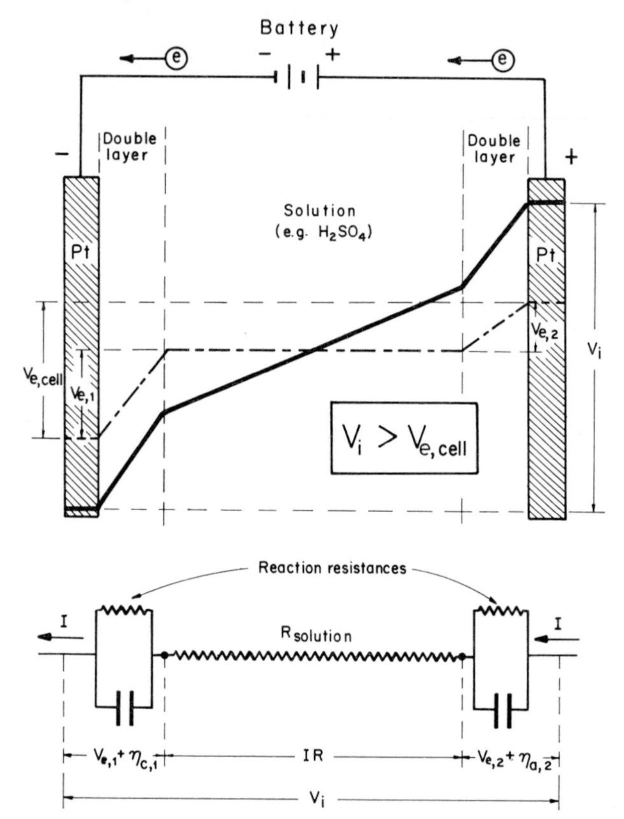

Fig. 4.22. A driven cell. When there is no net current, the cell has an equilibrium voltage, $V_{e,\text{cell}}$ (broken line). When the current is increased, the cell voltage V_i is larger by the sum of the overpotentials developed plus the '*IR*' drop (full line). Below, simplified equivalent circuit.

All these things add together in the case of a driven cell, and so the driven cell will go at a current given by a solution of the I in the equations in terms of the potentials which we have added, | | meaning absolute values since cathodic overpotential, η_c, is negative.

$$V_i = V_{e,\text{cell}} + |\eta_{c,1}| + \eta_{a,2} + IR. \tag{4.13}$$

If diffusion overpotentials appear because of the insufficient supply of reacting ions, the total cathodic overpotentials η_c, or anodic overpotential, η_a, are the sums of charge transfer overpotentials η, plus diffusion overpotentials η_d (e.g., $\eta_{c,1} = \eta_1 + \eta_{d,1}$).

In the case of the spontaneously-working, self-driving cell, everything is the same except that the overpotentials (the electron transfer ones, concentration ones, and the IR) all subtract themselves from the

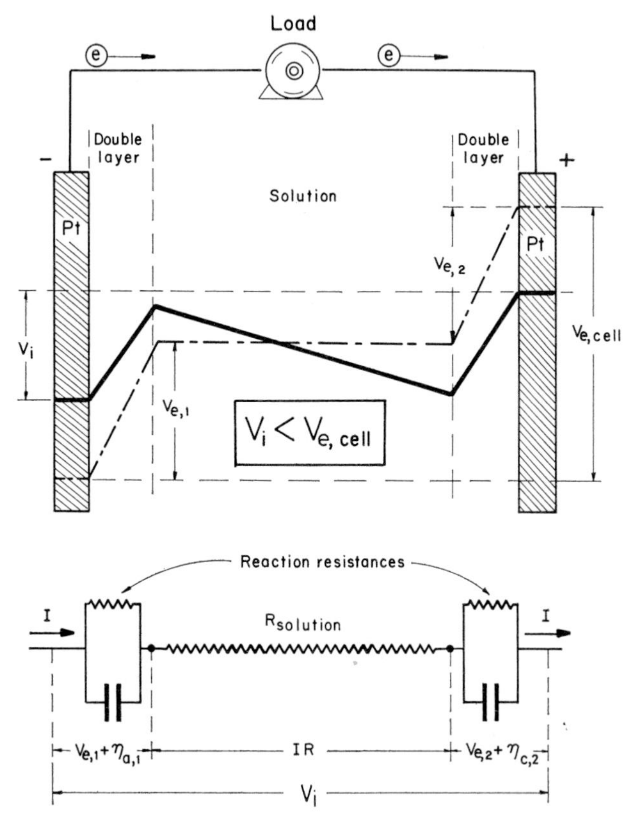

Fig. 4.23. A self-driving cell. The current direction is opposite to that of the current in the driven cell, and the overpotentials have opposite signs. The cell voltage V_i is less than $V_{e,\text{cell}}$, by (the sum of all overpotentials plus 'IR' drop).

total equilibrium cell voltage. The thermodynamic or equilibrium potential is a kind of 'total energy source' which the overpotentials can draw upon. They cannot overdraw what is, so to speak, funding them; and this source is always the reversible potential. The net potential which can be applied to any outside source (e.g., the motor the fuel cell runs) is the equilibrium cell voltage diminished by the overpotentials (see fig. 4.23).

$$V_i = V_{e,\text{cell}} - \eta_{a,1} - |\eta_{c,1}| - IR. \tag{4.14}$$

Basically, the same idea, but in terms of V–I curves for individual electrodes and overall cell voltage, is presented in fig. 4.24 for a driven cell, and in fig. 4.25 for a self-driving cell.

Now, you can see how a cell works. You can see the various components which make it a good or bad cell. A low solution resistance, R is always good; the highest i_0's are desirable; and the concentration of the solution must be as high as possible. In this extreme case, the current in the cell varies mainly with the external resistance of the load.

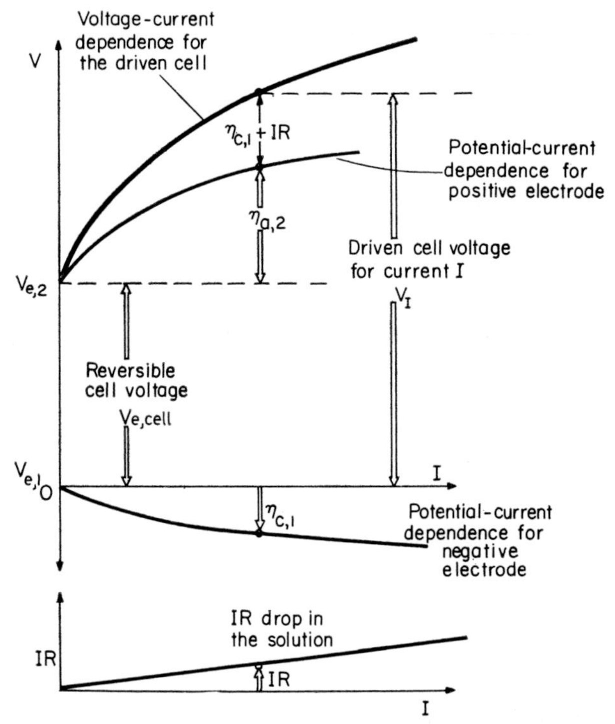

Fig. 4.24. V–I curves for electrodes, 'IR' drop, and overall cell voltage for a *driven* cell.

Cells in nature

We do know something about the existence of electrochemical cells in nature, especially those in corrosion (see Chapter 9) which are all around us, affecting our everyday living. To what extent electrochemical cells are the origin of activities in biological systems is on the edge of present-day electrophysiological research (see Chapter 10).

It is interesting for a moment to think of 'natural chemical activity' and to look at it from the point of view of what is thermal and what is electrochemical. Traditional chemistry, the chemistry of collisions and quantum transitions between molecules in the gas phase, looks at everything from the *thermal* point of view. It assumes that reaction originates from collision. Electrochemistry looks at everything from the point of view that the essential act is always the electron transfer,

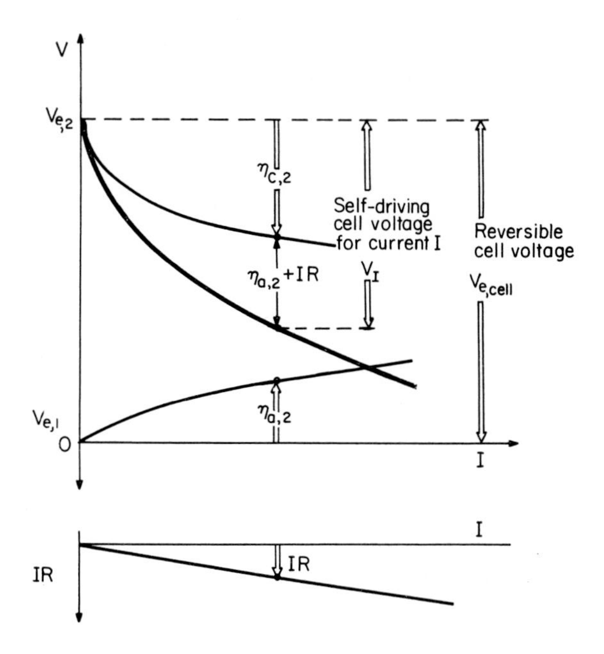

Fig. 4.25. *V–I* curves for electrodes, '*IR*' drop, and overall cell voltage for a *self-driving* cell.

and that reactants do not have to come into contact with each other, if they can come into contact with the same electronic conductor. Furthermore, although it has to be an electronic conductor, it does not have to be a metal. A semiconductor will do, and perhaps even some biological substances conduct electrons well enough to allow electrochemical reactions to take place on them. Many of the possibilities of electrochemical mechanisms in biophysics remain uninvestigated.

CHAPTER 5

electrocatalysis and electrosynthesis

Electrodes as Catalysts

CHEMICAL catalysis is a well-known phenomenon. A given reaction occurs at a different rate upon different substrates, and the action of the substrate in changing the rate is called catalysis. The substrate itself suffers no change. An example of chemical catalysis is given in Table 5.1 where it is shown how the velocity of the conversion of para-hydrogen into ortho-hydrogen depends on the substrate.

The situation is similar with reactions on electrodes. In Table 5.2 we give examples of the rate of the hydrogen evolution reaction at the equilibrium potential (exchange current densities, i_0) as a function of substrate. It will be seen that the reaction rates can change with different catalysts by a factor of 10^{10}.

Table 5.1. The effect of metals on the rate of para-hydrogen–ortho-hydrogen conversion reaction ($pH_2 \rightarrow oH_2$) at 300 K

Metal	Rate mol m^{-2} s^{-1}
Manganese	$10^{-2.68}$
Iron	$10^{-1.80}$
Nickel	$10^{-1.71}$
Palladium	$10^{-1.63}$
Cobalt	$10^{-1.11}$
Platinum	$10^{-0.42}$
Tungsten	$10^{+6.71}$

There are two distinct uses of the term electrocatalysis. One is simply to indicate that the electrodes increase the rate of a reaction whether or not there is any surface catalysis in the chemical sense of the term. Thus, if one increases the overpotential on an electrode, then according to the Butler–Volmer equation (eqn. (3.24)), for larger overpotentials (eqn. (3.26)):

$$i = i_0 \exp(-\beta \eta F/RT), \tag{5.1}$$

the reaction must go faster as the applied (negative) overpotential increases. However, this is a question of overvoltage rather than catalysis, and is *not* what is generally meant by electrocatalysis.

What the term electrocatalysis usually means is the variation of the rate of an electrodic reaction with change of substrate *at the same overpotential.*

Now, if we use the same overpotential, it is assumed that (if the coefficient β is the same for all the substrates on which we measure the reaction rate), the same electrical energy $\beta\eta F$ acts upon the activated state of the electrical reaction (see fig. 3.8). If, therefore,

Table 5.2. The effect of the electrode metal on the exchange current density (rate at the equilibrium potential) for the hydrogen evolution reaction in M H_2SO_4

Metal	Rate mol m^{-2} s^{-1}	Exchange current density i_0 A m^{-2}
Mercury	$10^{-13 \cdot 6}$	$10^{-8 \cdot 3}$
Lead	$10^{-13 \cdot 0}$	$10^{-8 \cdot 0}$
Thallium	$10^{-12 \cdot 3}$	$10^{-7 \cdot 0}$
Manganese	$10^{-12 \cdot 2}$	$10^{-6 \cdot 9}$
Cadmium	$10^{-12 \cdot 1}$	$10^{-6 \cdot 8}$
Titanium	$10^{-9 \cdot 5}$	$10^{-4 \cdot 2}$
Niobium	$10^{-8 \cdot 1}$	$10^{-2 \cdot 8}$
Tungsten	$10^{-7 \cdot 2}$	$10^{-1 \cdot 9}$
Gold	$10^{-6 \cdot 7}$	$10^{-1 \cdot 4}$
Nickel	$10^{-6 \cdot 5}$	$10^{-1 \cdot 2}$
Iridium	$10^{-5 \cdot 0}$	$10^{+0 \cdot 3}$
Rhodium	$10^{-4 \cdot 9}$	$10^{+0 \cdot 4}$
Platinum	$10^{-4 \cdot 4}$	$10^{+0 \cdot 9}$
Palladium	$10^{-4 \cdot 3}$	$10^{+1 \cdot 0}$

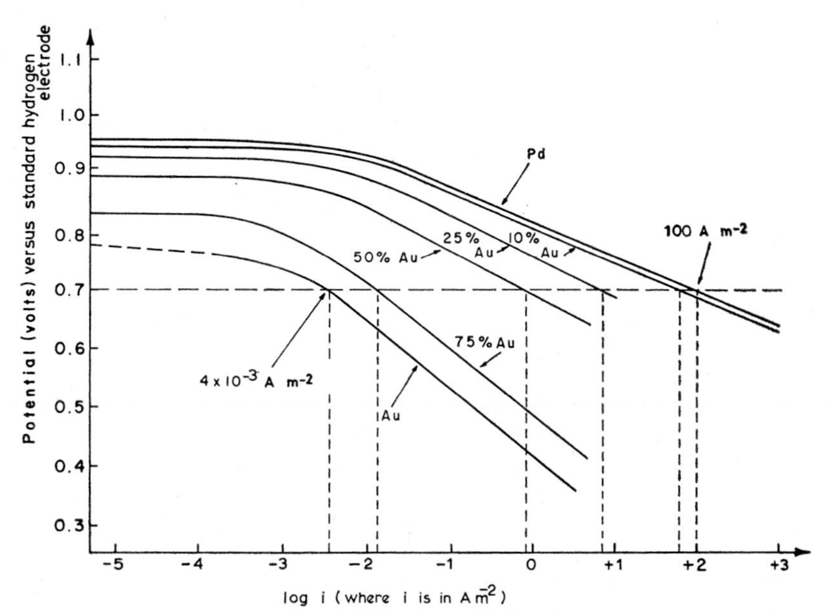

Fig. 5.1. Tafel lines for the electrochemical reduction of oxygen on gold, palladium and series of Au–Pd alloys, in 0·5 M H_2SO_4 at 25°C. Note the difference in current densities (rates) at the same potential (0·7 V).

we compare the rate of the single reaction on a variety of substrates, there will be a whole series of reaction rates, but the electrochemical component (the term exp $[-\beta\eta F/RT]$) will be the same. This need not be exactly true in practice, because the β factor may be a little different from one electrode to another. In so far as β *is* the same for the various substrates, however, the change in reaction rate is only going to depend on the catalytic powers of the substrate, and not directly on the exp $(-\beta\eta F/RT)$ term (for, in any comparison of the rates of *one* reaction on *several* substrates, this term will cancel out).

In fig. 5.1, the potential–log i curves for oxygen reduction at palladium, gold and several palladium–gold alloys are given. At the same potential (0·7 V) the rates of the electrochemical reaction can be seen to depend on the electrode material (although not so much as for the reaction of the evolution of hydrogen). On a palladium electrode the rate is nearly 25 000 times faster than on a gold electrode.

The best way of comparing the velocities of various reactions is to extrapolate each to the equilibrium potential (when η is zero). Thus, *electrocatalysis is measured by* i_0, *the exchange current density*, the equal (and opposite) rates of the electron emission and the electron acceptance when the electrode is at the equilibrium potential for the reaction concerned.

Let us consider an electrolysis cell, a substance-producer, and some situation in which we wish to act upon a cell to produce a definite current (see p. 148). Then we see that the applied voltage necessary to produce a given current—that is to say, a given rate of production of our substance—depends upon the η's present, by equation (4.13),

$$V_i = V_{e,\text{cell}} + |\eta_c| + \eta_a + IR. \qquad (4.13)$$

But,

$$i = i_0 \exp(-\beta F\eta/RT). \qquad (3.26)$$

And thus, for a given i (i.e., a given rate of production of new substance), the overpotential we need depends upon i_0. Hence, the potential we have to apply to get a given rate of production of substance depends upon i_0—or, more precisely, the logarithm thereof. It determines, in turn, the applied potential difference needed to make the cell function at the desired current density, i.e., to produce material at the desired rate. Of course, if the cell has to have a given applied potential difference (or voltage V_i) to make it function, the power which we have to use to generate our product, and the electrical energy we have to pay for one kilogramme of it, is directly proportional to V_i.

And, what is V_i? It is (see eqn. (4.13)) the equilibrium thermodynamic cell voltage, $V_{e,\text{cell}}$ plus the overpotentials, η. The cost per mole of producing a substance is proportional to the overpotential and this is proportional, at a given rate of production, to log i_0, to 'electrocatalysis' one might say.

An illustration of what we write here is given in fig. 5.2 for an electrolysis cell (e.g., hydrogen production). If we run the electrolysis at the certain current i, with the anode having an exchange current density, $i_{0,\text{anodic},1}$, the total cell voltage will be V_1 (plus the IR drop). However, if this anode is replaced by the other one, made of the material having larger exchange current density, $i_{0,\text{anodic},2}$ the same current can be passed through the cell at a lower total cell voltage, V_2. By *increasing* i_0, the cell voltage is *decreased* by ΔV.

Let us take a practical example: the electrolytic production of hydrogen is used for many industrial purposes, e.g., the hydrogenation of oil in margarine production. Hydrogen is obtained by electrolysis

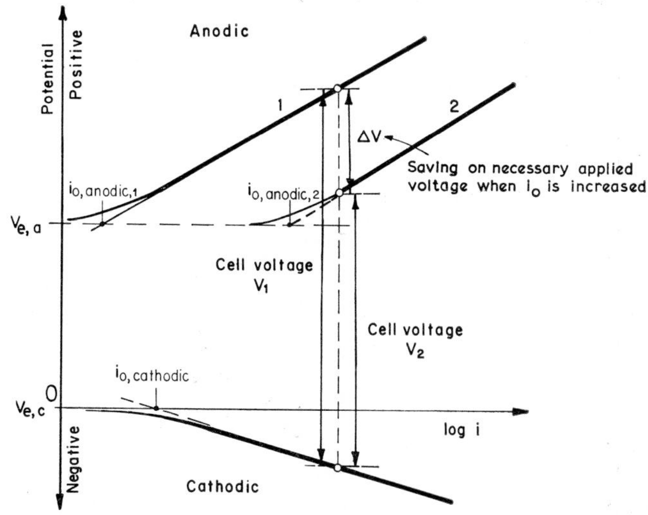

Fig. 5.2. The effect of an increase of i_0 on the anode overpotential and on the overall cell voltage. (1) and (2) are Tafel lines for the anodic reaction, for two metals with different values of i_0; ΔV is the saving in voltage.

of water in electrolysers containing a large number of unit cells, having steel cathodes and iron or nickel anodes. A typical electrolyser operates with about 2 volt per cell voltage, current density of 10^3 A m^{-2}, and can deliver 500 m^3 H_2 hour^{-1}. The average electrical energy consumption is 18 MJ m^{-3} H_2. Since the water used for electrolysis is very cheap, the main contribution to the price of the produced hydrogen is the cost of the electrical energy.

The operating cell voltage is about 2 V but the equilibrium cell voltage is 1·23 V, while the rest is the sum of overpotentials at the hydrogen and oxygen electrode and the IR drop between the electrodes of the cell. The oxygen overpotential at the anode is the largest contributor, being about 0·5 V, due to the relatively small i_0 value.

If we can replace the nickel used at present with some other material having i_0 only 10 times larger than that for the evolution on Ni, the oxygen overpotential would be reduced by about 0·1 V (see eqn. (3.25)), and the overall cell voltage would be reduced by 5%. Taking 0·3 cent per MJ ($\approx$ 1 cent per kWh) as the price of electricity, the savings achieved by this change, expressed in dollars worth in one year per one unit, would be:

$$\textit{Savings} = 500\ \text{m}^3\ \text{h}^{-1} \times 24\ \text{h} \times 360\ \text{days} \times 0{\cdot}05 \times 0{\cdot}003\ \$\text{MJ}^{-1} \times 18\ \text{MJ m}^{-3} = \$12{,}000\ \textit{per year unit.}$$

In large electrochemical plants, like those found in the electrochemical production of aluminium, a decrease of 0·01 V of overpotential is worth more than $1 million in the consequent reduction of the needed electricity.

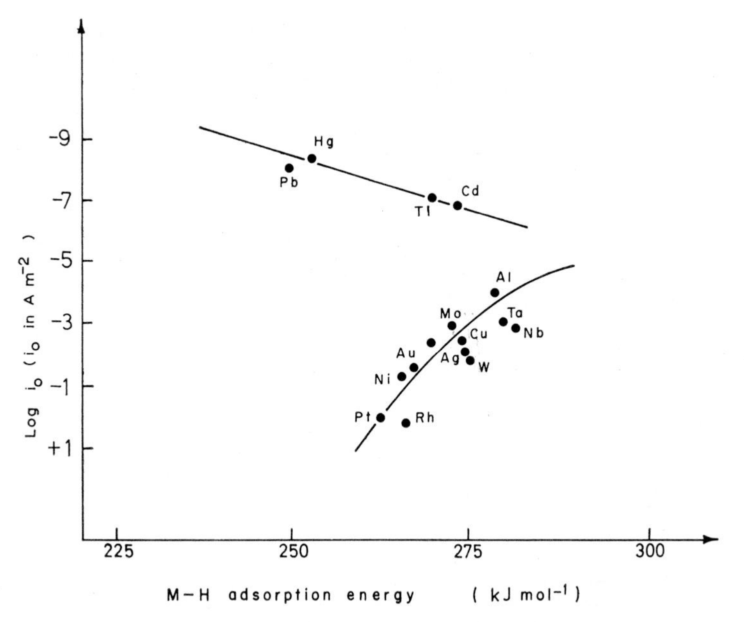

Fig. 5.3. Rate of hydrogen evolution reaction (log i_0) at different metals versus M–H energy.

The hydrogen evolution reaction

The clearest example of electrocatalysis is given by the hydrogen evolution reaction, $2H^+ + 2e \rightarrow H_2$, as it can be carried out on a variety of metals, so we have a good idea of the spread of results. In fig. 5.3, one can see how the reaction goes with the substrate.

What the graph tells us is that for metals with small values of hydrogen-adsorption energy (the bond strength of hydrogen to the metal being relatively small) the rate of the hydrogen evolution reaction at the equilibrium potential is also relatively small. As the strength of the bond of hydrogen to the metal increases, the current density i_0 at the equilibrium potential increases. These remarks apply to the way in which i_0 for mercury, cadmium, lead and thallium is related to the energy of adsorption of H atoms on the various substrate electrodes.

But at higher values of the hydrogen–metal bond the direction of the $\log i_0$–MH bond strength relation changes (or, for the lower group of metals in fig. 5.3). Now as the energy of adsorption *increases*, the velocity (i_0) of the hydrogen evolution reaction *decreases*. One cannot interpret these striking facts without more information. However, this is readily available.

On the four or five metals where the rate *increases* with *increasing* bond strength of hydrogen to the metal, it is found by experiment that the coverage with hydrogen, θ_H, is very *low*. On the metals where the rate of the reaction *decreases* with *increasing* bonding of hydrogen to the metal, the coverage of the electrode with hydrogen is very *high*.

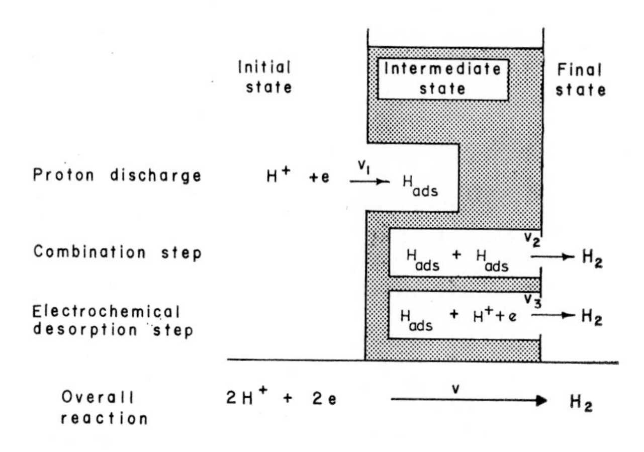

Fig. 5.4. Two possible reaction paths for H_2 evolution reaction. The intermediate, H_{ads} can either combine chemically or desorb electrochemically. Each step, depending on the situation, can be the rate determining step.

The section on the hydrogen evolution mechanisms, given in Chapter 3, showed (page 115) that a low coverage corresponds to a reaction mechanism in which *proton discharge* ($H^+ + e \rightarrow H_{ads}$) is rate-determining. As to the metals which evolve H_2 with a high coverage of hydrogen on the metal ($\theta_H \rightarrow 1$), *this* is consistent with a rate determining step which is called the 'electrochemical desorption reaction':

$$H^+ + H_{ads} + e \rightarrow H_2. \qquad (5.2)$$

To explain all this, let us first consider the metals mercury, cadmium, tin, lead and thallium for which, in acid solutions, the proton discharge reaction is rate determining, and examine the potential energy diagram (fig. 5.5 *a*) for this case when proton-discharge is the rate determining step.

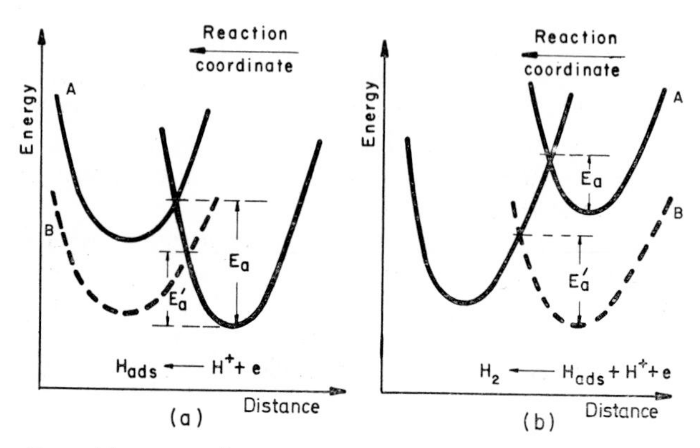

Fig. 5.5. Potential energy diagrams for (*a*) the charge-transfer step and (*b*) the electrochemical desorption step. (The dotted curves refer to another electrode metal which has a stronger M–H bond.)

The curves in fig. 5.5 refer to the vibrational energy of pseudo diatomic molecules. Thus, in (*a*), the right-hand curve represents the sum of the energy of an electron in the metal, and the energy of H^+–(OH_2), where H^+–(OH_2) is analogous to A–(B), and can be thought of for the purposes of this diagram as consisting of the atom H^+ and the pseudo 'atom' (OH_2). The distance coordinate refers to the distance between H^+ and O for the right-hand curve of (*a*). The left-hand curve of (*a*) represents the change of the energy of M–H as the H atom vibrates, with respect to the substrate. The H_{ads} is what is produced from (OH_2)–H^+ combining with an electron from the metal (together with H_2O left over and following back into the solution). When H^+–OH_2 stretches enough to reach the energy of M–H, and the curves intersect, H^+ picks up an electron and gets adsorbed. The height of the intersection of the two curves above the minimum of the one on the right determines the heat of activation in the reaction, and therefore the rate. The greater this height is, the *less* is the reaction rate.

When one changes the metal substrate, the line A is moved to B if the energy of adsorption of hydrogen is increased. Then the relevant point of intersection of the curves is *lower* than it was for a *lower* bond strength of hydrogen to metal ($E_a{}^1 < E_a$). From an energy standpoint, the proton has not to 'climb' so far before it reaches the conditions for quantum mechanical tunnelling (see Chapter 3). Hence, the straining

of the $H^+–OH_2$ bond is reduced when M–H bond strength is increased.†
Thus the reaction proceeds more readily with increased metal–hydrogen bond strength.

A relation can be easily established between the ease of bond-stretching and the reaction rate. The determining quantity is E_a in fig. 5.5 *a*.

As has been shown earlier (cf. eqns. (3.1) and (3.2))

$$\text{Velocity of reaction} \propto \exp(-E_a/RT), \tag{5.3}$$

so the smaller the value of E_a, the faster the reaction goes.

Less 'stretching' of a bond reduces E_a, and hence leads to a *faster* reaction rate.

The reverse of all this is true for the case of the electrochemical desorption, i.e., for the rate determining step $H^+ + H_{ads} + e \rightarrow H_2$ (known to be the path for the hydrogen evolution reaction on nickel, iron, chromium, tungsten, etc., the metals in the *lower* curve in fig. 5.3). To make this reaction go, the hydrogen has to be desorbed from the surface by the oncoming proton, and this is clearly more difficult as the metal–hydrogen bond strength increases (fig. 5.5 *b*).

Other cases of electrocatalysis

The hydrogen evolution reaction is a fairly easy reaction to study. Other cases of electrocatalysis cannot be explained so certainly and so simply as this one. The reactions are more complex and the reaction mechanisms much more difficult to sort out. The catalytic trends for some of them have nevertheless been explained fairly well, and one of these is the oxidation of unsaturated hydrocarbons.

The electrochemical *stability* of the substrate, quite a separate matter from its catalytic power, is important. Its stability is what makes *platinum* the best all-round catalyst for most anodic and even cathodic reactions taking place in fuel cells. The typical region in which hydrocarbon oxidation takes place at temperatures in the region of 100°C would be 0·3–0·9 V positive to the equilibrium hydrogen potential in the same solution.

Now, the difficulty is that this potential is often more positive than the potential at which many metals *anodically dissolve* following $M \rightarrow M^{2+} + 2e$. It is no use just calculating theoretically in terms of bond strengths on what would be the best catalysts for the oxidation of hydrocarbons, when those catalysts themselves will probably dissolve anodically. However, the noble metals *are* stable under these anodic conditions.

† In fact, to speak of *stretching* the bond is too classical. What is meant is that the activation needed for the reaction involves a greater number of higher vibrational states of $H^+–O$ (+ the energy of interaction with the surrounding continuum).

The unsaturated hydrocarbon, ethylene (ethene), can be electrochemically oxidized using noble metal electrodes, according to the overall reaction:

$$C_2H_4+4H_2O \rightarrow 2CO_2+12H^+ +12e. \tag{5.4}$$

It was found by Kühn and Wroblowa that the first three steps of the most probable reaction mechanism for this reaction are:

$$C_2H_4 \rightleftarrows C_2H_{4(ads)} \tag{5.5}$$

$$H_2O \rightleftarrows OH_{(ads)}+H^+ +e \tag{5.6}$$

$$C_2H_{4(ads)}+OH_{(ads)} \xrightarrow{\text{slow}} (\text{–}CH_2\text{–}O\text{–}CH_3)_{ads}. \tag{5.7}$$

The rest of the reaction steps, leading to the final product, CO_2, are still unknown. However, the important, rate determining step (r.d.s.)

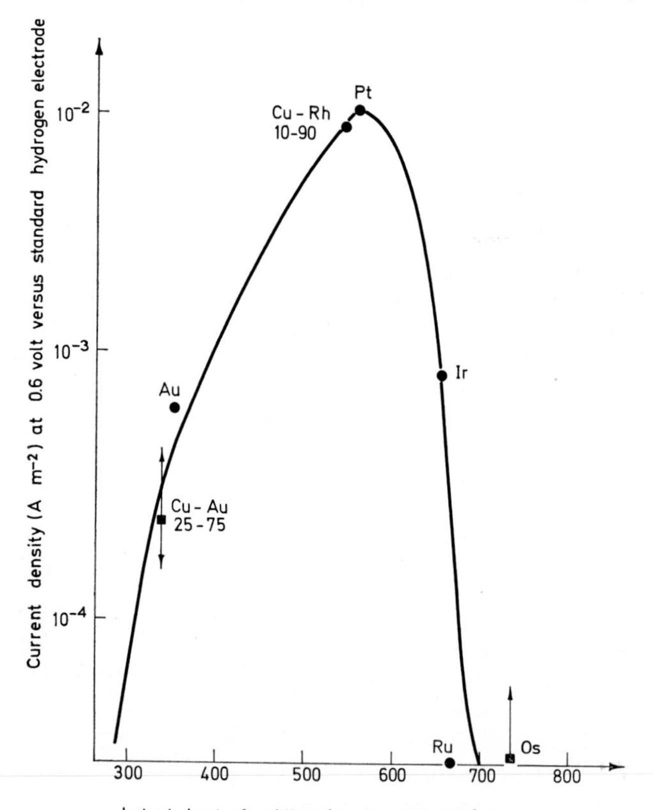

Fig. 5.6. Current density (rate) at constant potential versus latent heat of sublimation for different metals and some alloys (figures indicate atomic per cent) in the ethylene oxidation in 0·5 M H_2SO_4 at 80°C.

is reaction (5.7), controlling the overall reaction. It involves two adsorbed species, $C_2H_{4(ads)}$ and $OH_{(ads)}$. Therefore, it can be expected that the adsorption energies of these species, depending strongly upon the substrate, will affect the reaction rate considerably.

This has been found to be so experimentally, as can be seen from the graph in fig. 5.6 in which the oxidation rate (anodic current density) at constant potential is plotted against the specific latent heat of sublimation of the various metals used as the electrode. A 'volcano' relationship often found in chemical catalysis is obtained. Platinum appears to have the largest catalytic effect.

Platinum is fairly stable, with a high heat of sublimation and therefore strong metal–metal bonds, but it also has sufficiently high bonding power for reactants to stay upon the surface and *have time* to react. Some other noble metals (Os, Ir, Ru) have larger heats of sublimation

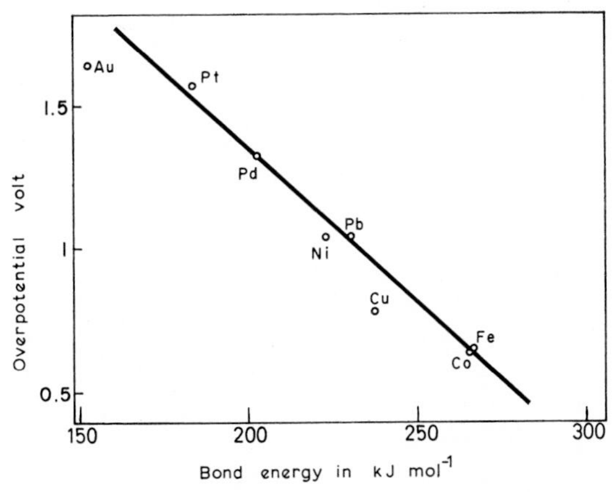

Fig. 5.7. Oxygen overvoltage at 10^4 A m^{-2} and 25°C in 1 M KOH for various metals as a function of the binding energy M–OH.

and much higher bonding power for carbon–metal or oxygen–metal bonds, and indeed they are more stable than platinum. But now their bonding power to reactants is *so* large that the reactants cling to the surface too much, and cannot get off again; they are too strongly adsorbed and *do not react* to go on to the end product of the reaction.

A good catalyst must possess balanced properties related to several aspects of the reaction concerned. For example, there must be similar interactions with the ions in the initial and final states of the reaction. The enviable advantages of platinum are medium–high metal–metal bonds which make the substrate stable enough to withstand potentials sufficiently positive (anodic) for the oxidation of hydrocarbons, but not *too* strong a bond adsorption strength, so that the hydrocarbon radicals, which must bond to the surface to react, cannot break free after reaction. Platinum's secret seems to be 'enough, not too much' of the central property of bond strength.

One more example of electrocatalysis is the oxygen electrode reaction. It is of great practical importance; the cathodic one (reduction of O_2) for fuel cells and batteries, and the anodic one (evolution of O_2) for various electrolysis processes. Its part in biological respiration may also have an electrochemical aspect.

The effect of the electrode material on the cathodic reduction rate has been already well illustrated by fig. 5.1. The effect of electrode material on the oxygen evolution reaction (anodic) is also considerable. It seems that it can be related to M–OH bond strength. As shown in fig. 5.7, the overpotential at constant current density for different metals is nearly linearly dependent on the strength of M–OH bond. Since the overpotential is inversely proportional to $\log i_0$, metals with the strongest M–OH bond have the largest i_0, i.e., they have the best catalytic properties for this reaction.

In acidic solutions, platinum is the best electrode material from the point of view of the electrocatalysis as well as the stability. In alkaline solutions, as shown in fig. 5.7, several other non-noble metals can be used rather successfully (e.g., silver, iron, nickel), since passivation effects (see p. 257) prevent the dissolution of these metals which would take place at the anodic potentials at which O_2 is reduced, in acid solutions.

In general, it seems now that platinum, and under some conditions nickel, are the best electrode materials for the reduction of oxygen. However, the exchange current density for oxygen reaction on platinum is about 10^{-6} A m^{-2} (compared to 10 A m^{-2} for hydrogen evolution reaction). This low i_0 value is the reason that in electrolysis cells (and in fuel cells as well) the largest overpotential (and loss of electrical energy) is at the oxygen electrode. It is obvious that the platinum is not a very good electrocatalyst for this reaction, just the least bad one. Perhaps, it should not be called a catalyst at all. But, at present we do not have anything better.

Electrocatalysis of the hydrocarbons as a historically important catalysis

Hydrocarbons can indeed be burned electrochemically, as was shown for the first time by the Americans Heath and Worsham in 1960. The difficulty is that up to now no other substrate has been found which does as well as platinum, and platinum is very expensive.

It is clear that, were it possible electrochemically to burn *oil* at somewhat the same efficiency as in thermal combustion, the owners of the oil wells would gladly countenance, and even support financially, the change to an electrochemically-driven transportation system. The result would be the elimination of smog-forming pollution. However, if it is not possible economically for the oil companies to have their oil turned to energy in a clean, electrochemical way, the oil will continue to be burned in a polluting way, in *chemical* internal combustion, with its ecological disadvantages, until taxes on the dirty old method have made a change to the new electrochemical methods financially desirable.

Is platinum the only good electrocatalyst?

Electrochemists usually examine electrochemical reactions at *metal*–solution interfaces, and most electrochemical knowledge and experience has been built up as a result of this work. Experience shows that, from the limited number of available metals, platinum seemed to be the most suitable substrate for a number of electrochemical reactions (if the price of platinum is not taken into account). One might ask, however, what about other materials: semiconductors or even insulators? The electrochemical reactions occur at their interfaces too, as shown by a number of electrochemists in the last 15 years. However, even if some of them would be good electrocatalysts, the inner resistance of these materials would introduce a large IR drop, so that all the gains in overpotential would be lost.

Have we come to a dead end with platinum, the too expensive catalyst? Is there any way to replace platinum with something better, but, above all, *cheaper*?

Several years ago, looking for some better electrocatalytic material, D. Sepa and A. Damjanovic used as electrode materials for the oxygen reduction reaction a number of compounds, known among physicists as 'bronzes'. 'Bronzes' are oxides of transition metals containing a non-stoichiometric quantity of alkaline metal (e.g., sodium–tungsten oxide Na_xWO_3, where $0{\cdot}3 < x < 0{\cdot}7$). The name of these compounds is derived from their colour, which resembles that of real bronze (Cu–Sn alloy). A peculiarity of these oxides is their very high electronic conductivity (near to metallic) and good stability against corrosion, even in strongly acid solutions, which is the prerequisite for any useful electrode material. It appeared that sodium–tungsten oxides, prepared in a proper way, exhibit exchange current densities for oxygen reduction close to that of platinum, while some oxides in alkaline solution have i_0 even larger than that on platinum.

Besides bronzes (the non-stoichiometric oxides), some nitrides behave in a similar way. Bronzes and nitrides are not the final answer to our question, since there are some problems with them, too. But it is this opportunity of exploring the electrochemistry of many known and still unknown electron-conducting compounds which is of tremendous importance for the development of cheap and stable electrocatalysts. Therefore, the task of finding a suitable electrocatalyst for hydrocarbons is an urgent one, and progress looks possible if sufficient effort by electrochemists is put into research in the direction of conducting oxides.

It is of interest to note that, in the U.S.A., for 1970–71, the cost of research for the production of non-polluting internal combustion engines (efficiency of energy conversion 8–15%), was in the region of hundreds of millions of dollars per year; and that for intrinsically non-polluting electrochemical hydrocarbon combustion (efficiency 30–50%) was less than $100 000 per year. In respect to the distribution of funds for research and the community-impoverishment which they imply, one might suggest the description: 'Seldom has so much been owed by so few to so many'.

Electrosynthesis

Most chemical syntheses involve oxidation or reduction reactions. Whether the substance can be oxidized by oxygen or reduced by hydrogen depends on the value of its electrochemical redox potential. The oxidation by oxygen is thermodynamically possible (which still does not say anything about the rate of oxidation) if the equilibrium potential of oxygen is more *positive* than the redox potential of the substance. On the other hand, the reduction by hydrogen is possible if the equilibrium potential of hydrogen is more *negative* than the redox potential of the substance. This puts some limits on our possibilities of chemical oxidation and reduction reactions. We cannot use oxygen for the oxidation of substances with redox potentials more positive than +1·23 V, and we cannot use hydrogen to reduce substances with redox potentials more negative than zero (potentials are referred to the equilibrium hydrogen electrode).

However, in electrochemical oxidations we can go up to about +3·0 V, and in electrochemical reductions to about −3·0 V, providing the proper solvent is used. This gives a span of potentials of about 6 V, compared to the chemically possible 1·23 V when oxygen and hydrogen are used. One might ask why we are talking about oxygen as the only oxidant. What about chlorate, perchlorate, permanganate, dichromate, etc., often used in chemical oxidations? With this question we come to our point. All these chemicals can only be produced by electrochemical means. When we use permanganate as an oxidant, we use *indirectly* the advantages of electrochemical oxidation. Instead of direct electrochemical oxidation of the substance in an electrolytic cell we produce permanganate electrochemically and use it as a carrier of the oxidative property. Among the naturally occurring substances oxygen is potentially the best oxidant. All the other, better oxidants, have to be produced electrochemically. A similar situation occurs with the chemicals used for reduction.

We said above that in the proper solvent electrode potentials of +3 V on positive and −3 V on negative electrode can be achieved, giving us a chance to perform many oxidations and reductions that could not be done chemically by oxygen and hydrogen. In most of electrochemical processes, water is the solvent. If somebody would now take the Nernstian, thermodynamic, approach, he would have to conclude that there is no difference between chemical and electrochemical systems. Thermodynamically, oxygen will start to be evolved on an anode at $+1{\cdot}23$ V, and hydrogen on a cathode at 0 V. Therefore, there seems to be no difference.

However, we know that to evolve oxygen or hydrogen at some finite rate we need *overpotential*. It is the overpotential which makes it

Table 5.3. Standard electrode potentials, at 25°C†

Electrode	Electrode reaction	V_e° volt
N_3^-/N_2, Pt	$\frac{3}{2}N_2+e = N_3^-$	$-3{\cdot}2$
Li^+/Li	$Li^++e = Li$	$-3{\cdot}04$
K^+/K	$K^++e = K$	$-2{\cdot}92$
Ca^{2+}/Ca	$Ca^{2+}+2e = Ca$	$-2{\cdot}87$
Na^+/Na	$Na^++e = Na$	$-2{\cdot}713$
Mg^{2+}/Mg	$Mg^{2+}+2e = Mg$	$-2{\cdot}38$
Be^{2+}/Be	$Be^{2+}+2e = Be$	$-1{\cdot}85$
Al^{3+}/Al	$Al^{3+}+3e = Al$	$-1{\cdot}66$
Mn^{2+}/Mn	$Mn^{2+}+2e = Mn$	$-1{\cdot}18$
Zn^{2+}/Zn	$Zn^{2+}+2e = Zn$	$-0{\cdot}763$
Cr^{3+}/Cr	$Cr^{3+}+3e = Cr$	$-0{\cdot}74$
S^{2-}/S	$S+2e = S^{2-}$	$-0{\cdot}51$
Fe^{2+}/Fe	$Fe^{2+}+2e = Fe$	$-0{\cdot}44$
Cr^{3+}, Cr^{2+}/Pt	$Cr^{3+}+e = Cr^{2+}$	$-0{\cdot}410$
Cd^{2+}/Cd	$Cd^{2+}+2e = Cd$	$-0{\cdot}402$
Co^{2+}/Co	$Co^{2+}+2e = Co$	$-0{\cdot}27$
Ni^{2+}/Ni	$Ni^{2+}+2e = Ni$	$-0{\cdot}24$
Sn^{2+}/Sn	$Sn^{2+}+2e = Sn$	$-0{\cdot}136$
Pb^{2+}/Pb	$Pb^{2+}+2e = Pb$	$-0{\cdot}126$
H^+/H_2, Pt Standard hydrogen electrode	**$H^++e = \frac{1}{2}H_2$**	**$\pm 0{\cdot}000$**
Sn^{4+}, Sn^{2+}/Pt	$Sn^{4+}+2e = Sn^{2+}$	$+0{\cdot}154$
Saturated calomel electrode	**$Hg_2Cl_2+2e = 2Hg+2Cl^-$ (satd. KCl)**	**$+0{\cdot}245$**
Normal calomel electrode	**$Hg_2Cl_2+2e = 2Hg+2Cl$ (1 N KCl)**	**$+0{\cdot}282$**
$Cu^{2+})Cu$	$Cu^{2+}+2e = Cu$	$+0{\cdot}337$
$Fe(CN)_6^{3-}$, $Fe(CN)_6^{4-}/Pt$	$Fe(CN)_6^{3-}+e = Fe(CN)_6^{4-}$	$+0{\cdot}36$
OH^-/O_2, Pt	$\frac{1}{2}O_2+H_2O+2e = 2OH^-$	$+0{\cdot}401$
I^-/I_2, Pt	$I_2+2e = 2I^-$	$+0{\cdot}536$
MnO_4^-, MnO_4^{2-}/Pt	$MnO_4^-+e = MnO_4^{2-}$	$+0{\cdot}564$
Fe^{3+}, Fe^{2+}/Pt	$Fe^{3+}+e = Fe^{2+}$	$+0{\cdot}771$
Hg_2^{2+}/Hg	$Hg_2^{2+}+2e = 2Hg$	$+0{\cdot}798$
Ag^+/Ag	$Ag^++e = Ag$	$+0{\cdot}799$
Br^-/Br_2, Pt	$Br_2+2e = 2Br^-$	$+1{\cdot}066$
Pt^{2+}/Pt	$Pt^{2+}+2e = Pt$	$+1{\cdot}2$
H^+/O_2, H_2O	**$\frac{1}{2}O_2+2H^++2e = H_2O$**	**$+1{\cdot}23$**
$Cr_2O_7^{2-}$, Cr^{3+}/Pt	$Cr_2O_7^{2-}+14H^++6e = 2Cr^{3+}+7H_2O$	$+1{\cdot}33$
Cl^-/Cl_2, Pt	$Cl_2+2e = 2Cl^-$	$+1{\cdot}359$
Pb^{2+}/PbO_2, Pb	$PbO_2+2e+4H^+ = Pb^{2+}+2H_2O$	$+1{\cdot}455$
MnO_4^-, H^+/MnO_2, Pt	$MnO_4^-+3e+4H^+ = MnO_2+2H_2O$	$+1{\cdot}51$
Ce^{4+}, Ce^{3+}/Pt	$Ce^{4+}+e = C^{3+}$	$+1{\cdot}61$
$SO_4^{2-}/PbSO_4$, PbO_2, Pb	$PbO_2+2e+SO_4^{2-}+4H^+ = PbSO_4+2H_2O$	$+1{\cdot}685$
H^-/H_2, Pt	$H_2+2e = 2H^-$	$+2{\cdot}2$
F^-/F_2, Pt	$F_2+2e = 2F^-$	$+2{\cdot}87$

†These potentials correspond to unit *activity* of the ions concerned (e.g. Br^-) but are often, as a rough approximation, equated to potentials for unit concentration.

possible to achieve much more positive or negative electrode potentials than thermodynamics predicts. If we choose the proper materials for the electrodes, having small i_0 (i.e., large overpotentials) and consequently negligible rate of H_2 and O_2 evolution, we can carry our oxidations in water solutions at electrode potentials up to $+2$ V (e.g., by using PbO_2 electrode), or reductions at potentials of -1 V (e.g., using mercury electrode). At these potentials H_2 and O_2 evolution become appreciable so that further increase of potential is no more economical (electrical energy would be wasted in producing large amounts of H_2 and O_2).

But, there is a way to extend the range still further; use of non-aqueous solution in which hydroxyl and hydrogen ions do not exist, for example, pyridine, formamide, acetonitrile, etc., or in molten salts, some of which (e.g., $AlCl_3 + NaCl$) are molten at temperatures as low as 180°C). With non-aqueous solutions it is possible to go positive to $+3$ V and negative to -2 V.

The second aspect that must be taken into account is that we can greatly reduce the temperature of electrochemical reactions compared with that of the corresponding thermal ones at which we carry the reaction out. This can be seen by our most elementary equation for an electrochemical reaction, in Chapter 3, equation (3.3) or (3.5). Thus, we can *reduce the energy of activation*, typically taken as 80 kJ mol^{-1}, down to, say 40 kJ by applying about a volt of overpotential (for 1 volt $\times$ 1 Faraday $\approx$ 96 kJ mol^{-1} and $\beta = 0{\cdot}5$). But a change of 40 kJ in the activation energy of a reaction will be equivalent to the reduction of the temperature at which it can be carried out at the same rate by about 300 degrees.

This can be deduced in the following way. The increase of the reaction rate by applying 1 volt of overpotential, and so changing E_a by 40 kJ is:

$$\text{increase of rate} = \exp\left(-\Delta E_a/RT\right) = \exp\left(40\,000/8{\cdot}314 \times 300\right) \approx \exp\left(16{\cdot}6\right) \approx 10^7. \quad (5.8)$$

Therefore, an electrode potential change of 1 volt increases the reaction rate some 10^7 times. We can calculate how much we must raise the temperature to obtain the same 10^7 increase of rate by thermally increasing the reaction rate using the integrated form of the Arrhenius equation

$$\log \frac{k_2}{k_1} = \frac{E_a}{2{\cdot}3R}\left(\frac{T_2 - T_1}{T_1 T_2}\right). \quad (5.9)$$

Assuming that E_a is 80 kJ mol^{-1}, and independent of temperature, and by taking $k_2/k_1 = 10^7$, $R = 8{\cdot}314$ J mol^{-1} K^{-1}, and $T_1 = 300$ K, we have

$$\log 10^7 = \frac{80\,000}{2{\cdot}3 \times 8{\cdot}314}\left(\frac{T_2 - 300}{300 T_2}\right). \quad (5.10)$$

When solving for T_2, we obtain:

$$T_2 \approx 600 \text{ K}.$$

Therefore, the rise in temperature needed to produce the same increase of the reaction rate as when 1 volt of overpotential was applied is:

$$\Delta T = T_2 - T_1 = 600 - 300 = 300 \text{ K}.$$

In short, reactions which may have to be carried out at high temperature, can be carried out at low temperature, with all the advantages which that spells out: for example, a lesser expense of materials, because materials for vessels for low temperatures are much less costly than those for high temperatures (corrosion problems), lesser stability of reactants or products (especially if they are organic compounds) at higher temperatures, etc.

The positive advantages of electrochemical syntheses compared with chemical ones are in summary:

(1) we can apply more energy to make things happen,

(2) we can often make them happen at room temperature, and

(3) we can be more selective about what reaction product we obtain.

The last advantage is explained by the fact that by using a potentiostat (an electronic device which holds the potential of the electrode at any chosen value) we can obtain only the material which corresponds to that potential, whereas we cannot be so selective using chemical means.

But there are disadvantages in carrying out electrosyntheses, and these have to be weighed against the advantages. The main penalty is the electrical energy which has to be paid for. Whether this power cost is an important item or not depends upon the cost of the material being made by the process. But there is also a second item which weighs against the electrochemical mode: electrochemical reactors are two-dimensional. The reactions happen in two dimensions (i.e., in the plane of the double layer), whereas ordinary chemical reactions happen in three dimensions. It, therefore, follows that the extra dimension gives an advantage, in the rate of reaction, to the ordinary chemical reaction. However, this can probably be overcome by using fluidized bed electrodes (see fig. 5.8). A fluidized bed electrode converts an electrochemical reaction from a two-dimensional to a three-dimensional process.

A basis for electrosynthesis

Let us consider the oxidation of a compound A to a compound B. The reaction would be represented by:

$$\text{A} \rightarrow \text{B} + n\text{e}. \tag{5.11}$$

(1) First we consider the thermodynamics. At what potential *could* this reaction begin to take place? This may be obtained, if it is not

known, by working out the standard free energy ΔG° of the overall electrochemical reaction. After this is known, we calculate the necessary standard equilibrium potential at the electrode V_e°, on the hydrogen scale, by the equation $-nFV_e^\circ = \Delta G^\circ$, where n is the number of moles of electrons which are taking part in the process, and F is the Faraday constant, 96 500 C mol^{-1}.

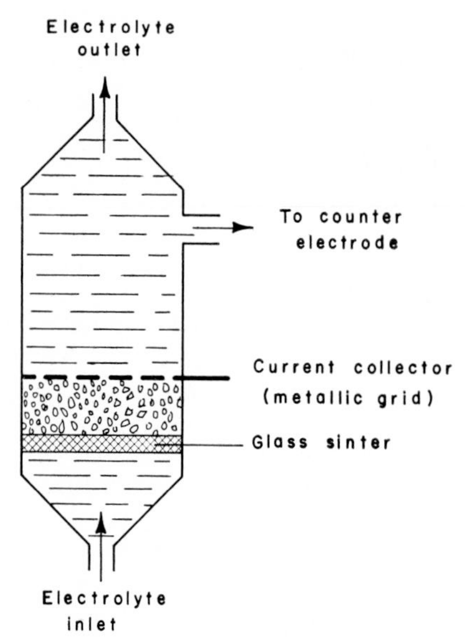

Fig. 5.8. A fluidized bed electrode. The electrode material is suspended in the electrolyte between the support (glass sinter) and metallic grid, serving as current collector when the particles touch the grid.

Suppose the reaction concerned is the oxidation of β-picoline to nicotinic acid, an intermediate in the production of nicotinamide:

$$C_5H_4N\text{–}CH_3 + 2H_2O \rightarrow C_5H_4N\text{–}COOH + 6H^+ + 6e. \qquad (5.12)$$

Then, we look *in books* for the standard potential V_e°, for this reaction. We shall find it only if the reaction is a well known one. If not, we calculate it from the free energy change in the reaction, ΔG°.

The electrode potential needed to get a finite reaction rate, and an appreciable current density, would have to be *at least* V_e°.† In fact,

† V_e° is the standard equilibrium potential corresponding to a concentration (or more precisely activity) of unity of each participant in the reaction. To find out the equilibrium potential V_e, for the actual concentration, equation (3.36 *a*) should be used. However, for rough estimates this is unnecessary, especially when n is large.

it will have to be more positive than that because of course V_e is the *equilibrium* potential, and overpotential is needed to make things actually work. We know that the sort of overpotential needed will be at least 0·2–0·5 volt. So our first concern is for the substrate, which must be chosen so that it will not itself

(*a*) partake in the reaction;
(*b*) provoke some other reaction, e.g., O_2 evolution,
(*c*) undergo an anodic reaction and dissolve, for example, $Ag \rightarrow Ag^+ + e$.

(2) The next thing is: does the substrate on which we intend to carry out the reaction *adsorb* the reactant we think of using? If it does not our ambitions are again going to be frustrated. As explained on p. 72, substances are adsorbed at different potentials on different substrates, the potential at which they are adsorbed having some relation to the potential of zero charge of the substrate. Thus, we must *know the potential of zero charge* for the substrate we are proposing as our catalyst.

If, therefore, the sum of potential V_e°, according to our calculation for thermodynamically equilibrium potential, plus the necessary overpotential to get an acceptable rate of reaction per unit area of catalyst, be in a region in which the coverage θ of the electrode is not less than 0·1, then we have some hope of accomplishing the synthesis.

(3) We now come to the overpotential. How shall we estimate it? We have argued our way to a substrate which does not itself undergo an independent reaction; our material does adsorb upon the substrate significantly at the potential at which the reaction may occur at a reasonable rate. But now comes the point: What overpotential shall we employ to make it go at a 'reasonable rate'? What is a reasonable rate? That is a question which cannot be answered without a knowledge of the economics (and the exchange current density i_0) of the particular reaction. However, if the reaction cannot be carried out at at least 100 amperes per m^2, it is doubtful that it will be of economic interest (for land occupied costs rent, and if one needs an enormous area to produce the desired tons per day from the plant, one may be approaching an uneconomic situation).†

Table 5.4. Factors to be considered for electrosynthesis

Factors
Equilibrium potential, V_e
Stability of electrode material
Adsorption of reactants
Solubility of reactants
Exchange current density, i_0, or
Rate at 'reasonable' overpotential
Possibility of interference of some other simultaneous reaction.

† The net decision about such matters used to be: which method would give a company the best profit? But, now, ecological, and thus social considerations must be weighed into the decision. The electrochemical choice may arise because it usually gives a less polluting process.

M

Also, we need to know the solubility of the substance. Dissolved to the saturation amount, and with no stirring (which *costs money* for the powering of the stirrer), will the limiting current be sufficient to give us the rate of production we need in respect to the limiting diffusion current (cf. eqn. 4.8)? Or, shall we have to stir the material so that, still dissolved, it will give us a *sufficient* limiting current for an economic production in kilogrammes per square metre? Or, shall we have to use the solute as a slurry, and veritably *fling* the solute at the electrode?

Lastly, the question of electrocatalysis: Suppose that we do have a reasonably high solute solubility and that it is diffusing reasonably to the electrode, will it need an overpotential which is economically too great? What would be 'too great' an overpotential? Two disastrous things may happen if one sets the applied potential too high. First, the total applied *voltage* may be so much that the kilowatthours† per kilogramme needed for a given amount of material may be too great for the economics of the situation. Also, another substance—oxygen in an anodic reaction, hydrogen in a cathodic—may be wastefully and irrelevantly evolved. Or, if we want to avoid oxygen and hydrogen by using a non-aqueous solvent, we may get embroiled in the difficulties of high resistance in the solution (and consequent 'lost volts'), or the non-aqueous solvent may turn upon us, itself undergoing oxidation or reduction.

These are some of the situations which we have to look into if we are going to make a satisfactory (and economical) electrosynthesis. Economical (and hence acceptable) electrosyntheses are likely with an increasing fall of the price of electric power. However, the rate determining step for commercial electrochemical syntheses at present is probably more the spread of the new knowledge in electrochemical science, and the education of electrochemists and electrochemical engineers rather than a fall in the cost of electric power.

Examples of Electrosynthesis

A few examples of industrial electro-organic syntheses will be sketched here.

Adiponitrile electrosynthesis, mentioned previously in Chapter 1, is one of the examples used in tonnage-scale production of adiponitrile, serving as the basic raw material for the synthesis of nylon. In 1963, the Monsanto Chemical Corporation opened a large plant using this process.

The basis of the process is the electrochemical reduction of acrylonitrile at the cathode, resulting in a hydrodimerization reaction. The process is known also as reductive coupling of unsaturated or olefinic compounds, and can be applied to other unsaturated compounds as well.

† 1 kilowatt-hour is $3{\cdot}6 \times 10^6$ J.

The overall cathodic reaction

$$2CH_2 = CHCN + 2H^+ + 2e \rightarrow NC.CH_2.CH_2.CH_2.CH_2.CN \quad (5.13)$$

is believed to proceed in two steps with the intermediate formation of a dianion

$$CH_2 = CHCN + 2e \rightarrow \overset{(-)}{\ddot{C}}H_2\text{–}\overset{(-)}{\ddot{C}}(H)\text{–}CN \quad (5.14)$$

$$2\overset{(-)}{\ddot{C}}H_2\text{–}\overset{(-)}{\ddot{C}}(H)\text{–}CN + 2H^+ \rightarrow NC.CH_2.CH_2.CH_2.CH_2.CN \quad (5.15)$$

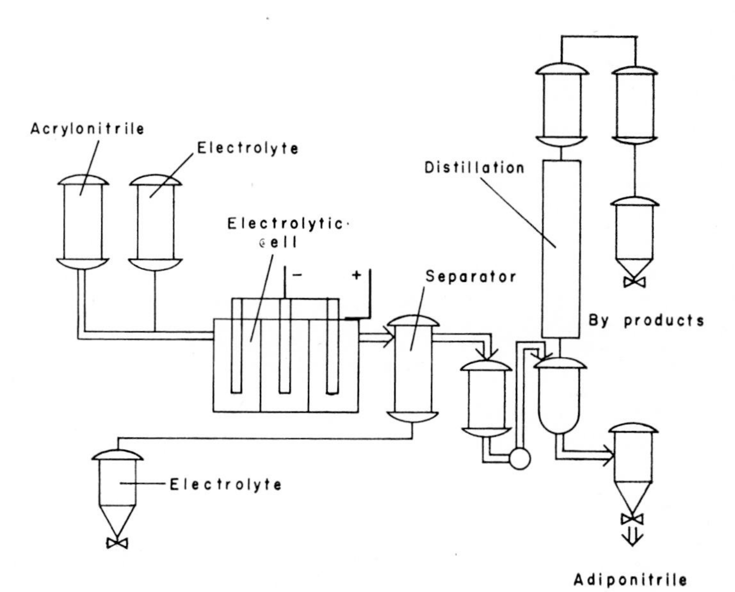

Fig. 5.9. Scheme of the electrochemical production of adiponitrile.

The scheme of the process is shown in fig. 5.9 the main part being the electrolytic cell. Since the potential at which the appreciable rate of the reaction occurs is more negative than $-1{\cdot}75$ V (on the standard hydrogen scale) a cathode with low i_0 for possible parallel H_2 evolution reaction should be used. Mercury or lead cathodes are used in the actual cells.

The solubility of acrylonitrile in normal aqueous solution is very low. Therefore, tetraethylammonium *p*-toluenesulphonate solution (30%

in water) is used as the electrolyte providing good conductivity and a rather high solubility of acrylonitrile (30–50%). The pH of the electrolyte is important and should be kept between 7·5 and about 9·5 to prevent side reactions, mainly the addition of water to the double bond of acrylonitrile. The yield of adiponitrile is more than 90%, the by-product being mainly propionitrile. Adiponitrile can be extracted from the electrolyte by a suitable separation process (by using solvents, distillation, etc.), and the electrolyte used again in the cell.

Another example of an electrosynthesis is the process of electrochemical bromination of hydrogen cyanide, as used by Standard Oil Co. in the production of melamine, a widely used plastic material. The whole process is sketched in fig. 5.10.

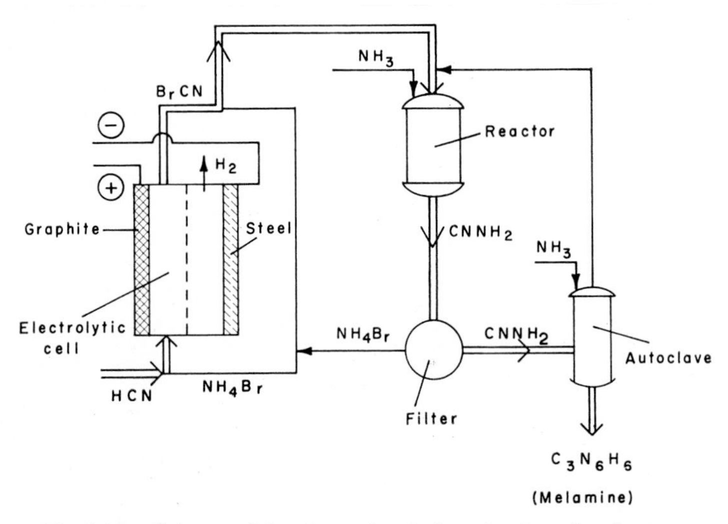

Fig. 5.10. Scheme of the electrochemical production of melamine.

The electrolytic cell is a two compartment cell divided by a semipermeable ion-exchange membrane, with steel cathode and graphite anode. The bromination occurs at the graphite anode by the reaction

$$HCN + Br^- \rightarrow BrCN + \tfrac{1}{2}H_2 + e. \qquad (5.16)$$

The electrolyte is the water solution of NH_4Br with 10% HCN. The yield is about 90%. In the further steps the process involves ammonolysis in a separate reactor

$$BrCN + 2NH_3 \rightarrow CNNH_2 + NH_4Br, \qquad (5.17)$$

and trimerization of the cyanamine in an autoclave under high pressure into melamine

$$3CNNH_2 \rightarrow C_3N_6H_6. \qquad (5.18)$$

A third example is a substitution reaction similar to the previous case, but performed in non-aqueous electrolyte in order to prevent formation of explosive by-products. This is the electrochemical fluorination of organic compounds by which a large number of known, and probably some still unknown, compounds can be synthesized.

The electrochemical cell used for fluorination is simple, made of iron, with nickel anodes and iron cathodes. The electrolyte is liquid hydrofluoric acid, kept in a liquid state by cooling to about 0°C. The electrical conductivity is achieved either by the presence of organic compounds or by the addition of another electrolyte (e.g., KF). A typical example of the industrially used fluorination reaction is the fluorination of organic acids, e.g., *n*-butyric acid, the overall electrode reaction being

$$CH_3.CH_2CH_2.C\lessgtr^{O}_{OH} + 18F^- \rightarrow CF_3.CF_2.CF_2.C\lessgtr^{O}_{F}$$
$$+ 8HF + F_2O + 18e. \qquad (5.19)$$

The process is excellent from an engineering point of view. It operates continually, the product is volatile and can be collected by passing an inert gas (nitrogen) through the cell, and the cell can be kept working for long periods, years if desired, with practically no attention. The current densities used are 100–300 mA m^{-2}, and the overall cell voltage 5–6 V (much of this is due to the relatively high resistivity of the electrolyte). The cell is versatile and a large variety of products, depending on what kind of organic material is fed into the cell, can be obtained. Heptafluorobutyric acid obtained in the example given above (when the gaseous product is hydrolysed with water) is the raw material for the production of a number of compounds which have both water-repelling and oil-repelling properties, so that textiles and shoes impregnated with them become both water-proof and grease-proof.

Spontaneous electrosyntheses

When we carry out a *chemical* synthesis, we usually do not drive it. We bring the substances into contact, and they 'react'—i.e., under the conditions of temperature and pressure, there is a net free energy which is negative for the synthesis concerned, and the reactants combine spontaneously to form the product (the by-product given out in chemical reactions is heat). An analogous situation occurs in a fuel cell, which can be regarded not only as a device for providing electrical energy, but also a spontaneously working substance generator.

In the normal fuel cell (see Chapter 7), particularly the only one which in the early 1970's has been well-engineered—the hydrogen–oxygen cell—the *chemical* product of the synthesis, water, is a very secondary consideration (though not to an astronaut: the electrochemical fuel cells which power space vehicles provide his supply of drinking water).

However, it is possible to consider *spontaneous* electrosynthesis—electrogenerative chemical reactions, or fuel cells, in which the electrical energy is secondary and the main thing is the chemical product ('synthesizer cells'). Just as a chemical reaction produces heat, so the spontaneously-working electrosynthetic plant would produce *electricity* as a by-product.

An example of this type of process is electrogenerative chlorination. Chlorine gas and an unsaturated hydrocarbon are introduced into cathode and anode compartments of the cell, which are separated by a suitable separator. Since the chlorine electrode potential is about +1·3 V and ethylene reacts at about +0·5 V, about 0·8 V difference can be obtained as the driving force for this spontaneous reaction. At the cathode (the *positive* electrode in self-driving cells (cf. fig. 3.1)), chlorine is reduced

$$Cl_2 + 2e \rightarrow 2Cl^-, \qquad (5.20)$$

while at the anode olefine is chlorinated

$$RCH = CHR^1 + 2Cl^- \rightarrow \underset{Cl}{\underset{|}{RCH}}-\underset{Cl}{\underset{|}{CHR^1}} + 2e. \qquad (5.21)$$

This process has two advantages. One is obvious. Instead of wasting the heat of the reaction, and heat-polluting the river nearby, one can produce useful electrical energy. The second is that no significant amount of ethylene glycol is formed as the by-product, as it is in traditional, chemical chlorination process.

Electrochemical polymerization

It has been known that by the electrolysis of many organic substances the effect of dimerization and even polymerization can be obtained. Thus, the example of adiponitrile synthesis given in the previous section can be understood as a dimerization reaction. A better example is the anodic reactions of different kinds of carboxylic acids in aqueous, aqueous–organic or organic media, often referred to as Kolbe's synthesis:

$$R.COOH \rightarrow R.COO^- + H^+ + e \rightarrow CO_2 + R \begin{cases} \xrightarrow{Pt} R\text{–}R \\ \xrightarrow{C} R^+ + e \rightarrow \text{product} \end{cases} \qquad (5.22)$$

Depending whether platinum or carbon anode is used, the product would be the dimer of two alkyl groups R (e.g., if acetic acid (CH_3COOH) is used, the product is ethane (CH_3–CH_3)), or the formation of carbonium ion R^+, which, depending on the composition of the electrolyte and potential, can give a variety of different products, even the polymerized material (see fig. 5.11).

Of recent years, particular interest has been shown in the possibility of electrochemical initiation and control of 'classical' polymerization reactions. Common plastic materials (polyethylene, plexiglass, polyvinyl chloride, etc.), are long chain molecules obtained by the polymerization of rather simple molecules (monomers, e.g., ethylene, methylmethacrylate, vinyl chloride). Polymerization to high molecular weight polymers is characterized as a chain reaction involving initiation, chain propagation and chain termination. Control of the chain length is important since the physical properties of the polymer depends on this. Many catalysts for polymerization reactions are used to provide

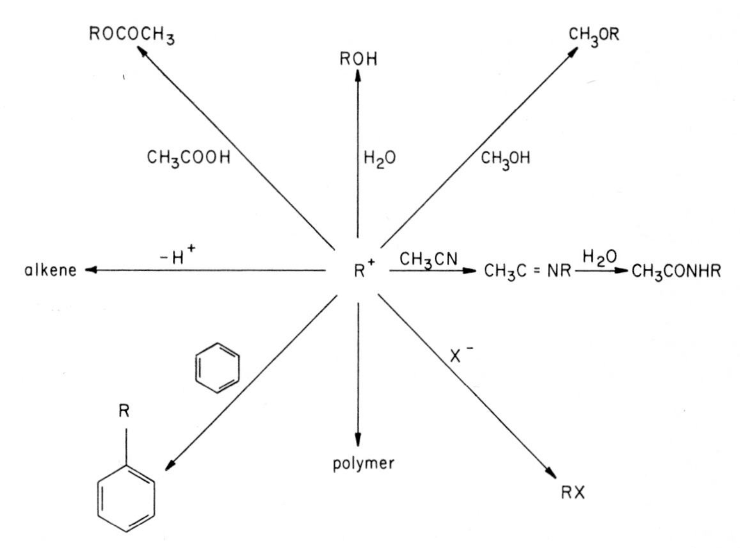

Fig. 5.11. Possible reactions of aliphatic carbonium ions in common solvents.

initiation and chain propagation steps; the mechanism is believed to be formation of the corresponding free radicals. It has been reported that the electrochemical generation of free radicals, with the possibility of controlling their concentration by properly choosing the electrode material and potential, can lead to polymers with similar chain lengths (e.g., in electrochemical polymerization of methylmethacrylate, vinyl chloride, vinyl acetate, etc.).

Final remarks

The examples of electro-organic reactions given in this section represent a tiny fraction of the possibilities which electrosynthesis offers. Besides, the obvious oxidations, reductions and halogenation reactions, it is possible to perform a great number of other reactions as for example, other substitution reactions (e.g., with nitro groups, thiocyanogen groups, various alkyl and aryl groups, etc.) or addition reactions.

It seems appropriate to finish this Chapter with a quotation from an extensive review of electro-organic synthesis.† 'Electrochemical reactions enable one to introduce a considerable amount of energy into molecules at low temperatures. The order of magnitude of this energy is in fact comparable to that of the strength of chemical bonds and this explains why many of chemical changes which are observed can take place. It is not surprising that many "high energy" chemicals which are used as oxidants or reductants in synthesis are made electrochemically.'

However, most of these reactions are quite complex and the further development and application of electro-organic reactions depends mainly on how soon the elementary processes involved will be fully understood.

† M. Fleischmann and D. Plestcher, R.I.C. Reviews, 2, 87 (1969).

CHAPTER 6

electrogrowth and electro-extraction

Two Aspects of Electrogrowth

ELECTROGROWTH is the growth of crystal forms on metals under the influence of electric fields. The essence of the electrogrowth process is the influence of the surface of the electrode on the crystal form. Ions come from their solvated state as in ordinary electrodeposition, but now the solid state physics of crystal growth, the electrochemical equations for the arrival of the atoms on the surface, and the properties of double layers which affect adsorption on the surface are all involved.

Electrogrowth is deposition on a moving, changing surface. It moves at a controlled potential-dependent rate, grows, for example, a Christmas-tree-like set of arms, which in turn grow arms, all at precise distances apart. It can be turned off, stopped, made to go back and dissolve each arm.

Electrodeposition means aluminium extraction, cheap houses, titanium for supersonic planes, bumpers and radiator covers for cars, most of practical extraction metallurgy outside ferrous metallurgy. There is a vast future in electrodeposition. For example the necessary thickness and mass of an aircraft wing must depend on the strength of its material. But the strength of a metal is much less (by a factor of about 100) than the theoretical maximum strength. This is because of the defects and dislocations in a real metal, which are formed when it crystallizes from the molten state. Could they be eliminated, or greatly reduced, in metals formed by electrocrystallization? Could we form thereby metals with few dislocations, metals of great strength, which would give us aircraft of one-tenth their present mass?

Electroseparation among a mixture of metals could inspire interest, too.

Electrodeposition

The pathways to the repeatable step

Assuming that the bulk crystal lattice is ideally perfect (i.e., no impurities, and each atom in its proper position, determined by the type of the lattice structure) the crystal surface in contact with the solution is never perfect and atomically smooth, but is composed of a number of unfinished atomic planes, which at their ends form edges and kinks (fig. 6.1). A metal ion after passing through the double layer might be discharged in one of several situations on the surface; the least stable position being as fig. 6.1 *a*, and the most stable as fig. 6.1 *d*.

However, the crystal lattice is never perfect, and there are several types of defect. One type is called a 'point defect', a vacant place in the lattice (fig. 6.1 *d*). Another type is an 'edge dislocation' (fig.

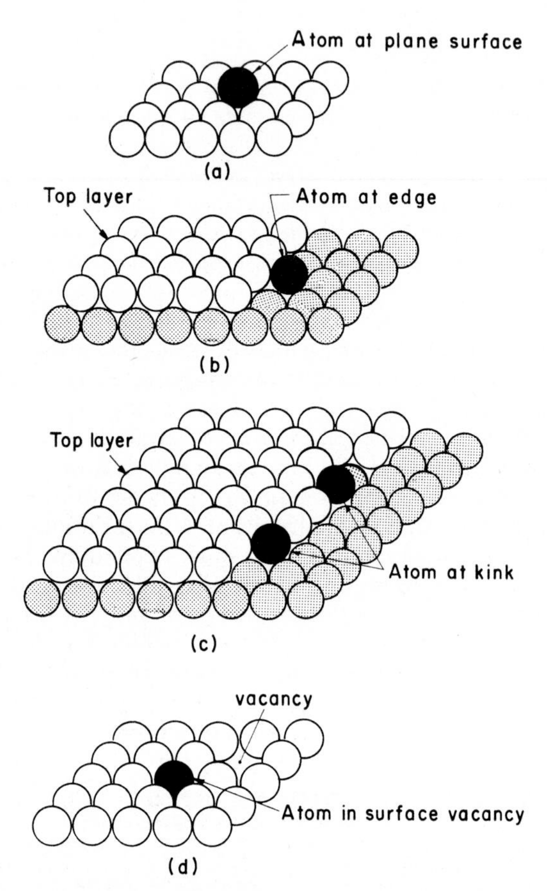

Fig. 6.1. At a plane surface the binding of an atom is much less than inside a vacancy.

6.2 *a*), appearing as an excess row of atoms in a layer adjoining another, regular one. Since there is not enough space in the regular lattice, the excess atoms deform the crystal lattice, forming a kind of vault and a tunnel through the crystal, into which neighbouring atoms move, leaving a new tunnel at their original position. So the edge dislocation moves until it reaches the surface layer (fig. 6.2 *b*) where it gives a new edge.

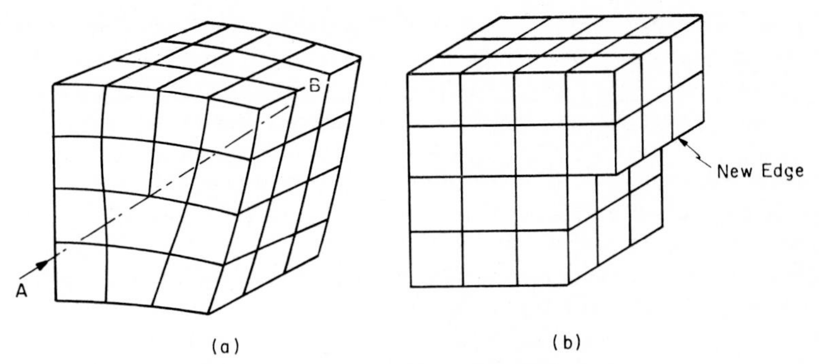

Fig. 6.2. (*a*) Edge dislocation produced by a row of excess atoms. (*b*) The excess atoms can reach the surface, producing an edge.

The most important type of defect is an 'emergent screw dislocation', usually caused by various faults in the lattice and by the action of stresses (external or internal) upon it. Imagine (fig. 6.3), that a part of the crystal lattice, has slipped under stress. The atoms which slipped for exactly one interatomic distance are again in the stable position, except the small number of atoms around the axis AB. The peculiar feature of this kind of fault is that the atoms are not situated in regularly ordered planes parallel to each other, but can be visualized as sitting on a spiral surface which winds round the axis AB, and gives an edge starting from the axis AB.

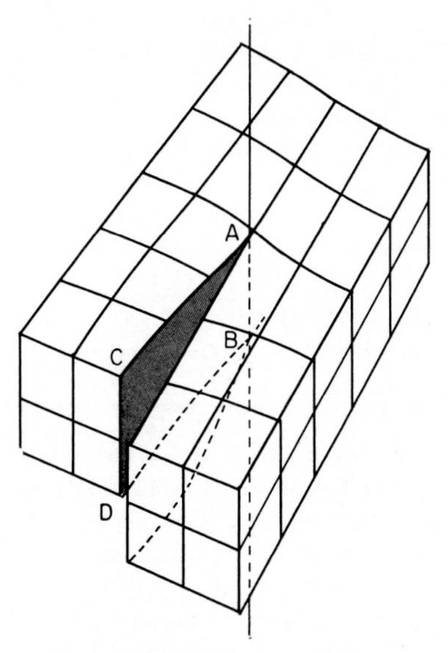

Fig. 6.3. Screw dislocation produced by the action of force upon a part of the lattice and slipping of atoms along the plane ABCD.

The kink sites along the edges arise as follows. Adsorbed atoms near the edges, and atoms in the lattice are effectively in dynamic equilibrium, some of them jumping out of the edge, creating new vacancies and kink sites, and a reverse traffic of an equal number of adsorbed atoms jumping back into the kink sites at the reversible potential for a charge-transfer reaction (p. 103). Under such conditions, the edges would not remain filled and smooth; an edge should be regarded as always containing plenty of kink sites (fig. 6.4).

We can now consider the deposition pathways available to an ion; there are two general ones, as a rule. An ion which has succeeded in diffusing up to the surface now has to decide whether: (*a*) it will cross the double layer from the point at which it happens to have arrived there, and then carry out the rest of its passage towards a resting place by diffusion on the metal surface; or, (*b*) it will search for a route by wandering about in the solution until it finds some suitable point on the metal surface which it likes, in which case it will pop across.

Thus, an ion might find a *point* defect particularly attractive. If it passed directly from its position in the double layer, landing directly into the hole in the metal, it would fit readily into the lattice. On the other hand, if energetic considerations are against this, the ion will land on a plane part of the crystal surface and thereafter diffuse to a lattice building point.

We can approach these two possibilities also in a theoretical way, as was done by Conway and Bockris, in 1958. They plotted the potential energies calculated for various paths which the ions could undergo. Some of their plots are shown in figs. 6.6 *a*, *b* and *c*.

What do such plots tell us? When one works things out for some imagined deposition pathway and it turns out, after these calculations, that the heat of activation for this possibility is enormously high—400 kJ per mole—then one is quite sure that the path is impossible.

This is so because the *rate* of a process depends on the heat of activation, according to:

$$V = cA \exp(-E_a/RT). \qquad (6.1)$$

Now, possible natural processes have energies of activation which can vary from a few kJ per mole to beyond 400 kJ mol^{-1} but those with heats of activation of more than 200 kJ mol^{-1} *do not actually occur at a speed which interests us*, for each of us is only here for a few decades. So, when we find 400 kJ mol^{-1} for a possible process, and look at equation (6.1), we say: 'its too slow (eqn. (6.1)) for me to worry about'.

In the calculations of Conway and Bockris referred to, the major effect which stopped the ions' jumping into holes was the displacement of the solvation sheath of the ions. An ion going through the solution may be pictured as in fig 6.7a. Correspondingly, as it comes from the solution, it has got to get rid of its solvation sheath—not entirely immediately, but at least it has got to leave some of it. As the ion

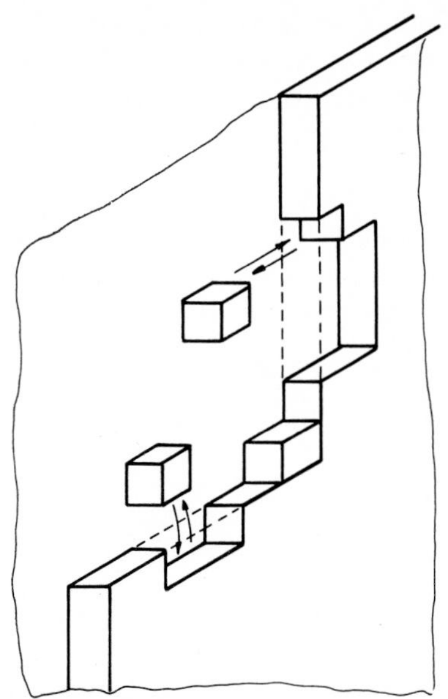

Fig. 6.4. Adsorbed atoms are incorporated into the lattice with a very small activation energy, so the edge is in dynamic equilibrium with surrounding adsorbed atoms always producing new kink sites.

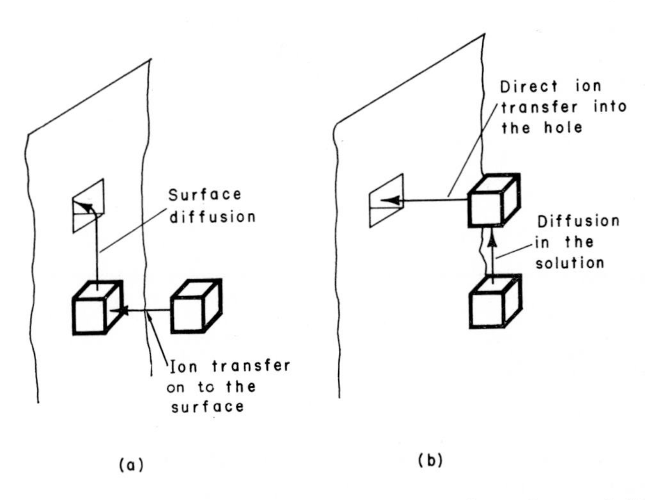

Fig. 6.5. An ion can be discharged at any position on the surface, and diffuse after that to the most stable position (*a*), or it can be discharged directly at the place where it is to be incorporated into the lattice (*b*).

approaches the cathode, the field surrounding it weakens, so that it cannot hold so many water molecule dipoles attached to it. Consider here, qualitatively, the attempt of the ion to enter the hole (fig. 6.7). It must *bend back* its solvation sheath, shear it off itself, and this costs a great deal of energy (for bending the ion–dipole bond, and trying to separate a charge from a dipole, has to do work against Coulomb forces). The energy of activation is far too high for such a step to occur at a reasonable rate.

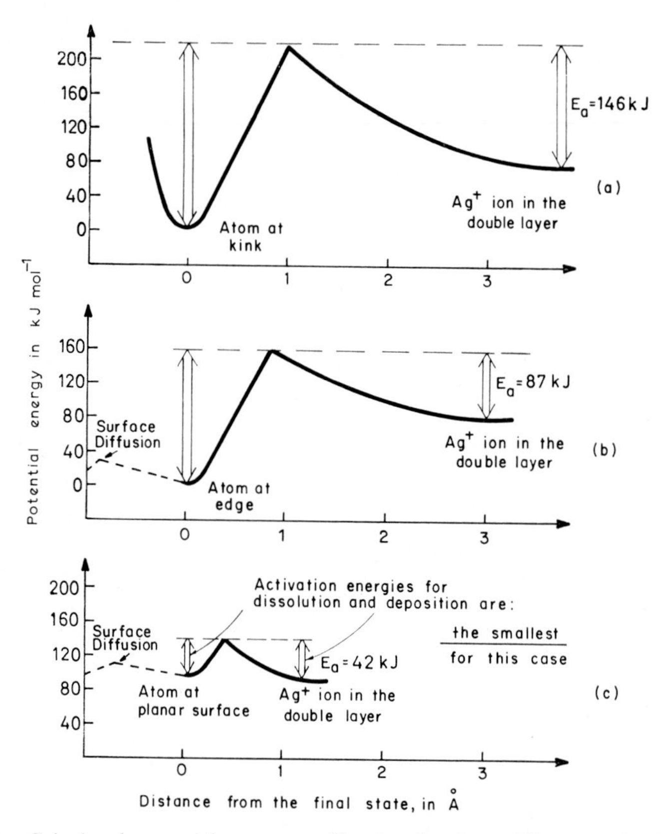

Fig. 6.6. Calculated potential energy profiles for the three different paths in silver ion electrodeposition. (*a*) Discharge into the kink; (*b*) discharge into the edge; and (*c*) discharge on to the surface. The lowest activation energy is for (*c*).

If the ion went directly to a kink site (fig. 6.8 *c*) this would need a similar, if not so large, increase in the energy of activation—and also be too slow to interest us.

The *only energetically feasible path* for the ion to take in crossing from the solution phase to the metal phase is the jump on to a plane

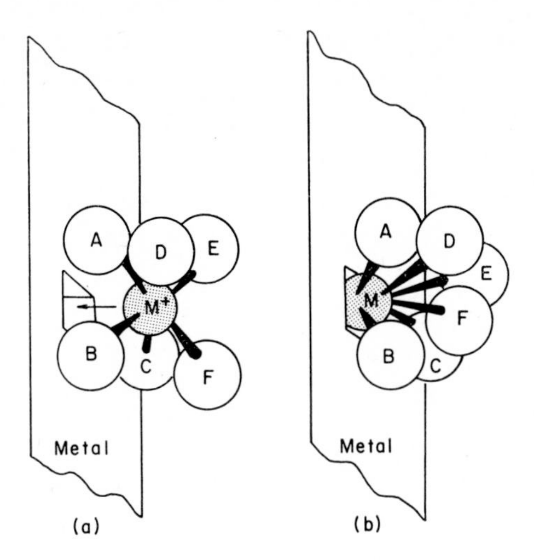

Fig. 6.7. For an ion to be discharged directly into a hole nearly all the hydration shell must be removed.

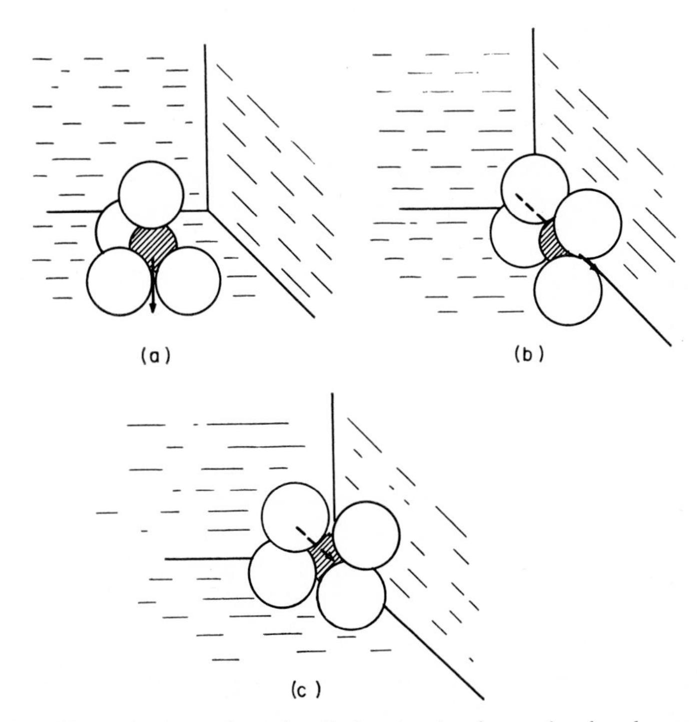

Fig. 6.8. To reach the surface, the discharging ion has to bend and remove the hydration shell. Least bending (*a*) is for discharge on a plane; (*b*) discharge into an edge; (*c*) discharge into a kink.

part of the surface, as shown in fig. 6.8 *a*. Here the sheath of solvated molecules around the ion is bent less than in the other cases.†

But what happens to the ion after it has reached the surface? The energy of activation for surface diffusion is quite low (see fig. 6.6), which means (for rate constant = constant × exp $[-E_a/RT]$), that surface diffusion is quick. The ion will execute a random walk (fig. 6.9) until it meets some point where it may bond better, with a greater

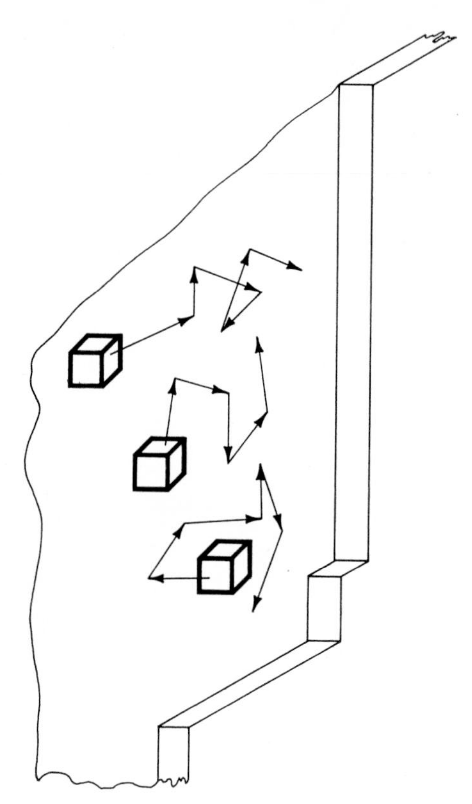

Fig. 6.9. Discharged ions (adsorbed atoms) move randomly over the plane surface.

negative potential energy, than elsewhere on the surface. For example, the ion may come to a crystal edge, and thereafter may diffuse along the crystal edge until it reaches a kink site (fig. 6.10). Here it will stop. Why? Because, at the kink site, it is surrounded by a greater number of coordinating metal ions (and so is bound more strongly) than at any other site. So it does not tend to diffuse away from it.

† There has been confusion on this point, which can be removed only by calculation. These show the barrier against transfer of charges at any place except on planar sites to be large.

For this reason, a kink site is called a 'site of repeatable growth'. An ion stops there, and other ions come along, find their way into other kink sites and also settle permanently, and so crystal growth begins.

We have not yet shown which one of the possibilities—transfer from

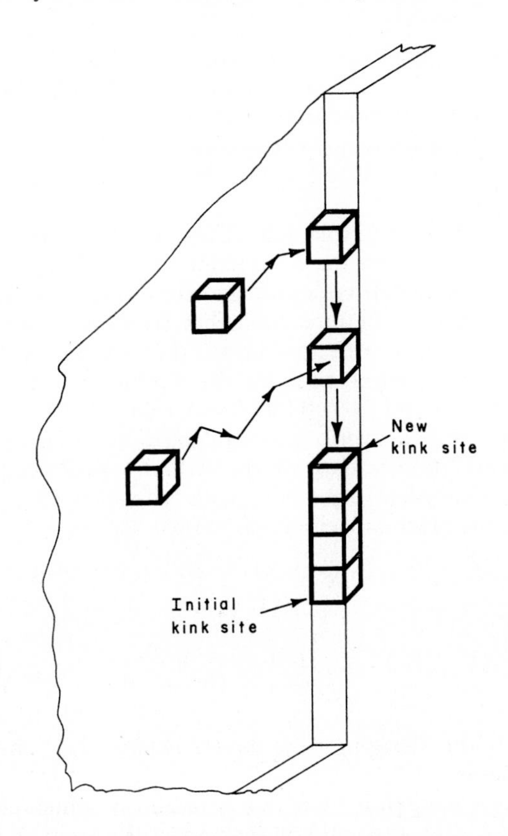

Fig. 6.10. The site of repeatable growth. Each atom incorporated into the kink site produces a new kink site.

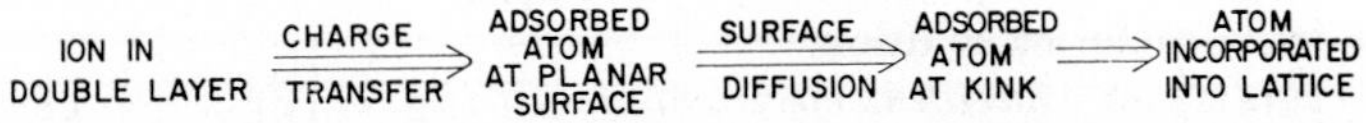

ION IN DOUBLE LAYER $\xrightarrow[\text{TRANSFER}]{\text{CHARGE}}$ ADSORBED ATOM AT PLANAR SURFACE $\xrightarrow[\text{DIFFUSION}]{\text{SURFACE}}$ ADSORBED ATOM AT KINK $\Longrightarrow$ ATOM INCORPORATED INTO LATTICE

Fig. 6.11. Three successive steps through which a metal ion has to pass in metal deposition.

solution to the surface, surface diffusion, or building into the kink site—would be *rate-determining*. This is a matter in which calculations alone cannot be fine-tuned enough to give an answer; the energies of activation are all not more than 20–40 kJ apart for the various steps, the accuracy of the calculations is perhaps not much less than that. The matter has to be decided by experiment, as we shall see in the next section.

The rate-determining step

The conditions under which we shall consider the question concerned are, firstly, those of low current density, when the potential is close to the equilibrium potention (eqn. (3.31)) and when the relation between current density and overpotential is linear. We may consider the following question: What will be the *relaxation time* of the double layer?

Let this question be explained: First of all, relaxation time in general means 'the time for the completion of something', some change. For example, if we switch on a voltage across a double layer and keep the potential within the bounds such that we never raise it to a value at which electron transfer reactions occur, then we can ask the question: 'What will be the relaxation time for the double layer to change from, say, zero on some scale to $+0{\cdot}005$ V on that scale?' As nothing is going across the double layer—it is not *leaking* at all (p. 33), one might say—then the situation is entirely that which could occur if we were *charging a parallel-plate capacitor*, with capacitance per unit area $0{\cdot}2\ \mathrm{F\,m^{-2}}$ (double layer capacitance). Since

$$C = \frac{\Delta q}{\Delta V} = \frac{it}{V}, \tag{6.2}$$

hence

$$t = C\frac{\Delta V}{i} = \frac{0{\cdot}2 \times 5 \times 10^{-3}}{10^{2}} = 10^{-5}\ \mathrm{s} \quad \text{if } i = 10^{2}\ \mathrm{A\,m^{-2}}.$$

Thus, we know the charging time *for the double layer* under constant-current conditions.

What will now happen if there is a situation in which *charge transfer* is occurring, i.e., the capacitor is leaking? We may at first suppose that the actual transition of the metal ion from the solution side of the double layer and its acceptance of an electron upon arrival on the surface of the metal, is the rate-determining step in the transfer of electric charge from metal to solution.

In terms of an *equivalent electrical circuit* (fig. 6.12), when electrons enter the metal they charge it up, and try to change its potential by filling it with electrons. This part of the equivalent circuit is represented by a *capacitance*. The electrons going over the double layer are equivalent to a 'leakage resistance' in parallel with the layer. When the capacitance has fully charged up, electrons are released from the metal, via the resistance, to ions in the solution.

We make things much easier for ourselves if we restrict our observations to the region of low overpotential, when (eqn. (3.31), p. 101)

$$i = \frac{i_0 F \eta}{RT},$$

hence

$$\frac{\mathrm{d}i}{\mathrm{d}\eta} = \frac{i_0 F}{RT} \tag{6.3}$$

or

$$\frac{\mathrm{d}\eta}{\mathrm{d}i} = \frac{RT}{i_0 F}. \tag{6.4}$$

In simple electrical theory, the ratio 'V/I' represents a resistance, so that, by analogy, it is reasonable to take $\mathrm{d}\eta/\mathrm{d}i$ as the differential resistance per unit area of the double layer. Thus, the situation which we have when we are charging up an electrode–solution interface is that we have a resistance of RT/i_0F (cf. eqn. (3.33)) and a capacitance C_{dl} as the capacitance of the double layer. As shown on p. 64 the capacitance of the interface often has a value in the region of 0·2 F m^{-2}.

We can calculate the rise time of a parallel R–C circuit (the time after switching on needed for the potential to reach its steady state value) from the values of the resistance and the capacitance.

The rise time, τ, is given by $\tau = 3{\cdot}98 \times$ *resistance* $\times$ *capacitance*, or approximately $4(RT/i_0F)C_{\mathrm{dl}}$.

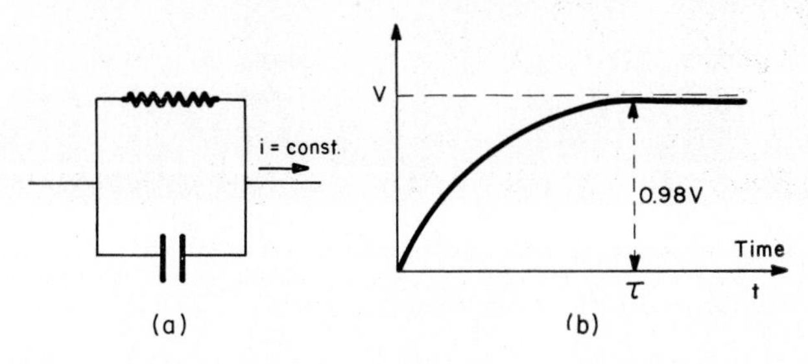

Fig. 6.12. (*a*) Equivalent circuit for the double layer. The double layer with charge-transfer reaction occurring can be regarded as the leaking capacitor, and represented by the equivalent circuit (*a*). (*b*) Charging at constant current. The rise time ($r \simeq 4RC$) is the time to reach 98% of the steady value.

Here, we know all the terms except i_0 and we can obtain this by extrapolating the overpotential versus log i plot to $\eta = 0$ (cf. eqn. (3.31)). So, we can calculate the rise time, and then compare it with the experimentally found rise-time. If the two results agree, then we can feel that the basic assumptions of that calculation may be sound.

Let us take actual figures here:

For $i_0 = 10^{-3}$ A m^{-2}, $C_{\mathrm{dl}} = 0{\cdot}2$ F m^{-2} and $RT/F = 0{\cdot}026$ V, the rise time for the simple charge-transfer reaction would be:

$$\tau = 4\left(\frac{RT}{i_0 F}\right) C_{\mathrm{dl}} = 4 \times \frac{0{\cdot}026}{10^{-3}} \times 0{\cdot}2 = 2 \times 10^{-5}\ \mathrm{s}.$$

In actual experiments, however, the rise time (fig. 6.13) *is much longer, several milliseconds.*

Thus, the predictive ability of the model we chose is poor. There is a *wide gap* between the rise time observed and the rise time calculated. We have clearly learned something: the charge transfer process is *not* a process which is rate-determining, in the case of the metal deposition reaction studied. (The figures were taken for a 0·1 M silver perchlorate solution.)

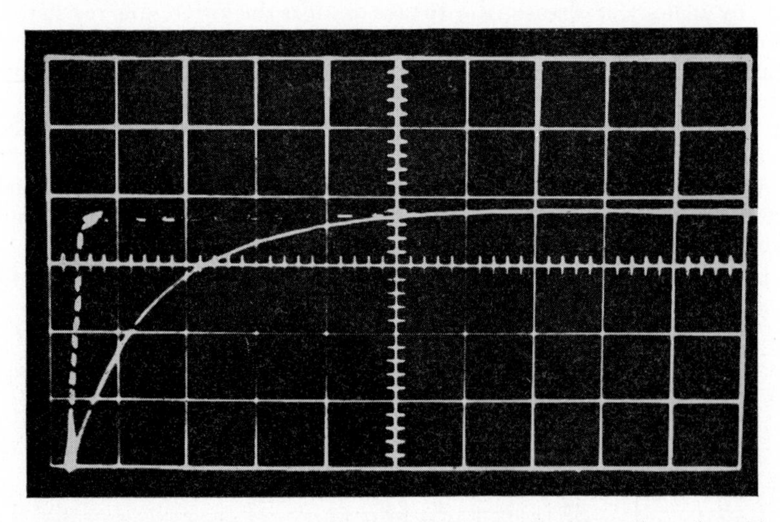

Fig. 6.13. The constant current 'galvanostatic' transient for silver deposition. $c_{AgClO_4} = 2 \times 10^{-1}$ M; $i = 2$ A m^{-2}. The dotted curve is what would be expected for the simple charge-transfer reaction.

What can we take as another possibility? Let us try out the possibility that there is a *diffusional* holdup after charge transfer of the ions has occurred.

We might consider the case when the first step (charge-transfer) is in pseudo-equilibrium, and the surface diffusion is the rate-determining step.

$$\text{ion} + \text{electron} \rightleftarrows \begin{array}{c}\text{adsorbed}\\ \text{atom}\end{array} \xrightarrow[\text{diffusion}]{\text{surface}} \begin{array}{c}\text{atom at}\\ \text{kink site.}\end{array}$$

It was shown by Mehl (for Ag in $AgClO_4$ at low η) that in this case the rise-time for the constant-current ('galvanostatic') transient pulse should be much longer than for the case when the charge-transfer step is the rate-determining step. The mathematics is beyond the scope of this book, so we shall use a rather simpler qualitative approach.

Of the total constant current i (per unit area) used in a constant-current pulse, part charges the double layer capacitor (i_{DL}). For the overall reaction the total current, i, may be written as: $i = i_{DL}+i_F$, where i_F represents the Faradaic process. If the charge-transfer step is in pseudo-equilibrium, then to achieve a steady state, there must be a new, higher surface concentration of adsorbed atoms. So, besides the charge on the double layer capacitor, further charge is needed in order to shift the pseudo-equilibrium of $M^+ + e \rightarrow M_{ads}$ to the right hand side, i.e., this reaction behaves as a pseudo-capacitor being charged with current i_{PC}. As the total current is constant and part of it used for an additional process (i_{PC}), ($i = i_{DL}+i_{PC}+i_F$), more time is needed to achieve the steady state condition, i.e., τ_{SD} should be larger when surface diffusion is the rate-determining compared to τ for the charge-transfer reaction.

It is therefore reasonable to assume that the conditions for the rate-determining step occur *after* the charge-transfer, as the calculation made, assuming it *is* charge-transfer, does not agree with experiment.

It turns out that the rate-determining step for many simple metal deposition reactions is *surface diffusion*, if the overpotential is low enough.† But at higher current densities, it often does become charge-transfer.

Why does the rate-determining step change at higher current densities? The probable explanation is somewhat as follows: If the rate-constant for the surface diffusional reaction becomes higher as the current density increases, surface diffusion becomes easy. The other alternative (the charge transfer reaction) then naturally tends to become the bottleneck again, the rate-determining step.

The reason for the change of the rate constant for surface diffusion is not too difficult to see. Down at the lower current densities, an ion, arriving in the middle, say, of a crystal plane, is a bit like an astronaut of the future out of the lunar module, roving around in an electrochemically driven lunar vehicle, but also with his batteries down and looking for a lunar base to reach before the oxygen gives out. There will be very *few* lunar bases, and on the metal surface, at the lower current densities, there are very few *active* dislocations, growth sites. It's a long way from a landing point to a growth site, on the average, and, because surface diffusion rates are inversely proportional to the thickness of the boundary layer, k_{Diff} is small under these circumstances of low surface occupancy. At higher current densities it's more like landing at the Kennedy Airport in New York City, the point is, can you find a *free* spot to get down on? Once you've done that, it's a very *short* way from touch down to one of the gates, to the growth site, and *that* part of the process isn't often rate determining.

† It may also sometimes be lattice building. Some recent work of Budewski (in which it was supposed that metal ions discharge at sites other than the planar ones!) seems to be interpretable in that way.

Thus, reference back to equation (4.8) shows that, for diffusion in solution, the rate constant is DnF/δ, which is the coefficient of c in the equation

$$i_{\text{Lim}} = \frac{DnF}{\delta} \times c \tag{4.8}$$

and depends on δ, the distance from the point of arrival of the ion near the electrode and on the point of arrival at the electrode plane. Very roughly speaking, the same sort of equation will apply in the surface case except that, now, δ will be the average distance between landing point and growth site (i.e., δ is the distance an atom has to diffuse over the surface), so it will be large for low current densities and small for high ones. In the latter case, the time for surface diffusion is negligible in the whole picture, and in the former case it is an important fraction of the whole. At low current densities, then, the surface diffusion may *tend* to be rate-determining.

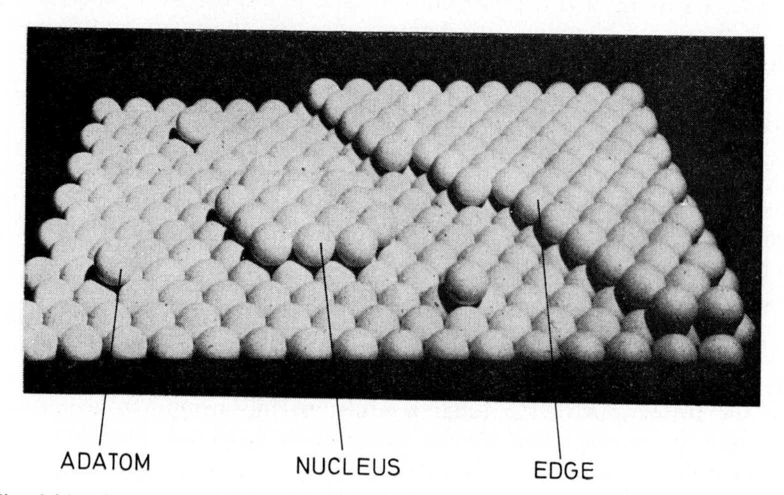

Fig. 6.14. Ping-pong ball model of a metal surface with an edge, adsorbed atoms, and a nucleus formed by the aggregation of a large number of adsorbed atoms.

Difficulty of crystallization in the absence of dislocations

Before about 1949 in the theory of crystal growth upon metals, crystals were thought to grow after a nucleation step: many atoms got together by a chance perturbation, and if they exceeded a critical number, the assembly was stable, and grew (fig. 6.14).

Of course, *eventually*, that means, if the rate of deposition was very, very high (i.e., the surface concentration of adsorbed atoms large), crystallization would occur in this manner. With a very great number of atoms on the surface, collisions would be so frequent that there

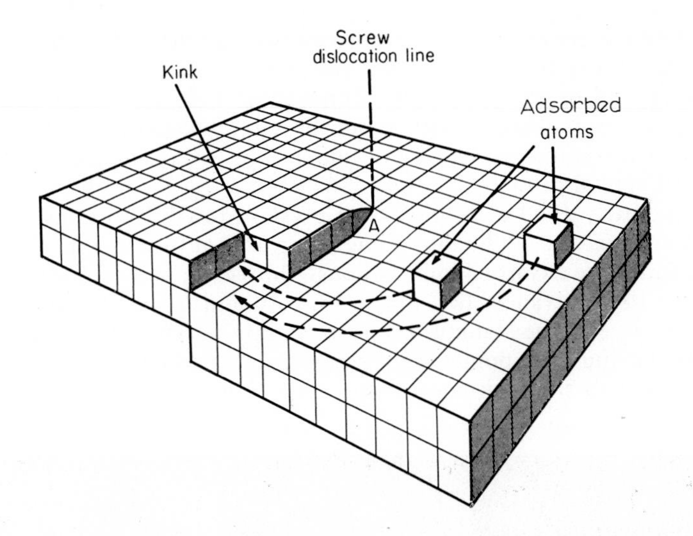

Fig. 6.15. Model of a screw dislocation with the adsorbed atoms diffusing over the surface to the kink site at the screw dislocation edge.

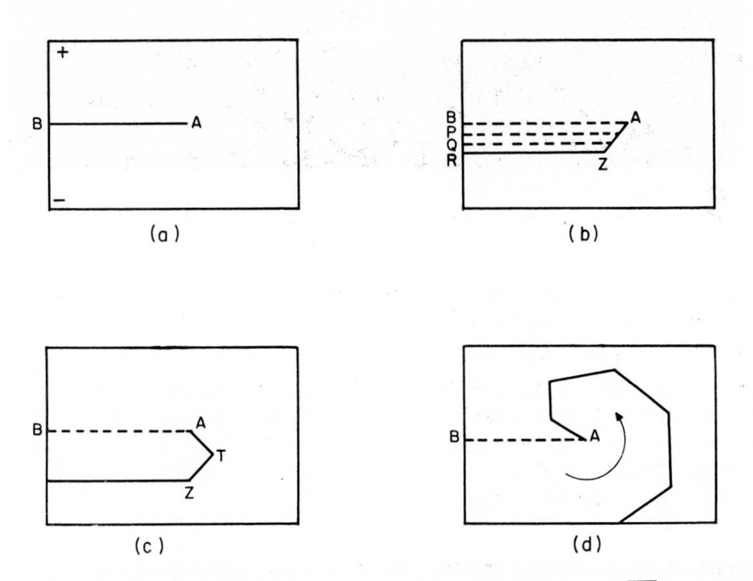

Fig. 6.16. Representing spiral growth at a screw dislocation. (*a*) $\overline{AB}$ is the initial edge; (*b*) the edge line moves as the crystal grows to $\overline{RZ}$, forming a new edge $\overline{ZA}$; (*c*) the growth continues at both edges, giving a third edge $\overline{AT}$; (*d*) continued growth makes new edges and results in a spiral.

would be the chance of multi-collisions between several particles at the same time; and then spontaneous nucleation of a crystal could occur. But this kind of crystal growth is unusual at best, and in any case has not been established under practical circumstances. Moreover, it greatly overestimates the magnitude of the overpotential needed to start off crystal growth.

In the early 1950's, the theory of crystal growth by means of screw dislocations arose. The ions come along and diffuse to kink sites. As more and more adsorbed ions, 'adions', diffuse to, and stick at, an edge, the step itself advances (see figs. 6.15, 6.16 and 6.17). Consider what happens if adsorbed atoms keep on adding to this step. A row of adions starting from points at the screw dislocation edge BA (fig. 6.16 *a*) will diffuse to the kink sites at the edge (not drawn in the figure for

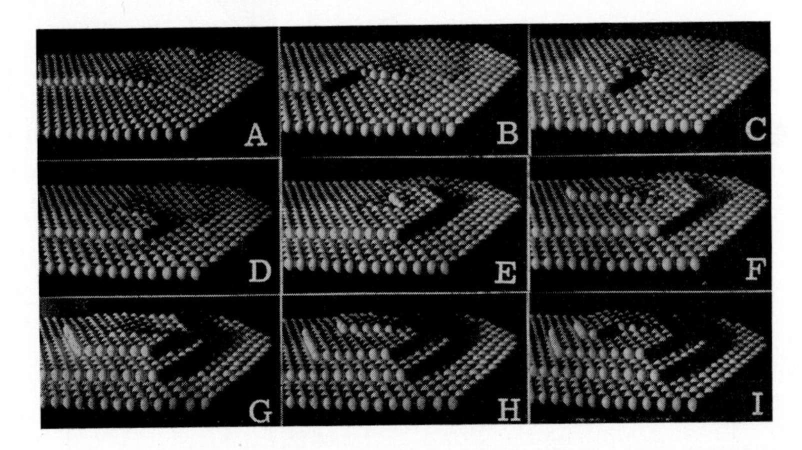

Fig. 6.17. Model of spiral growth. A, screw dislocation; B to I, various stages in the formation of the spiral.

simplicity), the edge will be filled permanently, so that the position effectively moves (fig. 6.16 *b*) to, say, the position RZ. However, a new, second edge AZ inclined to RZ is formed. Growth can now continue at both edges simultaneously, giving a third edge AT (fig. 6.16 *c*). Further new edges, each oriented differently from the original edge BA, result as shown in fig. 6.16 *d*, giving a screw-like growth around a dislocation axis at A. The similar growth stages are shown in fig. 6.17, on a model of the metal surface.

Deposition on individual crystal planes, and on real polycrystals

We must admit that so far we have not been describing any real case, but only deposition on to the highly-idealized situation of a single crystal plane.

In a real crystal the atoms are arranged in a certain order, the type of ordering depending on the properties of the atoms, and produce various types of crystal lattices (e.g., cubic, hexagonal, tetragonal, etc.). When we say single crystal we mean that the whole crystal has a repeating atomic arrangement which can be obtained by simply perpetuating the structure of the characteristic unit cell. For example, for a simple cubic single crystal, the whole crystal can be visualized as a large stock of cubes. Usually the unit cells are more complex, having more than just one atom at each corner of a cube. For example, silver has the face centred cubic lattice, i.e., in the centre of each face of a cube there is one additional silver atom (fig. 6.18 *b*).

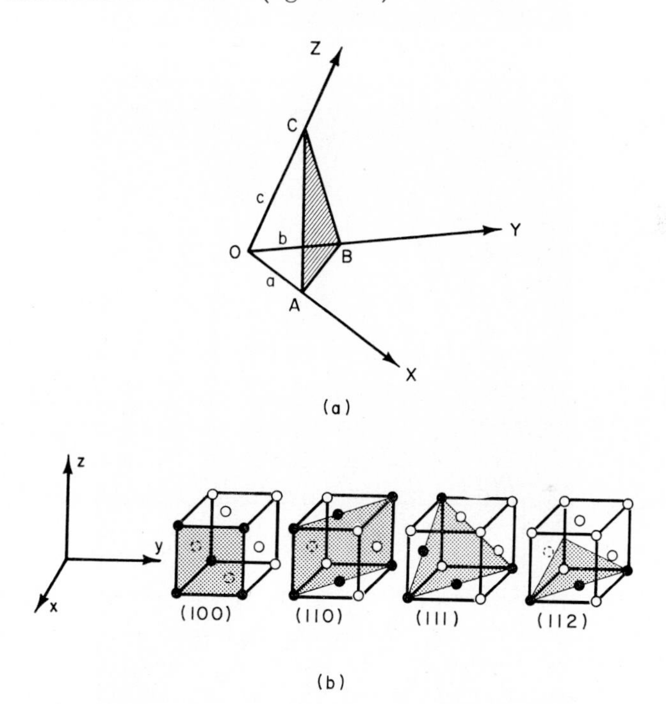

Fig. 6.18. Any plane through a crystal can be defined by the Miller indices (*hkl*). (*a*) a, b, and c are the unit cell lengths. Miller indices are: $h = a/\overline{OA}$; $k = b/\overline{OB}$; $l = c/\overline{OC}$. (*b*) Several illustrations of Miller indices for various planes in a face centred cubic lattice.

When cut, the crystal cleaves to give free plane surfaces along one of the planes populated with atoms. The distribution of the atoms in such a surface depends on the direction of this cleavage. The various possible faces of a crystal are specified with reference to a set of three axes which are mutually perpendicular for a cubic lattice (fig. 6.18 *a*). If we consider the plane ABC cutting the axes at A, B and C, and the

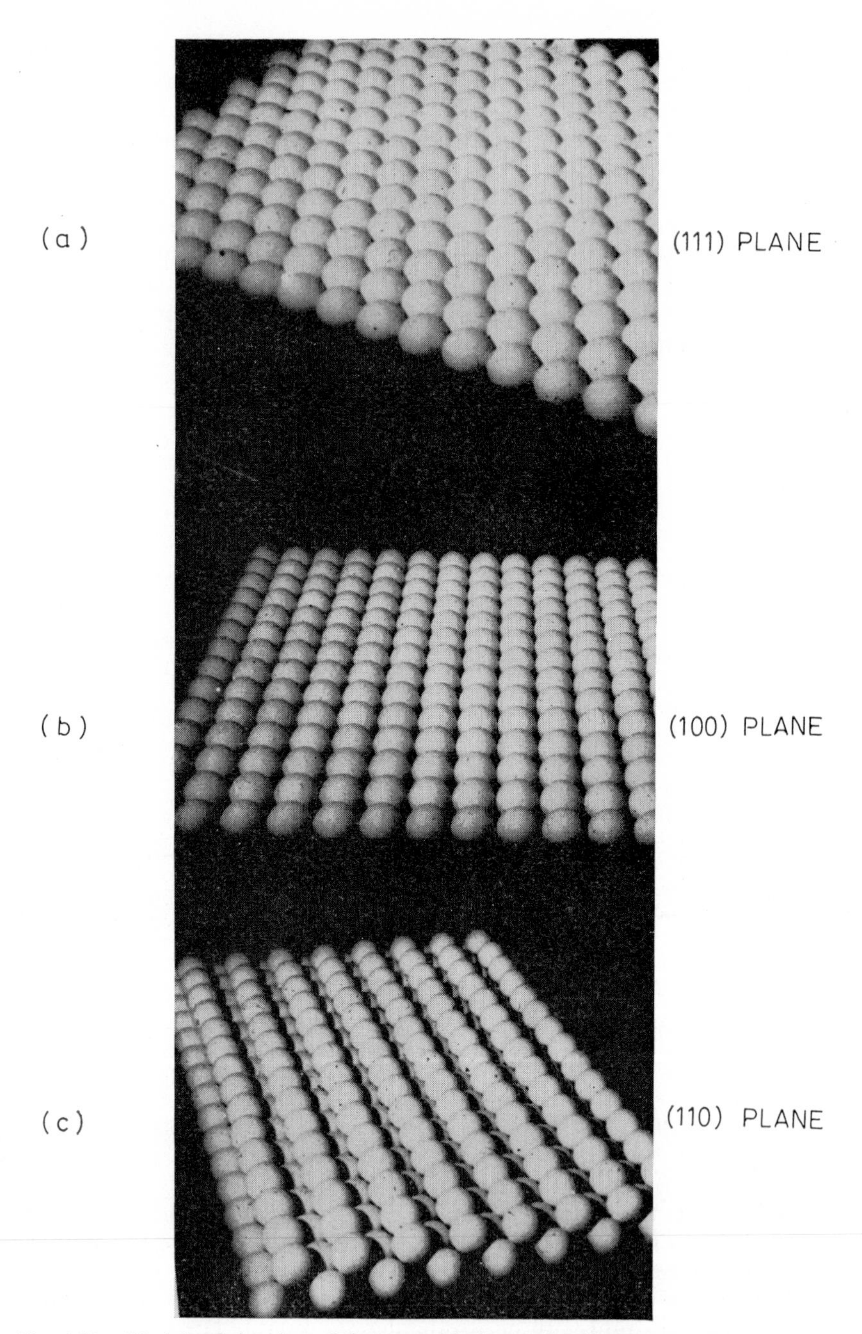

Fig. 6.19. Models of the view of three crystal planes of a silver crystal (face centred cubic lattice).

unit cell lengths along these axes are a, b and c, the length of the intercepts can be expressed as OA/a; OB/b, and OC/c, showing how many unit cell lengths can be put between O and either A, B or C. The reciprocals of these quotients are more useful, i.e.:

$$\frac{\mathrm{a}}{\mathrm{OA}} = h, \quad \frac{\mathrm{b}}{\mathrm{OB}} = k, \quad \frac{\mathrm{c}}{\mathrm{OC}} = l.$$

They are known as the Miller indices for the plane.

For the different crystal planes (fig. 6.19), each atom in the plane is surrounded in different ways by other atoms in the lattice. So the energy state of an atom at the surface is different for different planes, whence it is reasonable to suspect that the deposition rate should be also different for different planes.

Consider in fig. 6.19 the type of surface which will be 'seen' by an oncoming ion. In the (111) plane there will be stronger bonding (attraction) for an oncoming atom than in the (110) plane. Hence, the actual rate of transfer of the ion across the double layer on to the plane should be higher on the (110) plane than on the (111) plane. It is desirable to verify this by experiment, but here we run into a difficulty: how does one obtain a single crystal plane?

At first the answer looks simple. One takes a crystal, orients it in a certain direction, locates the plane desired using X-rays, and then cuts it in a direction parallel to that plane.

However, there is a fundamental flaw in this procedure, which has only recently been discovered. It is not possible to cut a plane so accurately that it is *really* parallel to a given crystal plane. The error is only perhaps one minute in angle, but this introduces a whole series of steps (fig. 6.20), interrupting the flat part which is the crystal plane we want. The vertical parts of the steps belong to quite different crystal planes from that which we cut, such steps may contribute to the rate of deposition at a given overpotential. And we should not know whether any change in rate, which we observe as we change from one crystal plane to another, was due actually to the effect of the new crystal plane which we had intentionally bared, or to the effect of these artificial steps introduced by our clumsy cutting process. The extra, artificial steps are the ones that we need to get rid of. How?

This problem has recently been partially solved in the electrodeposition of copper by Gerardo Razumney, who took advantage of an effect used in growing crystals from the gas phase. If a crystal is kept at a temperature just below its melting point, in a mixture of nitrogen, hydrogen and water, it is possible to make the unwanted steps diffuse away from their original position so that they bunch together in great steps many thousands of ångströms high (fig. 6.21). This has made it possible to observe large areas (*large* here means about 10–100 μm in diameter) which were indeed perfect single crystal planes, with an *exact* orientation, parallel to a certain plane of atoms.

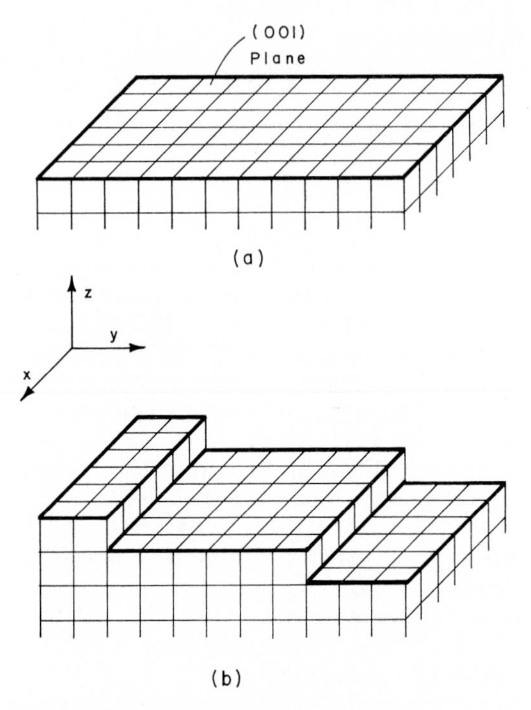

Fig. 6.20. (*a*) An ideal cut along the (001) plane. (*b*) The surface obtained if the crystal is misoriented (the misorientation is exaggerated).

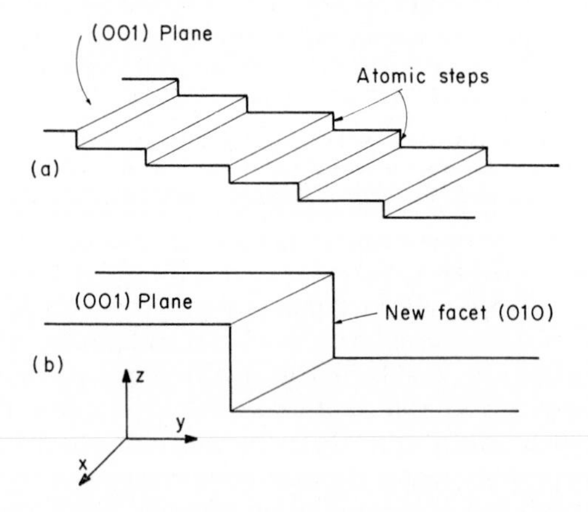

Fig. 6.21. The large number of small steps obtained by cutting can be reduced by thermal treatment, when small steps (*a*) bunch together, forming a larger facet (*b*).

Razumney was thereafter able to work on these planes. However, the order of accuracy obtainable in the measurement of the rate constants ($\pm 100\%$) has not yet made it possible to distinguish between the true effects of differently oriented planes of crystals upon the rate constants for deposition.

This all has important practical application. Real crystals, 'chunks of micro-metal', consist of many tiny *crystallites*, each of which has its own surface crystal planes oriented in a certain way with respect to some arbitrary axes. The ions come in from the solution and deposit on *all* of them. The fact that one plane may accept the ions

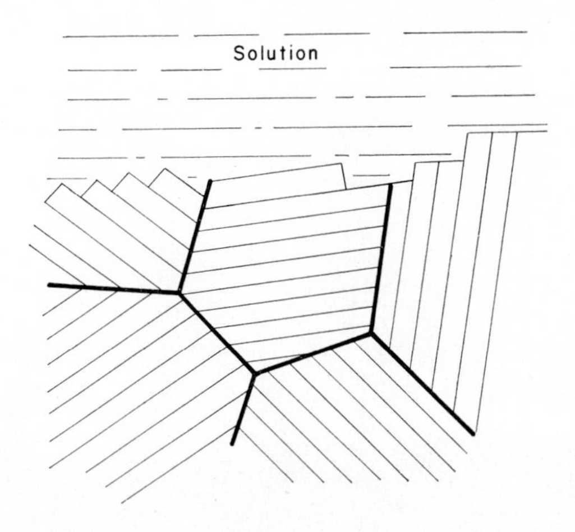

Fig. 6.22. The common metals are composed of large numbers of microcrystallites, each oriented differently, and exposing different planes to contact with the solution.

(have a certain i_0 for their deposition) in a different way from some other plane is now very important in determining how the actual real crystal will grow (see fig. 6.23). Sideways? Outwards? In big chunks? As a powder? Much will depend on these relative i_0's for different crystal planes—hence the need to know what these i_0's are.

Dendrites

The word dendrite comes from the Greek *dendrites*, a tree. Snowflakes are dendritic; and in the crystallization of a large number of metals from their melts, the first crystals are also shaped like dendrites. So if we understand why dendrites grow (and how they reach such shapes, see figs. 6.24 and 6.25), we shall understand much.

We shall describe a rather special case of dendritic growth, in which a central sphere is held at constant potential in a solution—perhaps silver nitrate dissolved in potassium nitrate at a temperature of 350°C.

It is found that after switching on the potential that nothing happens for a few minutes. After a certain critical time, a solitary dendrite shoots out from the surface of the metal. It is a remarkable sight, for it thrusts like a growing sword across from the central sphere towards any mechanical limitation imposed, such as the sides of the vessel. Shortly after this first growth, a number of exactly symmetrical swords

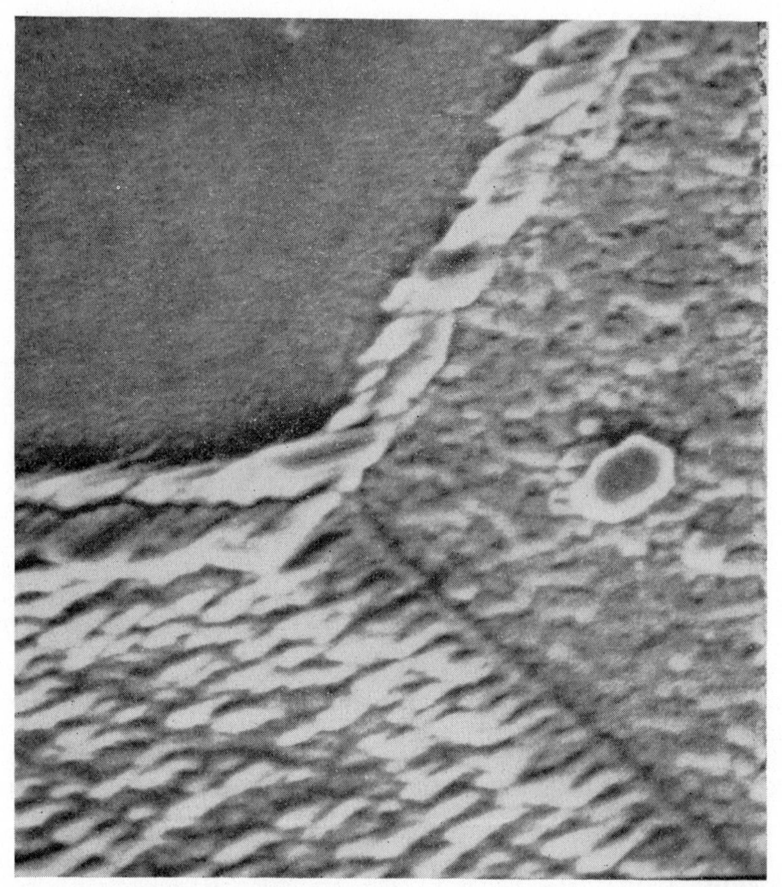

Fig. 6.23. Electron microphotograph of the zinc electro-deposit on a polycrystalline zinc metal surface showing a triple grain boundary and different forms of growth at differently oriented grains ($\times 2500$).

grow on the base of the growing sword, and on these other swords grow, so that finally one has a kind of two-dimensional Christmas tree, as shown in figs. 6.24 and 6.25.

To attempt a brief explanation of the kinetics of this growth is of course only to give part of the picture. Nevertheless, some essential points may be brought out briefly, at least as regards the growth of the primary stem.

Firstly, when dealing with diffusion problems and the application of Fick's diffusion laws (cf. p. 132) we must distinguish between linear, spherical and cylindrical diffusion, that is, whether the diffusing particles are moving towards a plane, spherical or cylindrical surface. Equation (4.8) for the limiting current is for *linear* diffusion (the usual case for diffusion towards an electrode).

Fig. 6.24. Electron microphotograph of silver dendrites grown from 0·1 M $AgNO_3$ solution at 100 A m^{-2}.

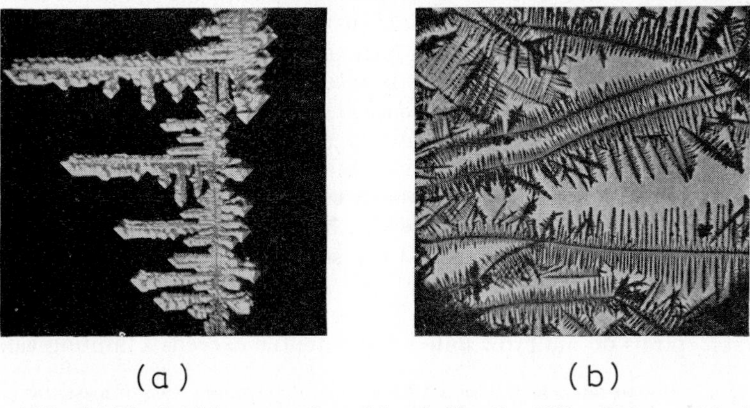

(a) (b)

Fig. 6.25. (*a*) Tin dendrite grown from 0·5 M $SnCl_2$ + 2 M HCl at 200 A m^{-2} (×25); (*b*) lead dendrites grown from 0·5 M $Pb(SO_3NH_2)_2$ + 2 M HSO_3NH_2 solution at 300 A m^{-2} (×25).

However, the limiting diffusion current for *spherical* diffusion is given (the derivation is rather lengthy) by

$$i_{\mathrm{Lim}} = \frac{nDFc}{r} \tag{6.5}$$

where r is the radius of the sphere (which should be *smaller* than δ, the diffusion layer thickness for linear diffusion). If δ is equal or larger than r, the linear diffusion equation (4.8) should be applied, even the surface is not ideally plane. Only if r is much smaller than δ, does the above equation apply.

If the radius of curvature of the substrate is less than the value of δ, the limiting current can be greater than that given by the normal equation (that which involves δ). Indeed, if δ is 0·01 cm, an increase of the possible diffusion rate of 10^4 times is possible, for r at a sharp tip of a growing crystal is sometimes about 10^{-6} cm.

Thus, to understand why it is that this single dendritic sword shoots out so rapidly from the substrate, we imagine that when we apply the p.d., if the potential is greater than the critical amount at which dendrites form, there will perhaps be a gradual growth of a spiral from the surface of the electrode. Some of these spirals will manage, after a certain time, to push out above the diffusion layer which is characteristic of the substrate on which they are growing (the δ of Chapter 4 is 0·05 cm). If the tip of one of these spirals, when it penetrates the diffusion layer characteristic of the sphere, and gets its own properties for diffusion, let us say, is *less* than δ, it will begin to grow at a rate corresponding to the *spherical* (and not the linear) diffusion formula, i.e., the current density at its tip (now proportional to 1/radius of curvature) will be much larger than the corresponding current densities on a planar substance. By comparison with other bits of crystal around (which are growing at the rate for plane diffusion) the dendrite, having the advantage of *spherical* diffusion, just shoots away.

Of course, this description assumes that the rate-determining step in the growth of the dendrite is diffusion (otherwise the growth rate would not be simply proportional to the inverse of the radius†), and this must be established case by case. It involves the assumption of very high i_0 values, usually one to two orders of magnitude higher than those obtained on the corresponding planar surface. Thus, a 'fresh' surface usually has a higher i_0 than one which has existed for a significant time in contact with the solution, and the surface of a growing dendrite is always new.

The reason why there must be a certain critical potential is that crystal spirals do not grow unless the potential exceeds a limiting value.

† For a growth rate which does not have a rate-determining step of mass transport to the surface—diffusion—then the rate would not be connected with the radius of the substrate at all, but with factors which make up i_0's analogous to those we touched on which we went over questions connected with electrocatalysis.

It can be shown that to grow spirally outwards from a crystal surface the atoms have to have a certain minimum surface charge, which means a minimum V. Until one has switched *this* on, no dendrites, because

Fig. 6.26. Microphotograph of the spiral growth of copper.

the originating spiral (or pyramid) will not grow out to penetrate the diffusion layer of the surrounding substrate.

The reason why the dendrites only grow at the tip, and negligibly on the sides, is that the radii of curvature of the sides are too large for the conditions of spherical diffusion to apply. Hence the maximum growth rate which the sides experience will be several orders of magnitude less than that which can be experienced by the tip.

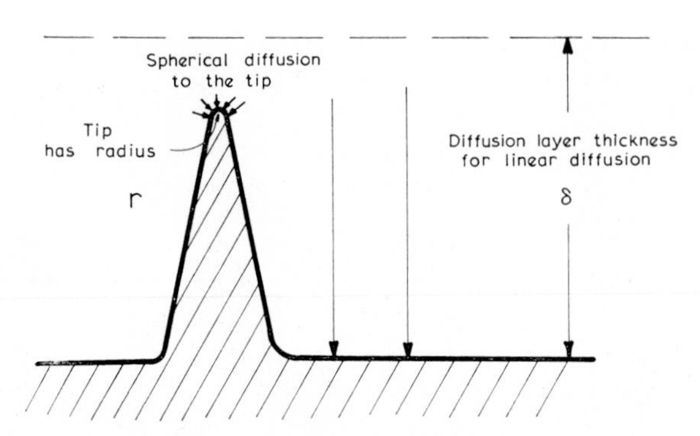

Fig. 6.27. The rate of diffusion is much larger at the tip of the dendrite than on the plane surface.

Principles of electroseparation

In traditional chemistry, one separated one ionic species from another by putting in a third, and precipitating the first, usually in the form of salt crystals.

In electrochemistry, one can carry out separations of materials, particularly metals, in a somewhat simpler and more controlled way. As we have seen in Chapter 3, equation (3.24), a substance will only begin to take part in a net electrode reaction after the electrode has been brought to a potential more negative than the equilibrium potential V_e, i.e., when overpotential is cathodic. Suppose, that we are depositing two metals, one of which deposits at +0·77 V and the other at +0·34 V. These are the equilibrium deposition potentials, so that when the potential is more negative (more 'cathodic') than the value stated, deposition of metal ions on the electrode will begin. The current will depend upon the overpotential by which the applied potential departs from the equilibrium potential (see eqn. (3.24)). Suppose now that the potential is made 0·1 V more negative than the equilibrium potential of +0·77 V for element A, i.e., the overpotential is 0·1 V negative. Element A will be deposited on to the electrode, and this can continue until about 99·9% of A has been deposited.

Then, the overpotential may be raised to, say, 0·2 V, negative to 0·34 V, the equilibrium deposition potential of the second metal. Suppose the first element is silver, and the second copper, we can slip another electrode into the solution and get the copper out of the solution though only after reducing towards zero the silver concentration.

During this second removal, the last traces of silver will be deposited too, so that the impurity in the copper would be of the order of 0·1%, but this could be reduced further if necessary.

In fig. 6.28 the potential–current relations for copper deposition and silver deposition are broken lines, while the solid line represents the total current. Between 0·77 V and 0·34 V the copper deposition current, i_{Cu}, is zero, the silver deposition current, i_{Ag}, is therefore at that stage the total current ($i_T = i_{Ag}$), so, in this potential range, only silver can be deposited. At 0·2 V (fig. 6.28), both metals will be deposited, the total current being

$$i_T = i_{Cu} + i_{Ag}. \tag{6.6}$$

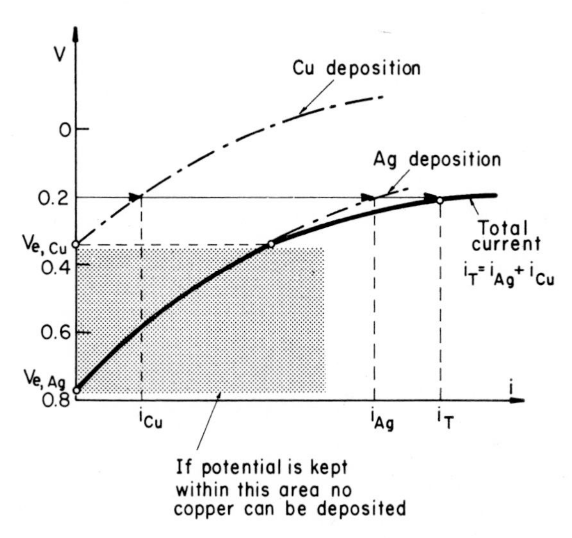

Fig. 6.28. Potential–current curves for the electrodeposition of silver and copper. Dotted lines—partial currents for each metal. Solid line—total current (sum of the two).

The diagram suggests that copper cannot be deposited from this system without the simultaneous deposition of silver. Basically, this is correct. But, if the potential had been kept for a sufficiently long time, before switching on the 0·2 V, at a value more positive than $V_{e,Cu}$, the concentration of silver ions would decrease with time, as silver is deposited at the electrode. As the concentration goes down (fig. 6.29) we get even smaller and smaller limiting diffusion currents. When most of the silver has left the solution, the potential may be switched to more negative values, e.g., 0·1 V. Both metals will be deposited again, but because of the low concentration of silver ions, the limiting diffusion current is small compared with that for the copper ions. The copper deposited will still contain a certain amount of silver (how much is determined by the ratio i_{Ag}/i_{Cu}).

In principle, the same technique can be applied to a mixture of a number of different metal ions, providing that their equilibrium potentials V_e, differ by at least 0·1 V, and that hydrogen evolution does not interfere too much (i.e., $(i_0)_H$ is sufficiently small) in the cases for which the corresponding V_e values are more negative than the hydrogen equilibrium potential.

The situation shown in figs. 6.28 or 6.29, can be utilized for alloy deposition, if the potential is adjusted *deliberately* to the value when both metals are deposited simultaneously. The composition of the alloy can be controlled by choosing the proper potentials and concentrations for the individual depositing metal ions. A well known example is brass, a Cu–Zn alloy.

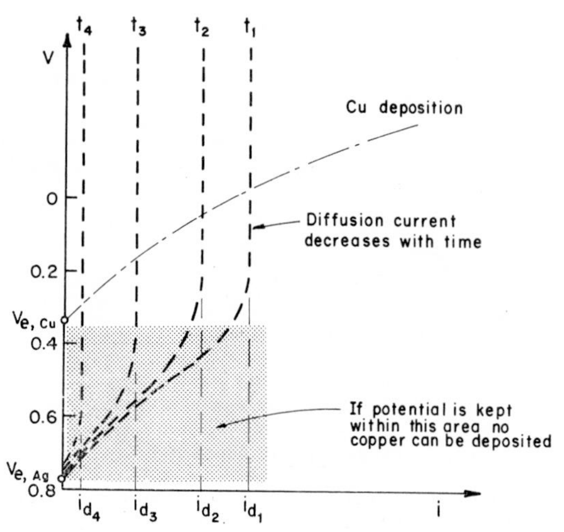

Fig. 6.29. Potential–current curves for electrodeposition of silver and copper, when the concentration of silver ions is small and decreases with time.

The *potentiostat* was introduced into academic electrochemistry by Hickling in 1942. The principle on which the potentiostat works is indicated in fig. 6.30. The potential of the electrode is set at a given value by comparing with a reference electrode which measures the potential of the working cathode. In so far as the cathode potential tends to wander from its set potential, the potentiostat observes this and immediately adjusts the current between the working and the counter electrode, to bring the potential of the working electrode back to where it was set. For example, if the working cathode is going in a too negative direction, the current is reduced to bring the potential of the working electrode back to the correct value. If it wanders in too anodic a direction, the potentiostat tells the counter electrode to send in a greater cathodic current.

Let us see, now, what can go wrong with the rather idealized account we have given on electroseparation in the above paragraphs.

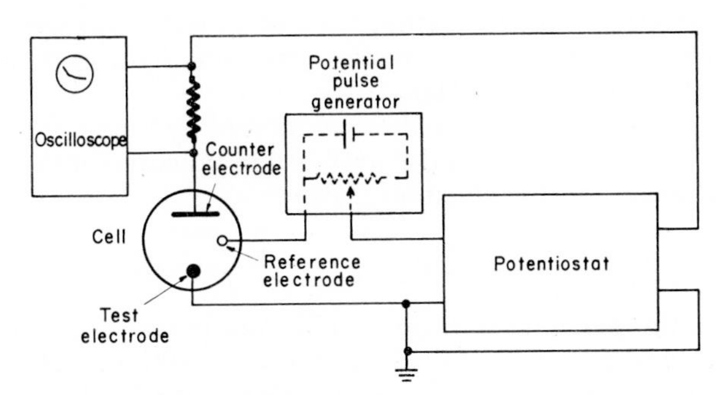

Fig. 6.30. Schematic diagram of the potentiostat, which adjusts the output current through the circuit so that the input potential is constant.

What can go wrong?

Limiting current density may intervene and reduce the current for the material which one wishes to remove to impracticably low values. For example, in the separation of copper and silver under the rough conditions we took (on p. 202) there would be 0·1% silver in the copper. To reduce this to 0·0001% it may be necessary to deposit the silver at current densities corresponding to very low concentrations. If we did not stir, and the concentration of the silver had been reduced to 10^{-4} M, the limiting current would be reduced to 2×10^{-2} A m^{-2}, and it would take a long time to remove the rest of the silver that way because the *rate* of deposition is so small at this current density. In this case, we resort to agitating the electrolyte, although stirring will not increase the limiting current density to more than, say, about 1 A m^{-2}. It has been mentioned above that special tricks can be used to decrease the boundary layer at the electrode–solution interface (i.e., to reduce δ, and thus, by equation (4.8), to increase the limiting current density, the maximum rate). One such trick is to induce turbulence by means of baffles, or *turbulence promoters.* The liquid is sent in a stream over such baffles, and the limiting current greatly increased, perhaps by another ten times or so, bringing the current density into the 10 A m^{-2} region, a tolerable value as far as further purification is concerned.

Another challenge may have to be faced when electrolysis has proceeded sufficiently so that the copper (Cu^{2+}) ion concentration has been greatly reduced. It may be (unless we are strict with the use of the potentiostat) that we start the evolution of hydrogen, which is the next thing along the potential series which should be available for electrochemical reaction (see also Table 5.3). The hydrogen equilibrium potential in a 1 M acid solution comes out on the scale of potentials which we so arbitrarily use, to be 0·00 V, and if the potential in our electrode is more negative (or cathodic) than this, and *if there is not enough of some other ion left in the solution* to take up the electrons which the electrode wants to emit, then eventually hydrogen ions will present themselves to the electrode as acceptors, hydrogen gas will be evolved ($2H^+ + 2e \rightarrow 2H \rightarrow H_2$).

It may be possible to reduce the evolution of hydrogen by increasing the pH. As the pH changes, the equilibrium potential of the hydrogen changes according to the equation (3.36):

$$V_{eH} = \frac{RT}{F} \ln c_{H^+} = -\frac{2{\cdot}3RT}{F} \text{pH}.$$

If we make the pH, say, +5, the equilibrium potential of hydrogen is reduced to about −0·3 V since $2{\cdot}3RT/F = 0{\cdot}06$ V. The point is that until the potential is more negative than −0·3 V, there will be no chance of hydrogen evolution. The thermodynamic equilibrium potential is the potential at which one must first start to *expect* it, but it will not actually occur until there is significant overpotential, i.e., until the potential is substantially more negative than the equilibrium potential. Thus, as the equilibrium potential for Cu^{2+} (from a solution containing about 1 mole per litre of Cu^{2+} ions) is +0·34 V, one can put on −0·64 V (−0·3−(+0·34)) of overpotential for copper deposition before there is a possibility of having H_2 evolved as well. At higher overpotentials for the Cu^{2+} deposition, and hence at higher current densities for that event, H_2 will evolve, too (see also fig. 4.14). There is a competition between them. Further theoretical considerations would be more detail than principle. Suffice to stress that, at sufficiently negative (cathodic) potentials in aqueous solutions, hydrogen will always evolve. (Sometimes one is driven by this fact to carry out the electroseparation of an alloy from a molten salt.)

Another trouble is that sometimes the deposition potentials of substances are too close together. For example, in the case of iron and nickel, the equilibrium potential of iron is −0·44 V and that for nickel is −0·23 V. After the appropriate overpotentials have been applied, it may be that a clear separation is not at all easy. In such cases one may be able to change the concentration of one of the materials, say, iron, considerably; one may, to this end, add a complexing agent and thereby (cf. the Nernst equation again, equation (3.36 *a*)) change the equilibrium deposition potential of iron, so that it would show a greater difference between iron and nickel potentials, and thus make separation possible. One way to do it is to use the fluoride solution which binds iron strongly into a complex, so that the free ferrous ion concentration is extremely low and V_e therefore very negative. There are many other complexing agents, of which one very often used is EDTA (ethylene diamine tetra acetic acid). Thus, the equilibrium potentials would be separated enough, and one could get a clear separation of the two materials.

The basic thing is that processes across metal–solution interfaces occur *as a function of potential.* (See eqn. (3.6), p. 86.) There is, therefore, less point in setting a certain current density, at which, say, silver only is depositing, and then coming back, later, knowing the current density is constant, and hoping that silver only, in the mixture of silver and copper, is still being deposited. This would probably not be so. As the silver was reduced in concentration, there would be a shift in electrode potential (cf. Nernst's equation, $V_e = V_e^0 + (RT/F) \ln c_i$).

But if the potential change brought in in this way, is sufficient, in a negative direction, some other ion with a nearby deposition potential (even the Cu^{2+}, perhaps) will begin to deposit. If this occurs at a significant rate, the silver deposit will be spoiled by the presence of the impurity. Hence, for electroseparation, potentiostats are important: as the potential begins to change, the information concerning this event is recognized by the potentiostat, which promptly intervenes to put the potential back where it was firstly told to stay. Hence, it is prevented from creeping off into a region in which deposition of another ion may occur.

Separating impurities from a solution

Electroseparation can be used to do many things. For example, as mentioned, it could be used to reclaim *all* the metal from scrapped cars. The compressed car would be suspended in solution and the iron and the more valuable metals, such as copper, nickel, and chromium, deposited separately. However, electroseparation can also be used for purification of solutions, for example, for removing small amounts of redox materials, or organic substances from solutions of, say, sulphuric acid, hydrochloric acid, sodium hydroxide, etc., which may be needed in a very pure state.

Let us see how the concentration of the impurity changes with time, assuming that the rate of removal (i.e., of the electrochemical reaction) is controlled by diffusion to the electrode. The rate of decrease of concentration is given by the simple differential equation

$$\frac{dc}{dt} = -\frac{i_{Lim}A}{nF \,.\, V} \tag{6.7}$$

where i_{Lim} is the limiting diffusion current for the impurity ($DnFc_s/\delta$, cf. eqn. (4.8)), in the solution of volume, V, and A total area of the electrode. If c_0 is the concentration as the beginning of the electrolysis, concentration c_t, after time t can be obtained by solving the above equation, i.e.,

$$c_t = c_0 \exp(-DAt/V\delta). \tag{6.8}$$

Of course, as the equation shows, enormous gains can be achieved by making the electrode area large. Such purifications can be made not only in an academic way; but also have some technological meaning, for example, in the removal of dissolved iron from sodium hydroxide.

Other Aspects of Metal Electrodeposition and Dissolution

After reading the previous sections of this Chapter the reader might ask himself: Why bother so much about the different kinds of electrodeposits? What is the difference if copper in electrolytic refining plants is growing at the cathode in spiral or ridge form? One of the answers can be the following.

At present, the current density used in copper refining electrolytic cells is 2×10^5 to 3×10^5 A m^{-2}. Why not use larger current densities when the limiting diffusion current is larger than that (electrolyte used in the cells is approximately 0·5 M $CuSO_4 + 2$ M H_2SO_4, and circulated continuously). It is because the copper deposited at higher current densities forms needles, nodules, bulges, etc., which in a short time reach out and catastrophically connect cathode to anode. At even higher current densities, copper powder may be produced, and fall down to the bottom of the cell. These things happen even at c. 10^2 A m^{-2} if pure electrolyte is used. The problem is partially solved at the present time by adding some glue or similar additive to the electrolyte, which seems to help to obtain smooth, compact copper deposits. No one seems to know why this works even though it is obvious that adsorption plays an important part (cf. p. 72). Why don't we double or triple the current density and double or triple the production of the plant? Well, we don't know what to add to the electrolyte to prevent the disturbing effects under these conditions. As long as we don't understand completely the mechanism of the formation of lumps, needles, powder and other undesired forms of electrodeposit, we shall not know how to *prevent* their formation. There is not much sense in experimenting irrationally with organic additives taken at random from the shelf.

Besides the basic electrochemical processes of obtaining and electrorefining metals, the electrodeposition or dissolution of metals is widely used at the present time in other aspects of modern technology. For example, electroplating on various metals (or even plastics†) covering them with a thin layer of another metal, 10–50 micrometre thick, is used either to prevent corrosion or for decorative purposes, or for both simultaneously. With some metals (copper, nickel, etc.) nice looking, bright deposits can be obtained, if the proper additives (usually organic compounds) are present in the electrolyte. Considerable saving can

† Electroplating on a plastic can be achieved if it is firstly covered by chemically deposited thin metal layer. For example, by chemical reduction of Ag^+ ions with glucose a layer of silver (silver mirror) well adhering to plastic can be obtained. Other metals can be electroplated on top of this.

be made in this way for it avoids the usually expensive mechanical polishing. But our knowledge is so *empirical.*

Similarly, most metals can be electro-polished to a high degree of brightness, by removing a thin surface layer by anodic dissolution in a suitable electrolytic solution.

Of the many other applications, we must mention the rapidly growing application of electro-forming and electro-machining to processes in modern technology. Electro-forming is the process in which metal parts of complicated shape can be obtained by cathodic deposition of metal using properly formed moulds as cathodes. In electro-machining the process is reversed. The metal piece to be machined is connected as the anode, and a cathode of the right shape, say, a rod with a channel inside it, is brought into electrolytic contact with the metal piece. The electrolyte is pumped through the channel and a large current (sometimes as high as 10 000 A) is passed, when the metal anode dissolves as required. By moving the cathode inside the metal piece to be machined, a hole can be bored in several seconds. The possibility of automation and the simultaneous boring of a large number of holes of all kinds in a single piece of metal is obvious.

CHAPTER 7

the direct conversion of chemical energy to electrical energy

The Present Method of Obtaining Energy

OUR present way of obtaining energy is to cause a chemical reaction to occur between hydrocarbons (oil, petroleum) and the oxygen of the air. The products of this reaction are principally carbon dioxide, and a number of unsaturated hydrocarbons (among them dangerous pollutants). But the main product, the one which we are interested in, is heat. The heat produced in the reaction oil + oxygen → carbon dioxide expands the surrounding gas, the expanding gas pushes a piston, and the piston turns a generator, whereupon the generator cuts the lines of force between the poles of magnets, and electricity is thus induced in the armature of the generator. This is the long way around which now constitutes the normal, *indirect* method of the conversion of chemical energy to electricity.

But the *indirectness* of the present method of obtaining electrical energy is not the main reason why our first objective in forming a viable world should be to eliminate it. There are three much larger reasons:

(1) The store of oil, coal, and natural gas arises from geological formations which occur every few hundred million years. This hydrocarbon store could be used to clothe and feed the one-third of the world population which at present suffers from malnutrition and want. We could elimiinate starvation and make a considerable change in living standards throughout the world. But what do we do with it? We *burn* it to get our energy.

(2) By burning our hydrocarbons in this prodigal fashion we poison the atmosphere and the seas. We use the sky as a sewer, we put into it not only the carbon dioxide but also the unsaturated hydrocarbons. What do they do? They combine with the nitric oxide which the internal combustion engine also produces and in the presence of light, and dust particles, they form a loose aggregate called *smog* (fig. 7.1).

But it is worse than that. We may be able some day partly to cut down the unsaturates which are emitted from 'internal' combustion engines, but the cleanest of engines burning fossil fuels is going to emit carbon dioxide in amounts too much for the (decreasing) green plants to take back and convert to oxygen by photosynthesis. We have thrown a vital ecological mechanism out of balance with our present method of producing mechanical and electrical energy.

(3) Lastly, our method of producing energy at the present time is inefficient; the efficiency of conversion of the chemical energy to

mechanical or electrical energy varies from about 10% in automobiles to perhaps 40% in modern and very large heat-to-system-to-electricity plants. If we take an average of about 25%, then three-fourths of the chemical energy released in burning oil or coal is simply wasted.

Heat has to *flow into and out of* a heat engine, which in the ideal (Carnot cycle) case operates between a high temperature T_1 and a lower temperature T_2. If a quantity of heat Q_1 is taken in at T_1, a quantity Q_2 rejected at T_2, and a quantity (Q_1-Q_2) converted into

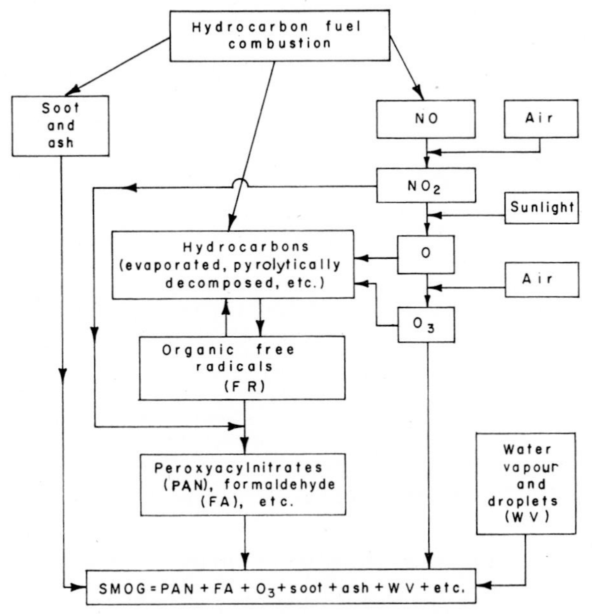

Fig. 7.1. Smog formation: a complex effect produced by unburned hydrocarbons, nitric oxide, air, water vapour and sunlight.

external work, the thermodynamic efficiency is $(Q_1-Q_2)/Q_1$. Now, $Q_1/T_1 = Q_2/T_2$, so the efficiency is $(T_1-T_2)/T_1$. This is a theoretical maximum limit imposed by thermodynamics, and no attention to design can ever improve on it.

Let us turn now to the possibilities of the *direct* production of electricity by the electrochemical conversion of chemical to electrical energy, and then ask about the efficiency of energy conversion of that.

The principle of the fuel cell

Let us here recapitulate what we said in Chapter 1 about the simplest example, the hydrogen–oxygen fuel cell. The hydrogen passes over the electrodes, dissociates to atoms, and the atoms give up electrons to the electrode forming H^+ ions. These electrons pass around the circuit, and must pass through any 'load' (for example, an electric motor) placed in their path. Having *driven* their load (and thus got rid of their energy), they then come down to the electrode over which oxygen is bubbling, and combine with the oxygen and H^+ ions coming through

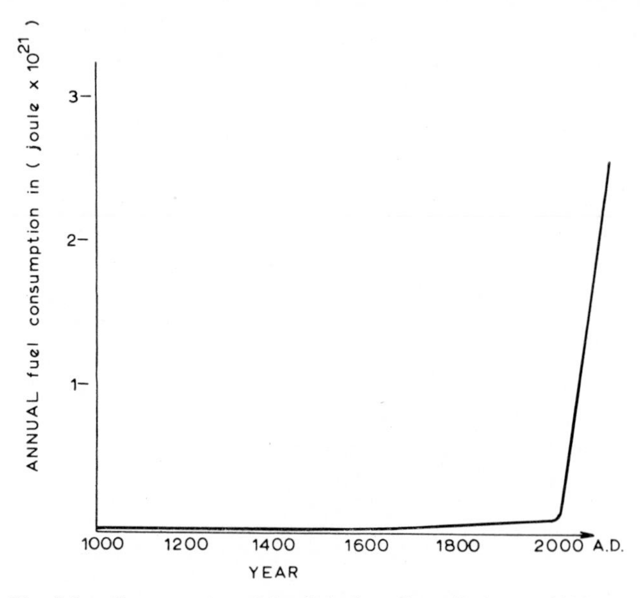

Fig. 7.2. Consumption of fossil fuel; and prediction to 2000 A.D.

the solution from the other electrode, thereby producing water† at this electrode. The driving force of the whole reaction, the bank account from which we take the energy, is the free energy, ΔG, of the overall cell reaction:

$$\begin{array}{ll} \text{Anode:} & H_2 \rightarrow 2H^+ + 2e \\ \text{Cathode:} & \tfrac{1}{2}O_2 + 2H^+ + 2e \rightarrow H_2O \\ \hline \text{Overall reaction:} & H_2 + \tfrac{1}{2}O_2 \rightarrow H_2O. \end{array}$$

But the energy is converted when the current has to pass through a potential difference, the potential difference caused by its flow through the external resistance or load. There, theoretically, *all* of the bank account can be used up (whereas, for any heat engine, much of the heat gets rejected).

† In alkaline solutions the electrode reactions are different but the overall reaction is the same again

$$\begin{array}{ll} \text{Anode:} & H_2 + 2OH^- \rightarrow 2H_2O + 2e \\ \text{Cathode:} & \tfrac{1}{2}O_2 + H_2O + 2e \rightarrow 2OH^- \\ \hline \text{Overall Reaction:} & H_2 + \tfrac{1}{2}O_2 \rightarrow H_2O \end{array}$$

The fuel cell has no moving parts, nothing to wear out. It is silent, and it could be made in virtually any size (for hearing aids and heart pacers to multi-megawatt power stations). It could burn virtually any fuel which would undergo a spontaneous reaction with the usual reactant, oxygen from the air. Which fuels are practicable, however, depends on the energy per unit cost of basic fuel, and, as we shall see, the important electrochemical factor of the *exchange current density* by which (and via electrocatalysis, cf. Chapter 5) the electrochemical reaction of the fuel can be persuaded to function at the electrode concerned, without using up too much of the total available potential as overpotential.

The efficiency of electrochemical energy conversion

Let us first of all deduce the efficiency of an ideal fuel cell, an impractical sort of fuel cell, but one which we can talk about easily. We refer to a fuel cell which would have 'infinite i_0 values', i.e., no overpotential. We have seen (eqn. 3.24.) that if the exchange current density were infinite, one could have any current one desired without involving overpotential.

The heat evolved while burning coal or oil is equal to $-\Delta H$, the enthalpy change for the combustion reaction. It is ΔH which is taken as the basis calculating the efficiency of a heat engine.

However, the voltage of the reversible electrochemical cell is directly proportional to the free energy change (ΔG) for the cell reaction (see equation (5.9)). ΔH and ΔG are related to each other through the well-known relation

$$\Delta G = \Delta H - T\Delta S, \tag{7.1}$$

ΔS being the entropy change, and T the temperature.

The ideal, maximum, efficiency for converting chemical energy into electrical energy may be defined by

$$\varepsilon_{\max} = \frac{\Delta G}{\Delta H}; \tag{7.2}$$

or, using the relation between free energy ΔG and reversible potential V_e, $\Delta G = -nFV_e$

$$\varepsilon_{\max} = -\frac{nF}{\Delta H} V_e. \tag{7.3}$$

Since the numerical values for ΔG at room temperatures† are usually close to that for ΔH (i.e., $T\Delta S$ is small compared to ΔH) the ideal, maximum efficiency $\varepsilon_{\max}$ is usually close to one. For example, in the combustion of propane to CO_2 the overall reaction is:

$$C_3H_8 + 5O_2 \rightarrow 3CO_2 + 4H_2O.$$

$$\Delta G^\circ = -2107{\cdot}95\ \text{kJ mol}^{-1};\ \Delta H^\circ\ (= \Delta G^\circ + T\Delta S) = -2221{\cdot}66\ \text{kJ mol}^{-1}.$$

† Fuel cells operate usually at low temperatures 25–100°C. We are talking here about the 'cold combustion of fuel'.

Let us calculate the maximum possible conversion efficiency for the hydrogen–oxygen fuel cell reaction. The overall reaction is the combustion of hydrogen ($H_2 + \frac{1}{2}O_2 \rightarrow H_2O$) and in the tables of standard thermodynamic functions one can find that: $\Delta H^\circ = -241{\cdot}95$ kJ mol^{-1}: $\Delta G^\circ = -228{\cdot}72$ kJ mol^{-1}, and $\Delta S^\circ = -43{\cdot}95$ J mol^{-1} K^{-1}. Then the ideal maximum possible conversion efficiency would be

$$\varepsilon_{\max} = \frac{-228{\cdot}72}{-241{\cdot}95} = 0{\cdot}95, \tag{7.4}$$

or 95% of the total energy content can, in the ideal case, be converted into electricity at 298 K.

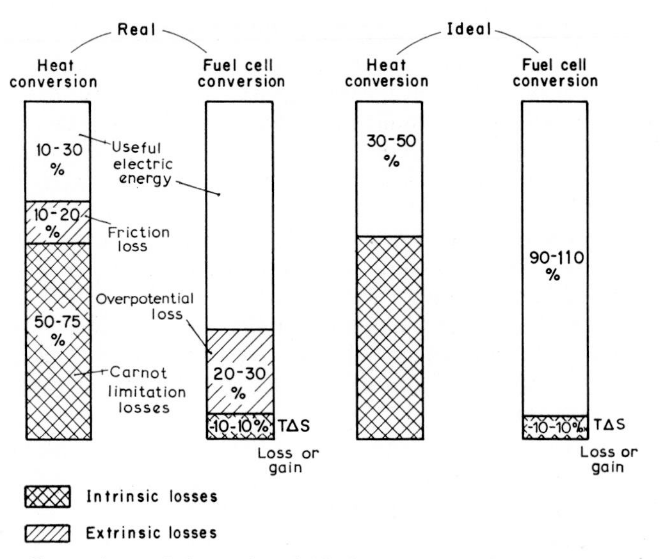

Fig. 7.3. Comparison of the real and ideal conversion efficiencies (and losses) of enthalpy (ΔH) for classical and fuel cell production of electricity.

We have here a very attractive aspect of electrochemical energy conversion; and before we consider the difficulties let us admire its high efficiency. There is no Carnot efficiency to worry about, no intrinsic limitation. Here, in principle, every electron which leaves the double layer can do its full complement of work, and produce electrical energy. It does not *have* to stream out again at some intermediate potential with half or more of its kinetic energy still in it, as is the case for the working substance in a thermal engine.

The real efficiency of the electrochemical energy converter

The real efficiency of the electrochemical energy converter is always lower than the ideal efficiency, since a part of the energy is used to propagate the reaction. Since it is the equilibrium voltage V_e, which appears in the efficiency relation (7.3), it is obvious that for the efficiency of a real cell producing current density, i, one has to replace V_e by the actual cell voltage V_i at the current density i, thus

$$\varepsilon_{\text{real}} = -\frac{nF}{\Delta H} V_i. \tag{7.4}$$

Or, taking into account the relation between V_e and V_i (eqn. (4.14))†

$$\varepsilon_{\text{real}} = -\frac{nF}{\Delta H}(V_e - \eta_a - |\eta_c| - IR). \tag{7.5}$$

Assuming that for a real hydrogen–oxygen fuel cell one obtains 0·9 V as the terminal voltage at $i = 2$ A m^{-2} the efficiency would be

$$\varepsilon_{\text{real}} = -\frac{2.96500.0.9}{-241\,950} = 0{\cdot}72.$$

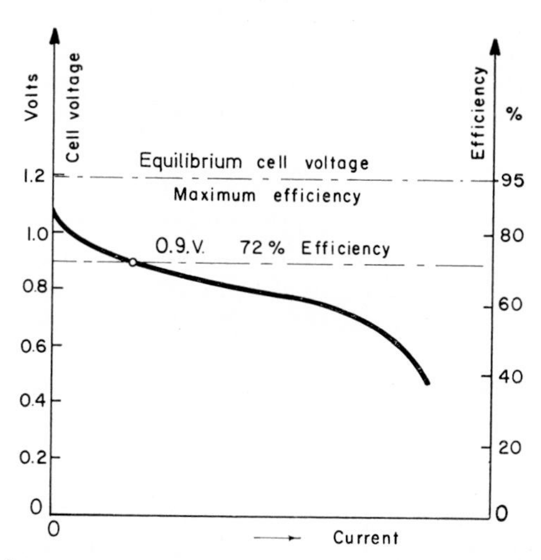

Fig. 7.4. The voltage–current line for a hydrogen–oxygen fuel cell also represents the efficiency–current relation (since $\varepsilon = -(nF/\Delta H)\, V_i$).

Since the cell voltage *decreases* with increase of current density, it is obvious (fig. 7.4) that the fuel cell efficiency decreases with increase of current density. The larger the current (i.e., the more *power* we want to have from one cell) the more energy is lost inside the fuel cell, due to the existence of various overpotentials. The real efficiency of the electrochemical energy converter will be more like 60% than 90% (compare internal combustion, 20%).

† ΔH is usually negative for the combustion of fuels. V_e is always positive. Hence, ϵ is positive.

The realist may say, 'Ah-ha, for the thermal engine you have your Carnot efficiency, and for the electrochemical engine you have this overpotential . . . so!'. The point is that in the Carnot cycle the limitation is intrinsic; *nothing* can be done about it. However vibration-free and friction-free the engineers might be able to make the mechanical devices in a heat engine, there is always the reduction in overall efficiency due to the Carnot limit. In fact, when we say that the Carnot efficiency of a heat engine is, say, 25%, its real efficiency is less than that, because we have neglected the other, extrinsic, energy-losing processes, such as friction. In the electrochemical case, it is *only ex*trinsic factors which bring down the efficiency: *they* are then open to research and development.

Efficiency and the rate of working (power)

The expression for the efficiency of a fuel cell (eqn. (7.5)) immediately shows us that the higher the overvoltage, the less the efficiency. If we are content with a very small *power* output ($V_i \times i$) from our fuel cell per unit area, and use a small current density, we can have greater efficiency. An infinitessimally small power would give us the efficiency of the equilibrium situation (eqn. (7.3)).

The power produced by an electrochemical reactor

A fuel cell can be regarded as an electrochemical reactor, but also as an electrical generator. One of the important characteristics of all electrical generators, including fuel cells, is their power characteristic (power per unit surface of the electrode or assembled cell, power per unit volume, or power per unit mass). The more power one can get from the same volume or mass, the better is the power source.

Since power is the product of current and actual cell voltage

$$P = I \times V_i \tag{7.6}$$

one can easily calculate the dependence of P on I, if the voltage–current dependence is known (fig. 7.5). In the *ideal* case, assuming that the equilibrium cell voltage V_e can be obtained when a current I passes (i.e., that overpotentials are negligible), the power–current line would be a straight line (broken line in fig. 7.5), with a slope V_e. However, in a real case, V_i is smaller than V_e, according to the equation (4.14)

$$V_i = V_e - \eta_a - |\eta_c| - IR_{sol}.$$

At larger currents, overpotentials are larger and V_i is smaller than V_e (cf. fig. 7.4). Consequently, the power line would deviate from the straight line more and more, as the current increases.

Equation (7.6) can be written in more complete form if we remember that both anodic and cathodic overpotentials can be complex, being composed of charge-transfer and diffusion overpotentials.

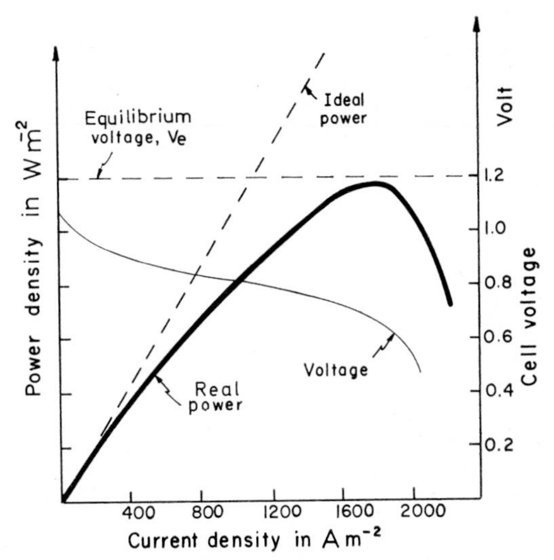

Fig. 7.5. Voltage–current and power–current lines for hydrogen–oxygen fuel cell. The dotted lines are for ideal, maximum voltage and power.

The charge-transfer overpotential is (eqn. (3.47))

$$\eta = \frac{RT}{\alpha F} \ln \frac{I}{Ai_0}, \tag{7.7}$$

and diffusion overpotential (by rearranging eqn. (4.12)):

$$\eta_d = \frac{RT}{F} \ln \left(1 - \frac{I}{Ai_{\text{Lim}}}\right), \tag{7.8}$$

where A is the real electrode surface, I is the total current (i.e., $i = I/A$), α is the transfer coefficient† (often $\alpha = \beta = 0{\cdot}5$), i_0 is the exchange current density and i_{Lim}—the limiting diffusion current density. Then the power equation (7.6) can be written in more complex form:

$$\begin{aligned}
P = {} & I \times V_e && \text{Maximum available power.}\\
& - \frac{IRT}{\alpha_a F} \ln \frac{I}{A_a, i_{0,a}} - \frac{IRT}{\alpha_c F} \ln \frac{I}{A_c, i_{0,c}} && \text{Power losses due to charge transfer overpotentials.}\\
& - \frac{IRT}{nF} \ln \left(1 - \frac{I}{A_a i_{\text{Lim},a}}\right) - \frac{IRT}{nF} \ln \left(1 - \frac{I}{A_c i_{\text{Lim},c}}\right) && \text{Power losses due to diffusion problems.}\\
& - I^2 R_{\text{sol}} && \text{Power losses due to the resistance of the solution.}
\end{aligned} \tag{7.9}$$

† See page 110.

P

This equation plainly shows how the power density of a fuel cell can be enlarged. Larger exchange current densities i_0 (i.e., good electrocatalysis), larger limiting current densities i_{Lim} (better diffusion conditions) and better electrical conductivity (higher concentration of electrolyte) or smaller R_{sol} are the means to increase the power density of a fuel cell battery.

The necessity for porous electrodes

If we try to make a fuel cell with planar electrodes, such as are often used for various electrolyses, the cell voltage V_i drops down to very small values, even at current densities of a few milliamperes. The reason is the low solubility (or concentration) of oxygen and hydrogen in the electrolyte and therefore the small diffusion limiting current. The solubility of these gases in aqueous electrolytic solutions is roughly about 10^{-4} mol litre^{-1}, which if replaced in equation (4.8) for i_{Lim}, gives only about 0.1 milliamperes cm^{-2} as the limiting diffusion current for an unstirred solution ($\delta = 10^{-4}$ m, $D \simeq 10^{-9}$ m^2 s^{-1}), both for the cathode and anode. Therefore, if replaced in equation (7.9), these i_{Lim} values limit the overall cell power to a few watts m^{-2} (e.g., $P = 0{\cdot}5$ V $\times$ 5 A m^{-2} = $2{\cdot}5$ W m^{-2}).

Thus, even with relatively high i_0 values of 10 A m^{-2}, etc., the electrical output of a fuel cell is very small, assuming the use of *planar* electrodes. What are planar electrodes? They are essentially sheets of metal dipping into the solution, and on these sheets the electrode reaction is to take place. With this type of electrode, the likelihood is a small power density. Indeed, it is so poor that many workers on electrochemical science who contemplated fuel cells for the first time, perhaps about 1960, thought that fuel cells would never produce power which, in terms of some factor of practical usefulness such as kilowatts per kilogram, would be comparable with the much-criticized internal combustion engine.

On closer inspection of the power equation (7.9), we find the surface area, A, in the denominators of both the charge-transfer and diffusion overpotential terms. In other words, even with rather small i_0 values, or small solubilities of gases producing small limiting current densities, i_{Lim}, a larger power density can be obtained if a larger real surface area of the electrodes can be utilized.

This was the beginning of the use of *porous* electrodes (fig. 7.6). At first the ideas were naïve, in the sense that it was thought that the more pore area one had inside, the greater would be the area available for reactivity. This is by no means so.

Thus, if we think of a point just inside a pore, where we have electrochemical activity at an overpotential η, it is as though it were on the surface. But if we go further inside the pore, then we have a loss of net electrical potential by the IR drop, which occurs down the pore (fig. 7.7 *b*). Thus, pores waste electrical energy, as well as helping to increase the amount available per unit area.

On this basis, we would have to say that the amount of electrical energy which one pore contributed per unit area simply got less as the pore got longer. Only the parts of the pore near its mouth, in contact with the external solution, would be effective. However, there is

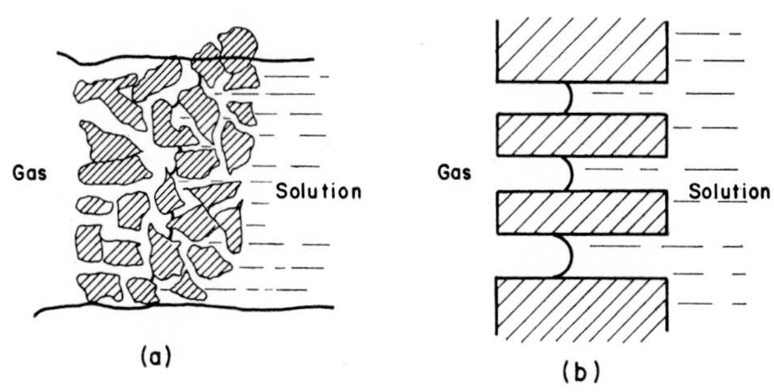

Fig. 7.6. (*a*) Cross-section through part of a porous electrode. (*b*) Idealized pore, and three-phase boundary (solution–gas–metal) at the meniscus.

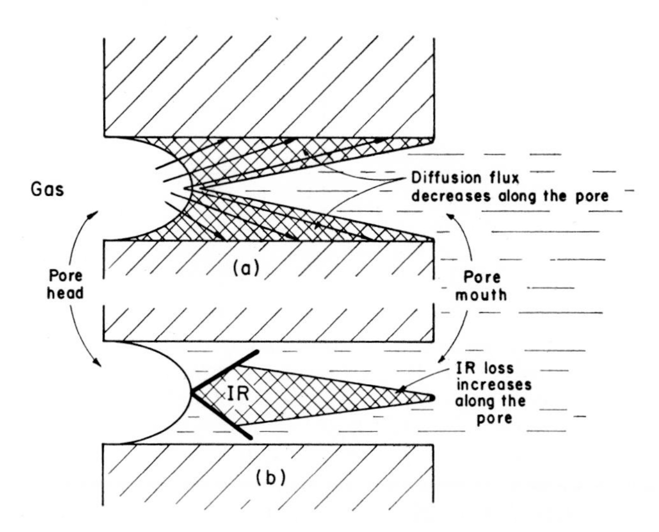

Fig. 7.7. (*a*) Diffusion flux is largest at the pore head. (*b*) Ohmic (*IR*) drop increases as we go along the pore from the solution side to the meniscus.

another factor which must be coupled with this one (fig. 7.7 *a*). The hydrogen fuel arrives at the pore *head*, the end opposite to the mouth. It then has to get dissolved into the liquid in the pore and *diffuse* through this liquid. As the length of the pore, now measured from the head rather than the mouth, gets longer, so the rate of supply of fuel to the active zones at various distances up the pore from the head to the mouth decreases. It is clearly more difficult for the fuel to reach a point far up the pore at the same rate as it can reach zones just inside the head, to which it has only a small distance to diffuse.

Hence, there are two factors to be considered: (*a*) the loss in useable potential, which gets worse as one goes from mouth to head; and (*b*) the lack of available reactant (fuel), which gets worse as one goes from head to mouth. Somewhere between mouth and head there is an optimum position between the two counter-indicating factors, and here the local current density in the pore would be at a maximum.

But all this is an oversimplification, even for a very elementary account.

Thus each pore has a meniscus, and this can be looked at in the following way (fig. 7.8). As the meniscus grows up from a limiting value of a few ångströms at its 'edge', where it begins to wet the material, it

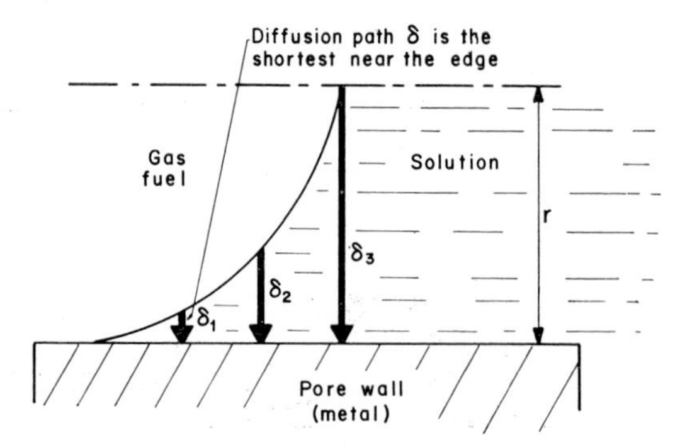

Fig. 7.8. Diffusion paths at the meniscus.

makes an arc, perhaps approximately circular, along the other side of the wall of the pore. Hence, if one takes the surface of the meniscus and draws the straightest line to the nearest 'shore', it is clear that this varies and may extend to a depth of half the radius of the pore. Now, if we look back to equation (4.8), the value of the limiting current is inversely proportional to δ, the depth of the boundary layer. Therefore, one can have a δ which is extremely low near the beginning of the meniscus, a δ of perhaps 10 nm. Now, the normal δ on a surface in unstirred solution is about 0·5 mm (p. 135), so we have a decrease of δ by a factor of about 50 000 times. Equation (4.8) shows that we should have, when δ is 10 nm, an *increase* in limiting current density compared with what we would have for the limiting current density at a planar electrode of some 50 000 times.

It would be quite wrong to assume that this very high limiting current density applies to the situation all down the pore, because the meniscus covers only a very small region (fig. 7.9). One might expect, because the limiting current density is so large there, that the major activity would be just near the head, where the thinnest part of the meniscus is. We have seen that the diffusion of fuel from the head is a counteracting factor to avoid. But suppose the gas is very soluble, and plenty of fuel diffuses down the meniscus. Then there is another factor which prevents the very thinnest part of the meniscus from being active. At a sufficiently small thickness, there is a high solution resistance, which will not allow the escape of ions produced in the reaction. What is meant by this? Suppose we are burning hydrogen electrochemically. The reaction will be $H_2 \rightarrow 2H^+ + 2e$. The protons have got to escape down the pore, out to the solution. If they are to go through a part of the meniscus which is only a few hundred ångströms in thickness, there

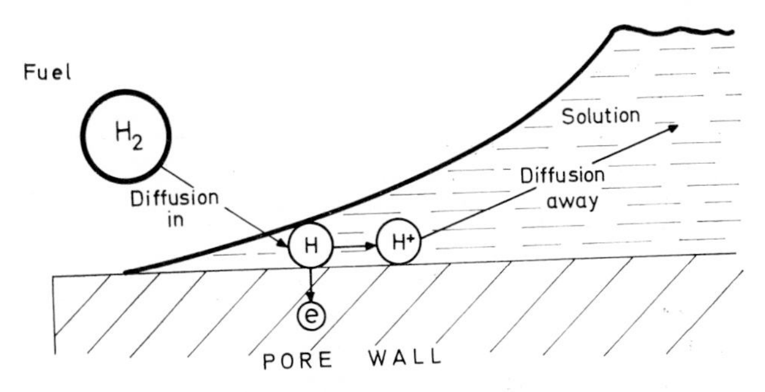

Fig. 7.9. Action at the end of the meniscus.

will be a large resistance against their passage, because the resistance is proportional to 1/area. Hence, the relation of current to pore extent, starting at the head and working towards the mouth, has the shape shown in fig. 7.10.

Thus, as the meniscus thickens, the resistance lessens, the *IR* drop decreases, and the current increases (reaching a peak). However, as one proceeds to a still thicker layer of solution (see fig. 7.8), or even goes inside the bulk of the pore, the δ value becomes much bigger than the few hundred ångströms inside the meniscus, the limiting current falls, and hence there is a fall of current density.

It follows that, if reactant solution and diffusion are plentiful, the major production of current, so far as the limiting current is concerned, will be near the beginning of the meniscus, and the other parts of the pore will be of less importance.

All this concerns one important type of porous electrode, that in which there is partial wetting of the substrate by the liquid. One can conclude:

(1) Diffusion control of the current is important in porous electrodes. The properties of a pore in giving high current densities are due essentially to its provision of small boundary layer thicknesses, δ, in certain regions, so that here (eqn. (4.8)) the limiting current density is very high.

(2) Only a small part of any pore is active.† Porous electrodes work due to the large limiting current at the three-phase boundary (fig. 7.8). They allow much greater limiting current densities than corresponding planar electrodes. A comparison of porous and planar electrodes for the same conditions is given in fig. 7.11, showing the dramatic difference in limiting currents.

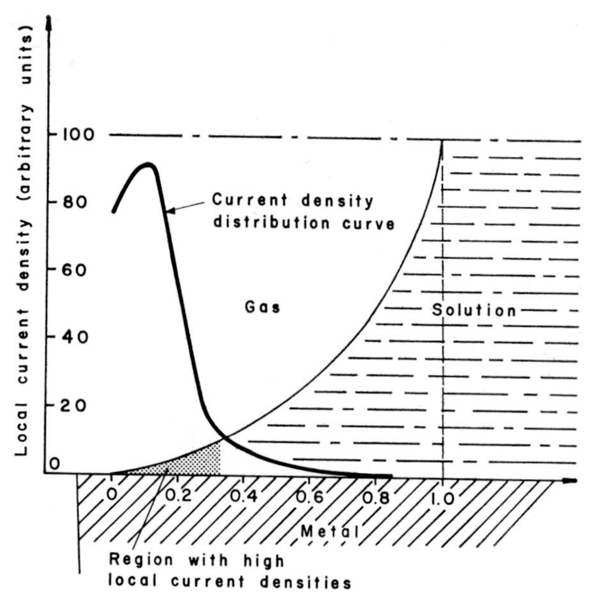

Fig. 7.10. Distribution of local current densities along the meniscus in an ideal single pore.

Catalysts (e.g., powdered silver for oxygen reduction) are put inside porous electrodes to help make the exchange current densities as high as possible, and hence, for a given current density, the overpotential is as low as possible. The catalyst is deposited throughout the pores of an electrode, often by heating some thermally unstable salt of the material inside the porous electrode and letting the metal deposit

† The degree to which this is so depends not only on the details of the i_0 of the catalyst, but also upon the model. We have assumed in our discussion that the essential model, of course, an oversimplification, is a series of parallel pores. Now, there may be essentially different structures and the degree to which much of the catalyst is unused then remains not yet quite clear.

randomly. Note that there may be a waste of some of the catalyst here, because in some porous electrodes, as explained above, the activity is extremely localized, whereas the catalyst is put down everywhere. As the cost of the catalyst is an important part of the fuel cell cost, this inability to control the extent of the location of the catalyst to the active region brings one to a research boundary in electrochemical engineering.

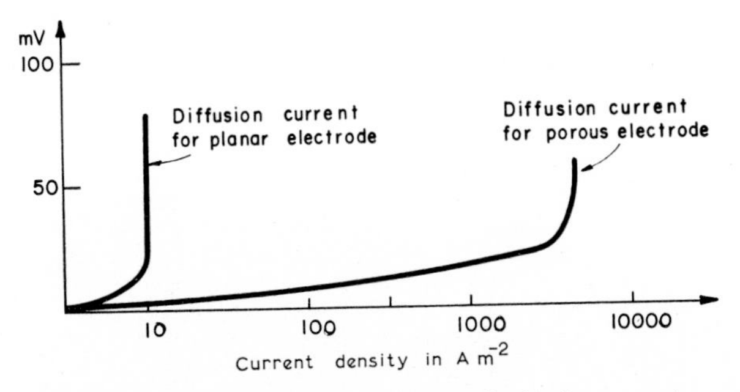

Fig. 7.11. Limiting currents for the hydrogen ionization reaction at a planar platinum electrode and at a porous nickel electrode.

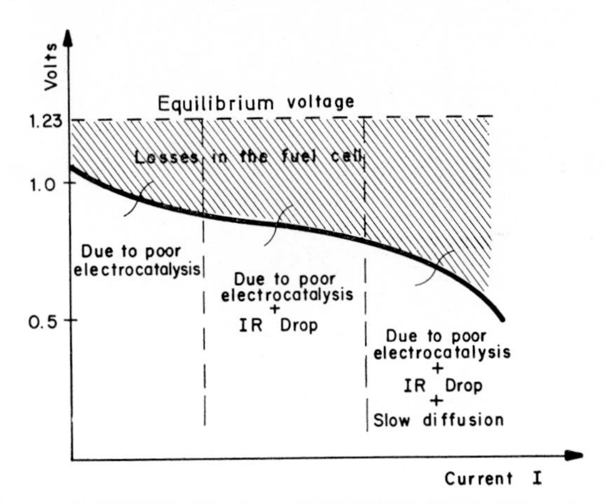

Fig. 7.12. Losses in a fuel cell.

Diffusion, electrocatalysis, corrosion, high temperatures, and fuel cells

Let us say a word very briefly about all these topics, which, as we shall show, are related. First, we have shown already that easy and rapid diffusion is a vital part of the electrochemical engineering of making fuel cells of high power. (The maximum power so far reached is about 4×10^2 kW m^{-2} for a fuel cell working at 700°C). Electrocatalysis is important, because it controls (eqn. (3.26)) the amount of overpotential, i.e., *energy loss*, in the production of energy from the available energy of a chemical reaction. In the idealized diagram of fig. 7.12 one sees the regions of the current density–potential diagram which indicate the parts played by electrocatalysis, by *IR* drop, and by diffusion. The figure shows that it is the energy loss in the first part of the polarization, before the current density is large enough for diffusion and resistance to become important, which is controlled by electrocatalysis.

High temperature is the other side of the penny to electrocatalysis in fuel cells. If electrocatalysis cannot get the i_0 sufficiently high, and

Fig. 7.13. The General Electric ion-exchange membrane (IEM) hydrogen-oxygen fuel cell battery; 1 kW module used in the Gemini spacecraft.

therefore the overpotential sufficiently low, the alternative is to increase the temperature. This is satisfactory if the lifetime of the cell could be short, say days or weeks. But increase of temperature increases not only the rate constants of the reactions, but the rate constants of the electrochemical corrosion reactions, which cause the materials of the cell to decay, split up, and break. The lifetime of a cell becomes not years but months or even weeks. Once more, one comes to a research frontier: how can such corrosion reactions be controlled, or can we increase electrocatalysis and work at medium (100–500°C) or low (25–100°C) temperatures?

The Most Important Fuel Cells of the 1970's

The first is without doubt the hydrogen–air fuel cell, one of the few fuel cells for which the electrochemical engineering has been done thoroughly. The cell has become of great practical interest because of a significant decrease in the price of hydrogen in recent years.

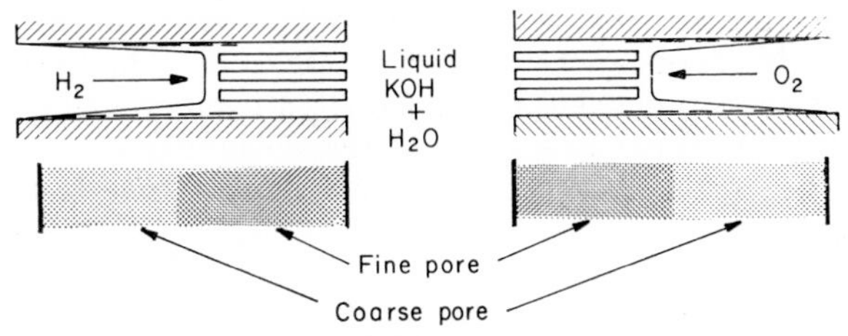

Fig. 7.14. Dual-porosity sintered metal electrodes used in many types of fuel cell

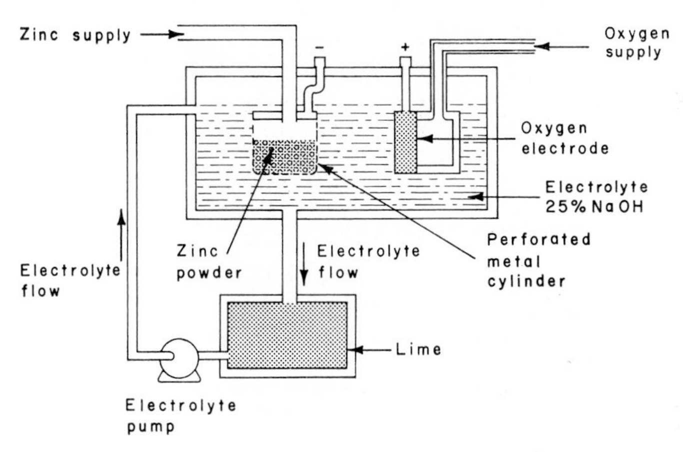

Fig. 7.15. Schematic of a zinc–air fuel cell.

The hydrazine–air fuel cell is another cell on which the engineering is advanced. Hydrazine (N_2H_4) is an excellent way of 'carrying hydrogen', attached to nitrogen, for it is a liquid at room temperatures and pressures. The disadvantage at present is that it costs too much to manufacture†; but the elements of which it is made are easily available, and a reduction in its cost is predicted should a market for very

† In 1972, the cost of hydrazine, in the form of the crystallized hydrate, was *c.* \$1 per lb in the U.S.A. and \$0.60c. in Japan. Mass production corresponding to the amounts needed to supply an electric car population of tens of millions would bring the price down, in the U.S.A., to about \$0.40c. However, the main cost of manufacturing hydrazine is the separation of the hydrazine from saline solution by evaporation. In potential fuel cell use, the hydrazine would in any case have to be dissolved in an electrolyte so that possibly saline dissolved hydrazine can be produced sufficiently cheaply, *even by the present Raschig process*, to make it viable as a competitor for gasoline.

large quantities of the fuel develop. Were it possible to go below the cost of gasoline in hydrazine manufacture, then there would be a fuel cell revolution in transportation, for the distribution of hydrazine to service stations would be no more difficult than that of gasoline.

Metal–air cells, for example, magnesium–air, aluminium–air, zinc–air (fig. 7.15), are undergoing research at the present time. The advantages are the absolute safety and ready availability of the metal fuel, particularly for magnesium and aluminium. The disadvantages are that some corrosion takes place and hydrogen would be evolved, which would have to be collected and reused perhaps in an auxiliary fuel cell. The corresponding economic balances have not yet been clearly worked out.

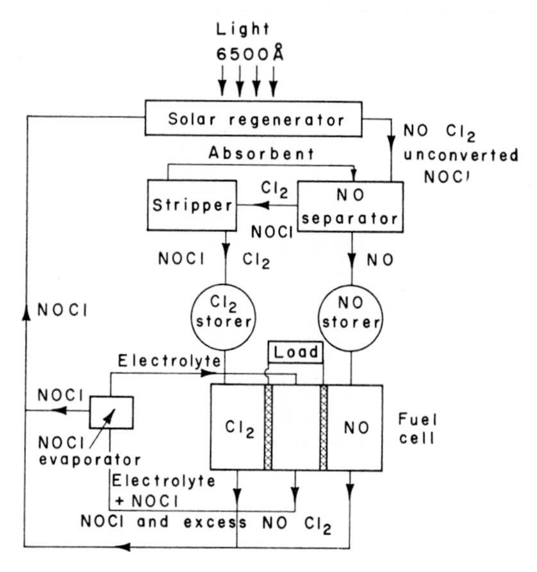

Fig. 7.16. Scheme of a photochemically regenerative chlorine–nitric oxide fuel cell. NOCl produced by the fuel cell reaction is decomposed by light and used again in the cell.

Photogalvanic cells use light to dissociate the chemical which is formed in the fuel cell. The cell is thus called a 'photochemically regenerative cell' (fig. 7.16). For example, if one leads nitric oxide over one electrode and chlorine over another, the compound formed is nitrosyl-chloride, which then can be made to undergo decomposition by light, forming the NO and Cl_2 again for more use in the cell. The overall reaction is light energy → electrical energy.

Lastly, reformer type fuel cells: one of the goals of petroleum companies is to convert the energy of the burning of hydrocarbons with air directly to electrical power, i.e., to engineer fuel cells working with hydrocarbon fuels. However, such efforts are frustrated at present because only noble metal substrates catalyse the anodic oxidation of hydrocarbons to CO_2 with a sufficiently small overpotential at reasonably high current densities. The necessity of using noble metals makes the cell uneconomic. Research on substitutes is not being pursued.

Uses of Fuel Cells which are Feasible Now

Henri, the Belgian fuel cell engineer, made an economic and engineering survey of the use of fuel cells in 1968, and it is on his estimates that we rely here in summarizing very briefly the areas in which fuel cells, on the basis of the *present* research position, would appear to compete favourably and sometimes dominatingly with traditional alternatives.

(1) Space power: The use of fuel cells as uniquely suitable power sources for space vehicles arises because they allow maximum energy to be carried with minimum weight.

(2) Power sources for isolated areas: The transportation costs of fuel are often a very significant fraction of the cost of power, so that if one has to carry only $\frac{1}{2}$ to $\frac{1}{3}$ the amount of fuel, for the same energy output, the situation becomes favourable to fuel cells.

(3) Vehicles which involve idling and stopping, and where the motor is in the 10 kW range, in particular, where work in an enclosed space is important.

(4) Railway traction, particularly shunting engines, where fuel cell power can be shut off at every stop and internal combustion engines would be left to idle.

(5) Naval propulsion: For submarine propulsion the fuel cell is unique in the advantage it offers: it is silent and need not emit presence-indicating exhaust.

(6) Basic power plants for electrometallurgical situations (where high *d.c.* is needed); peak power units; in isolated centres, e.g., mining camps, farms.

(7) Prosthetic (biological) applications. Fuel cell-powered heart pacers may last for an indefinite time; batteries have to be recharged every few years. An internal fuel cell power source (burning glucose and oxygen present in blood) to drive a pump to work the circulatory system is under research.

(8) Recreational applications: Power at camp sites or for scuba diving, land yachts, boats, trailers, all would have to carry about half as much fuel as they now do for the same amount of energy.

(9) Fuel cells in cars: Fuel cell powered electric cars with a 230-mile radius at an average speed of 40–50 miles per hour have been made and tested. A cheap, electrochemically-burnable fuel (hydrazine?) would make fuel cell-powered electric vehicles (which are already scientifically possible and socially desirable) economically attractive.

CHAPTER 8

the electrochemical storage of electrical energy

The Lead–Acid Cell

THE basic cell (fig. 8.1), out of several of which the actual battery is made, consists of two electrodes of porous lead, the pores being filled with scarcely soluble lead sulphate. The solution between them is sulphuric acid, saturated with lead sulphate. Upon charging, the electrode which is cathodic reduces the Pb^{2+} ions present (Pb^{2+} ion concentration is constant as long as $PbSO_4$ is not consumed), and these

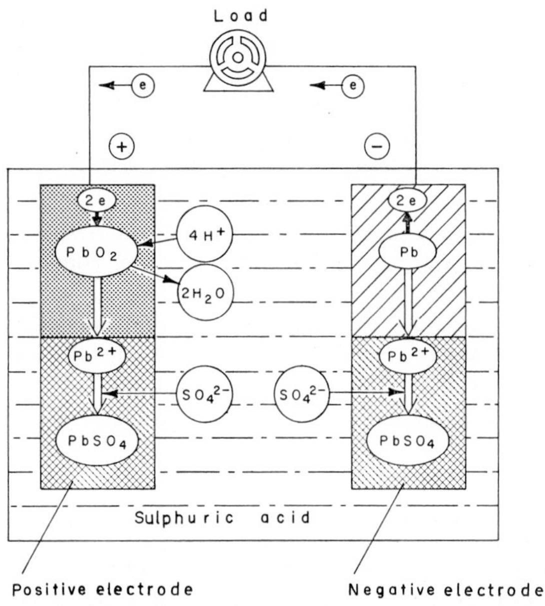

Fig. 8.1. The discharging process in lead–acid storage battery.

deposit onto the lead sheet, making more lead. At the other electrode, the Pb^{2+} ions yield electrons to the lead plate, and become Pb^{4+}, after which they undergo hydrolysis to form crystalline PbO_2. Thus, one might say that the charging reactions are

$$Pb^{2+} + 2e \rightarrow Pb \tag{8.1}$$

at the negative electrode; and at the positive electrode the reaction would be

$$Pb^{2+} + 2H_2O \rightarrow PbO_2 + 4H^+ + 2e. \tag{8.2}$$

Now, after the battery has been thus 'charged', i.e., sufficient lead (IV) oxide has been piled up one plate and sufficient lead from the lead sulphate piled up on the other plate, one may connect the two terminals to a resistor, load, motor, etc., and drive something. During the driving the battery discharges—that is to say, the plate which was formerly an anode, that on which lead oxide was formed, now becomes a cathode and the reaction

$$PbO_2 + 4H^+ + 2e \rightarrow Pb^{2+} + 2H_2O \tag{8.3}$$

occurs. Of course, the other electrode is now an anode, and the reaction which occurs at it will be

$$Pb \rightarrow Pb^{2+} + 2e. \tag{8.4}$$

The overall reaction must always be

$$2Pb^{2+} + 2H_2O \rightleftharpoons Pb + PbO_2 + 4H^+. \tag{8.5}$$

This is really the *cell* reaction. As it is customary to write the cell reaction in the form of complete chemical reaction, we can write

$$2PbSO_4 + 2H_2O \rightarrow Pb + PbO_2 + 2H_2SO_4. \tag{8.6}$$

It is interesting to note that the by-product of charging is H_2SO_4. This is the reason for increase of density of acid while charging.

One of the good features of the lead–acid battery, for the starting of internal combustion engines, where a high current is needed for a short time, is that the i_0's for the two reactions mentioned are large, so that (cf. eqn. (3.24)) little polarization develops. The competing reaction of the discharge of hydrogen on lead is so slow that it can be neglected, because it happens that lead has a very low exchange current density for hydrogen evolution (see Table 5.2), so that (by eqn. (3.26)) the overpotential which would have to develop to make the hydrogen discharge reaction compete with lead deposition would be very large.

Electrochemical storers and converters: batteries and fuel cells

The mechanism of the working of a battery is not *essentially* different from the working of a fuel cell, or a corrosion couple, or indeed any spontaneously-working electrochemical cell. The additional special features of the electrochemical energy storer are:

(1) The materials which take part in the reaction are all present in the one box. They do not come from outside fuel tanks, as they do in a fuel cell.

(2) The reaction can be sent backwards and forwards at will, e.g., lead sulphate may be made in the battery while discharging, and then it may be reduced to lead while charging. If one were converting methanol in a fuel cell to carbon dioxide, one could not catch the carbon dioxide and then reconvert it back to methanol. (The reduction of carbon dioxide to methanol is *possible*, but it is by no means direct.)

(3) If an electrochemical energy storer is to be successful, it must be rechargeable to an order of a thousand times. Changes at the plates—for example, the growing together of small particles into large particles which then do not give so much material in contact with the solution—is one of the basic troubles in the life of electrochemical energy storers.

To investigate a given electrochemical storer, we can apply the equations already deduced for the current in cells.

For example, if the overall cell reaction is known, the maximum equilibrium cell voltage can be calculated, using equation (3.36 *a*). From thermodynamic tables we can find that ΔG° for the lead–acid battery reaction is -394 kJ. Then the expected equilibrium cell voltage would be:

$$V_e^\circ = -\frac{\Delta G^\circ}{nF} = \frac{394\,000}{2\times 96\,500} = 2{\cdot}05 \text{ V}. \quad (8.7)$$

This *is* approximately the open circuit cell voltage that we really can measure at a lead–acid battery.

Under load, the cell voltage becomes smaller, as with a fuel cell, following the general relation (cf. eqn. (4.14))

$$V_i = V_e - \eta_a - |\eta_c| - IR. \quad (8.8)$$

Important quantities in a battery

There are important differences, however, in the behaviour of electrical energy storers (batteries) and that of fuel cells or other energy converters. In fuel cells, when a certain current density is applied, after a short time (a maximum of several minutes) the steady state is established. That means that the balance between the inflow of the reactants, current, overpotentials and outflow of reaction products is established. Usually this balance does not change for long periods of time. In other words, for a certain defined current density value the steady overpotential (or cell potential) value is obtained. Therefore, a potential (or cell voltage)–current density diagram is a reproducible and specific characteristic of a fuel cell (cf. fig. 7.9).

With batteries this is not the case. In every storage battery both reactant and reaction product remain close to the position of the electrochemical reaction. For example, lead is transformed into $PbSO_4$, which remains inside the pore, being able to react backwards in the charging cycle. During the process of discharge (as well as in charging), the fine structure of the electrode changes (pore size, shape, length, etc.) changing the values of overpotentials, particularly diffusion overpotentials and *IR* drop (ohmic resistance of the solution in the pores). The overall result is often that the voltage–current density line is different if taken at a different degree of discharge of the electrode, as shown in fig. 8.2 *a*. Therefore, one has to specify what was the degree of discharge, when referring to an experimental figure of the important

V–I characteristic of the battery (often it is at 50% discharge at the nominal current).

Another important quantity in a battery is what is called the *storage capacity*. It shows how much charge, Q (current × time), one can take out of the battery. In other words, how long a battery can operate without interruption (recharging). A good battery should have good storage capacity properties, i.e., large storing capacity per unit volume (coulombs/litre) or per unit mass (coulombs/kilogramme). However, again, due to changes in the microstructure of the pores in the electrodes, part of the active material in the reaction (e.g., lead)

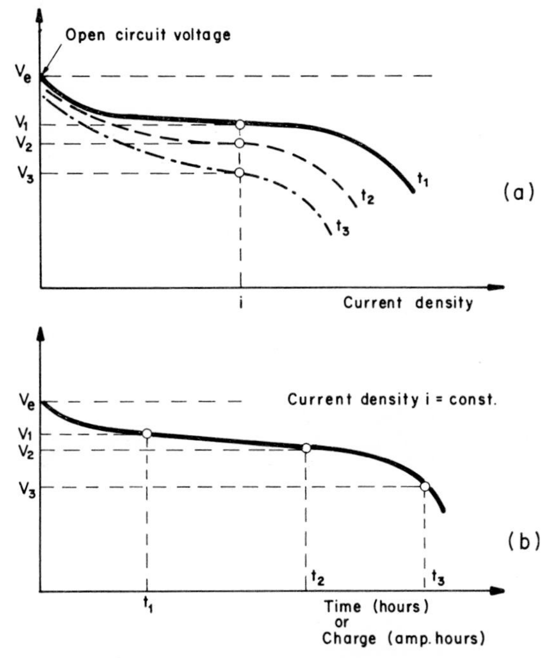

Fig. 8.2. (*a*) Voltage–current line, and (*b*) voltage–charge (or time) line. Since the cell voltage depends on the degree of discharge ($V_3 < V_2 < V_1$), various voltage–current lines can be obtained for the same cell at different stages.

might be blocked by the reaction products (e.g., $PbSO_4$). If this blocking is effective (lead loses contact with the solution), the blocked part of the lead electrode cannot operate further and is effectively lost for the discharge process, thus the overall capacity of the battery to provide electricity becomes smaller. This gradual loss of capacity with use is a property of all storage batteries involving solids

As a rule, the maximum storing capacity is obtained at small discharge rates. The larger the current one takes from the battery the smaller is the available charge capacity (fig. 8.2).

The third important quantity is the *energy density*, the amount of energy which can be extracted from a given mass (or volume) of the device.

The energy density can be calculated by multiplying charge density by the actual cell voltage, usually taken at the middle of the discharging curve (fig. 8.2 *b*).

$$\text{energy density} = \text{charge density} \times \text{voltage}.$$

It is interesting to note here, that energy density is dependent on the *kinetics* of the electrochemical plate reactions through both terms—charge density (as shown before) and also voltage because this is

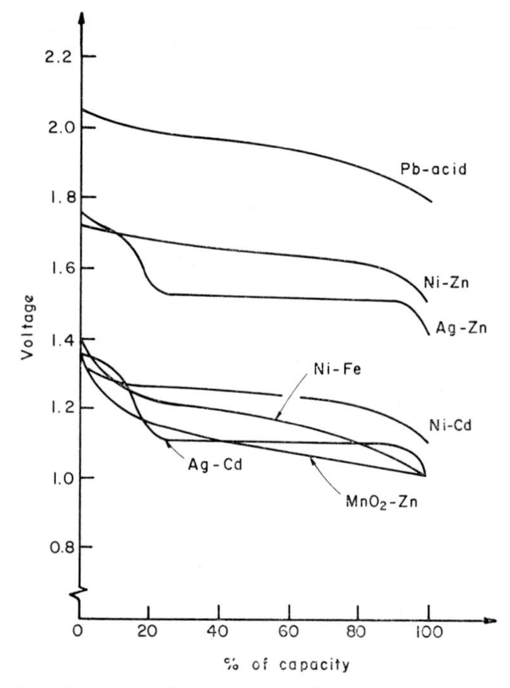

Fig. 8.3. Discharge characteristics of various types of battery.

affected by the overpotentials of the electrode reactions. (cf. eqn. (8.8)). The energy density decreases usually rather fast as the rate of discharge increases.

The fourth important criterion of a battery is the *power density*—that is to say, the watts per kilogramme or the *rate* of delivering energy per unit mass, rather than the *energy* per unit mass. Thus, one must have a certain amount of energy per unit mass; but one could conceivably have a cell in which the energy per unit mass was extremely high but

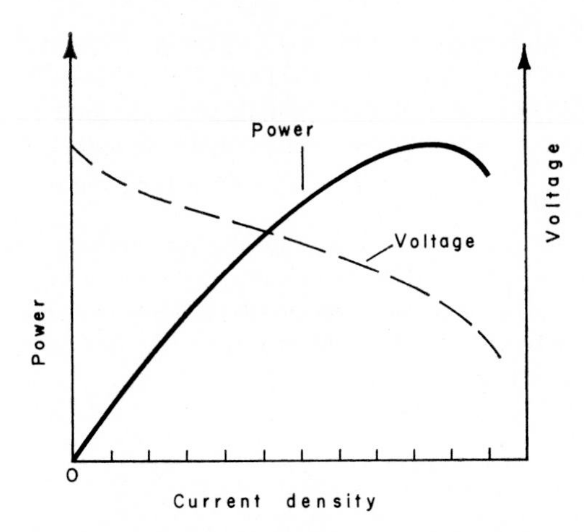

Fig. 8.4. Power density of a battery as a function of current density.

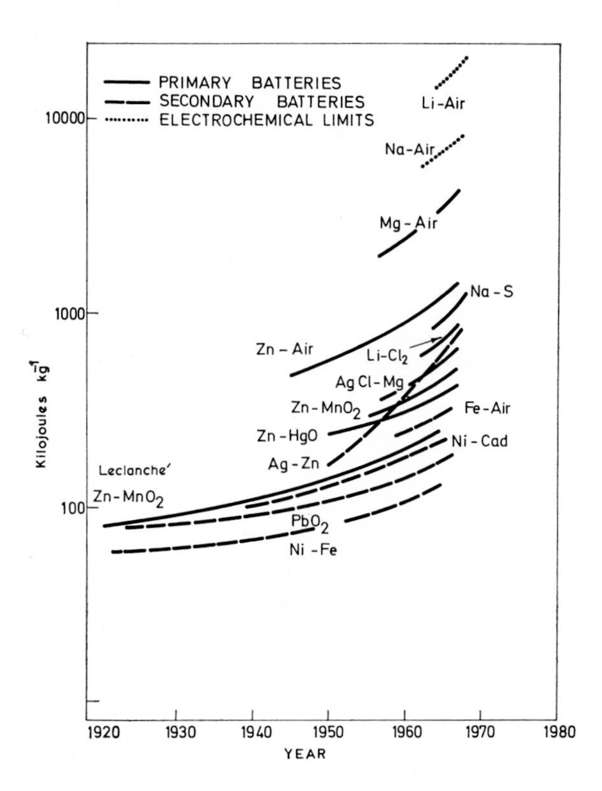

Fig. 8.5. The improvement of energy density for various types of battery during the last 50 years. Metal–air batteries seem to have the steepest curves, promising high capacities in the 1980's.

the power per unit mass low because of a large overpotential, which would decrease the voltage available from the cell. The same sort of considerations apply here as those which were applied to the power in a fuel cell. As the amount of current density demanded from the fuel cell or battery increases, its power per unit mass increases and passes through a maximum (fig. 8.4).

Silver–zinc batteries have particularly high energy densities, going up to about 400 kJ kg^{-1}. This is already sufficiently high to be applied in electric cars. It is the high cost of silver, however, and the tendency of the cell plates to change shape after only a few hundred cycles of life, that prevents its wider use at present.

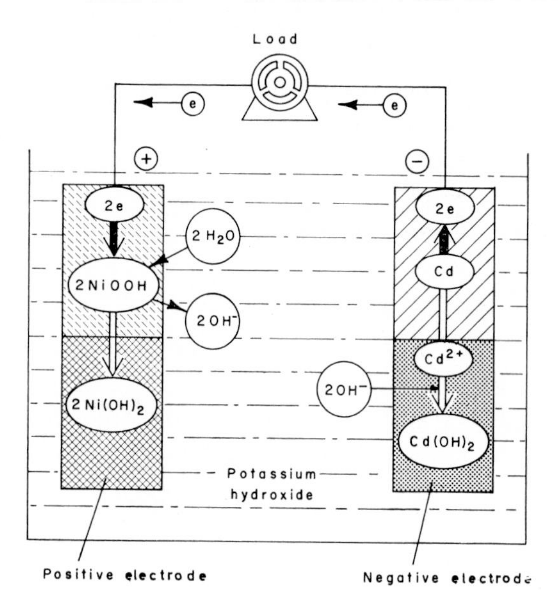

Fig. 8.6. Discharge process in the nickel–cadmium alkaline cell.

The necessity for reliable and cheap high energy density batteries, particularly for application for traction (cars, boats, railroads, etc.) is the reason for the great interest of electrochemists in some other promising systems. A typical power in a good, high energy density battery at the present time would be 200 W kg^{-1}.

Extrapolation of historical trends in batteries would show (fig. 8.5) that 5000 kilojoule per kilogramme for energy per unit mass and 1 kilowatt per kilogramme for power per unit mass would be reasonable aims for battery performance during the next decade or two.

Batteries of the Near Future

What other batteries are there at the present time which are commercially available? There are two, the nickel–cadmium battery (fig. 8.6) and the silver–zinc battery (fig. 8.7). Batteries with sintered nickel electrodes have energy densities up to 160 kJ kg^{-1} and power densities up to 150 W kg^{-1}. These characteristics are much better than for lead–acid batteries, and much less maintenance of them is needed than for lead–acid. But the relatively high price of nickel and cadmium, compared with lead, limits the use of nickel–cadmium batteries to the application where the initial investment is not of the primary importance (military, railroads, aircraft, ships, etc.).

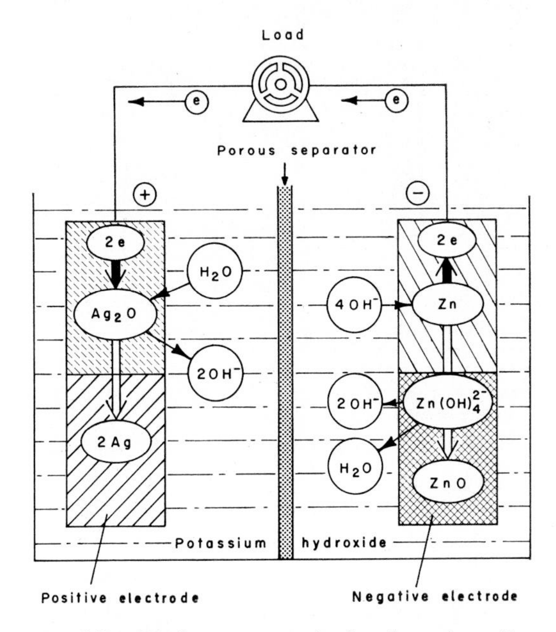

Fig. 8.7. Discharge process in the silver–zinc cell.

The most important batteries of the near future are as follows:

(1) *Metal–air batteries.* Advances made during the intense activity in fuel cell research for the American space programme between about 1958 and 1968, have been used to develop good air electrodes, which can now be coupled with fairly active metals such as magnesium, aluminium, and zinc, which may be rechargeable (the zinc in aqueous solution, the aluminium in non-aqueous solutions and in molten salts). These batteries offer good possibilities of energy per unit mass of 400–800 joules per kilogramme and powers per unit mass of 800–1000 watts per kilogramme. They use cheap metals (fig. 8.8).

(2) *High temperature cells.* There are several high-temperature cells which offer very striking performance. The lithium–chlorine cell is one kind (fig. 8.9). The chlorine storage may be in liquid form even at ambient temperatures under pressure, or it may be stored in the porous carbon of the electrode. Cells of this type give by far the best energy density performance with 1000 kJ kg^{-1}.

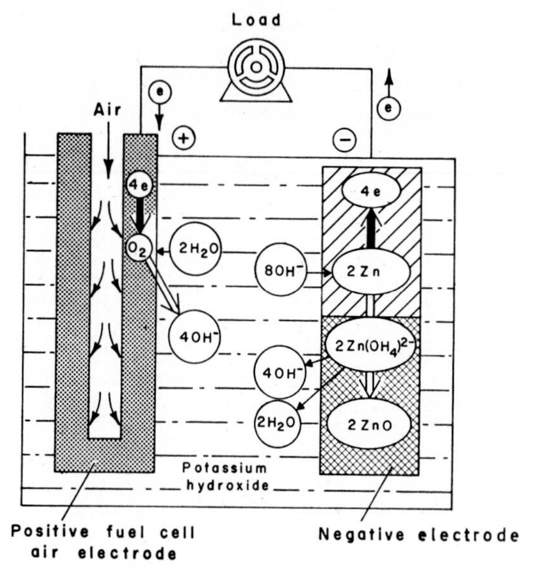

Fig. 8.8. Discharge processes in the air–zinc cell.

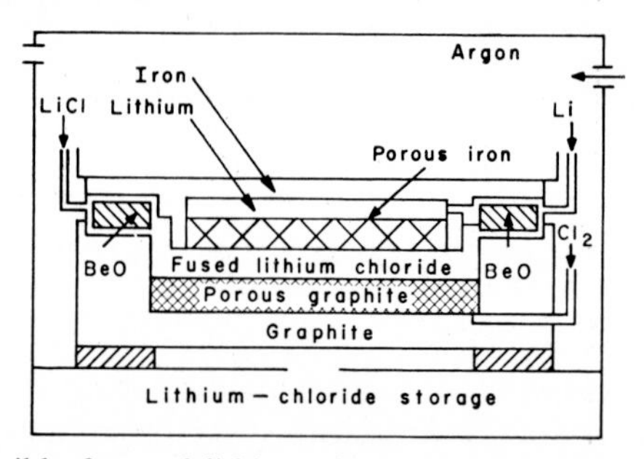

Fig. 8.9. One possible form of lithium–chlorine rechargeable cell. By charging, Li and Cl_2 are produced again and stored in separate vessels (not shown). Porous graphite is the positive (chlorine) electrode, and porous iron the negative (lithium) electrode.

Of course, there are points against high temperature cells. They need a definite start-up time to be 'thawed out' (though several devices for doing this which reduce the start-up time to minutes or less have

Table 8.1. Realized and idealized energy-storage-density parameters for some cell systems

System	Thermodynamic equilibrium potential V_e, V	Realized energy density (mean), kJ kg^{-1} (kWh kg^{-1})	Idealized energy density, kJ kg^{-1} (kWh kg^{-1})	Ratio of realized to idealized energy density
Single discharge				
M–O_2–KOH–Zn	1·64	540 (0·15)	1580 (0·44)	0·34
m-DNB†–$MgBr_2$–Mg	2·84	790 (0·22)	5580 (1·54)	0·14
Ag_2O_2–KOH–Zn	1·81	396 (0·11)	790 (0·22)	0·50
HgO–KOH–Zn	1·34	396 (0·11)	790 (0·22)	0·50
Hypothetical single discharge				
Li–F_2	6·0	—	5400 (1·5)	
Mg–O_2	3·1	—	4700 (1·3)	
Be–*m*-dinitrobenzene	2·6	—	11 100 (3·1)	
Be–nitrobutanol	2·3	—	13 300 (3·7)	
Multiple charge–discharge				
PbO_2–H_2SO_4–Pb	2·04	72 (0·02)	650 (0·18)	0·11
NiO(OH)–KOH–Cd	1·48	144 (0·04)	790 (0·22)	0·18
Ag_2O_2–KOH–Zn	1·70	396 (0·11)	1580 (0·44)	0·23
Hypothetical multiple charge–discharge				
Be–BeF_2–F_2	4·5	—	11 800 (3·30)	
Al–$AlCl_3$–Cl_2	3·02	—	7900 (2·20)	

† *m*-dinitrobenzene

been suggested). Furthermore, there are always psychological difficulties in the concept of having a hot liquid as the centre of a power source for cars, and this certainly cannot be minimized. Against this must be weighed the relatively favourable energy–density of these cells. However, the life over more than mere months of service has as yet to be proved. Up to now, they have tended to break down at longer times, because of *corrosion*, but as yet fundamental investigations of the reasons for this have not been carried out.

Problems Still to be Solved

We must solve the following problems, so that batteries will function close to their theoretical efficiency.

(1) In many batteries, the electrode reactions are not understood. We do not know, for example, how zinc becomes an oxide when the zinc–air cell discharges. What is the rate-controlling step?

(2) We do not understand very many *side* effects, the very things which cause the storer to give much less than it ought to—that is, we don't understand its illnesses. For example, we don't understand the mechanism by which the solid particles grow together and form *less available surface* as the charge and recharge process goes on.

(3) Corrosion gives us many problems. We have understood it in principle for about thirty years. But only now are texts about corrosion being written with real mechanistic electrochemistry in them (see Chapter 9). The thermodynamic view has prevailed too much.

(4) Electrocatalysis is little explored. Even well-functioning batteries without illnesses have overpotential, which detracts from the power they can give. Electrocatalysis and high i_0 values are the needed entities, and it is true that we are only just getting the solid state physics tied on to the exchange current values which (see Chapter 3) determine the over-potential.

CHAPTER 9

the stability of metals

LET us take a piece of iron, and put it in an acid solution containing iron (II) ions. For example, sulphuric acid with some quantity of iron (II) sulphate. Hydrogen will start evolving, and at the same rate as hydrogen evolves, iron will dissolve into solution, that is, it will corrode (fig. 9.1).

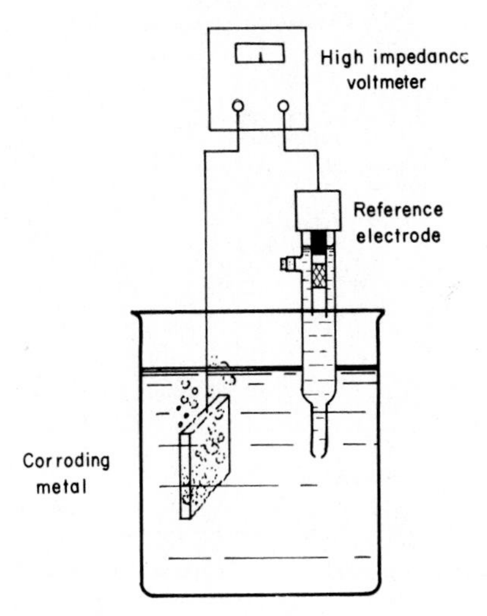

Fig. 9.1. The potential of a corroding metal (corrosion potential) can be measured by means of a reference electrode and a high-impedance voltmeter.

How much it will corrode, what is the corrosion rate, and what will be the potential of the corroding metal are the most important questions we have to answer when considering corrosion problems.

If there were no dissolution of metal in the solution, as would be the case if the metal were platinum or copper, the metal would have a potential corresponding to the equilibrium hydrogen potential in this solution, $V_{e,H}$.

If we could somehow stop the hydrogen ion discharge, and H_2 evolution at the iron surface, the iron would achieve a potential corresponding to the equilibrium iron electrode, $V_{e,Fe}$, in the same solution, which one can calculate by using the Nernst equation (eqn. (3.36)).

However, this cannot be done simply, because in acid solutions iron corrodes; in other words, iron dissolves electrochemically. Simultaneously, at the same surface, an equivalent amount of hydrogen evolves at the same rate. But this does not prevent us from making a thought experiment by separating these two simultaneous reactions, so that they occur at two different electrodes (fig. 9.2) and make a self-driving cell. By adjusting the resistance R, we could vary the current through the cell, and by means of the reference electrodes and high-impedance voltmeters, we could determine the potentials of each electrode at any chosen current. In other words, we could construct potential–current lines for each electrode, i.e., for each, separate, electrochemical reaction, as shown previously in fig. 4.25.

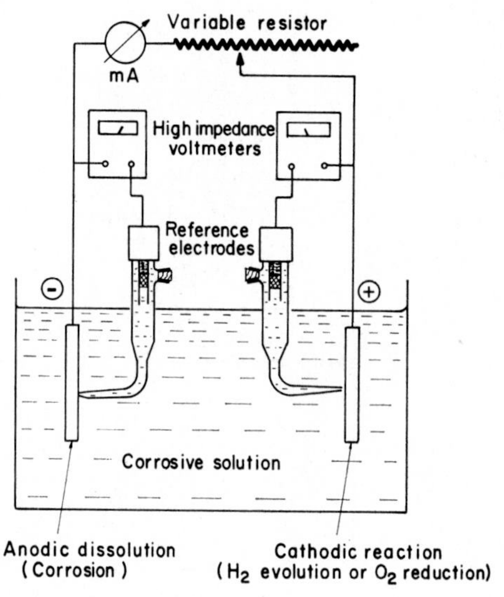

Fig. 9.2. The 'thought experiments' explained in the text for the separate measurements of the anodic and cathodic potential–current relationship.

Let us assume, to make the reasoning simpler, that the rates of both cathodic and anodic reactions are determined by charge-transfer processes, and that the potential–current relationships follow a logarithmic dependence (eqns. (3.25) and (3.26)).

A potential–current diagram of the type shown in fig. 9.3 should be obtained (sometimes referred to as an Evans diagram). If the external resistor is short-circuited ($R = 0$) and internal resistance of the solution is taken again to be small enough to be neglected ($R_{sol} \simeq 0$), then the current flowing through the cell would be the current which corresponds to the intersection point of two potential–current lines. Since this current is at the same time the current by which the metal dissolves, i.e., corrodes, it is the rate of corrosion expressed as corrosion current. The potential corresponding to the intersection point, being the same at each electrode, is the so-called corrosion potential, and is the potential which we really can measure experimentally (fig. 9.1).

The corrosion diagram in semi-logarithmic coordinates is perhaps clearer to present. The charge-transfer processes may be assumed to be rate-determining, and the potential–current lines are straight lines. In fig. 9.4, a diagram of this type is given, where the roles of exchange current densities, i_0, and gradients $(RT/\alpha F)$, for both processes in determining the corrosion rate (the intersection point), are more obvious than in the potential–current diagrams in fig. 9.3.

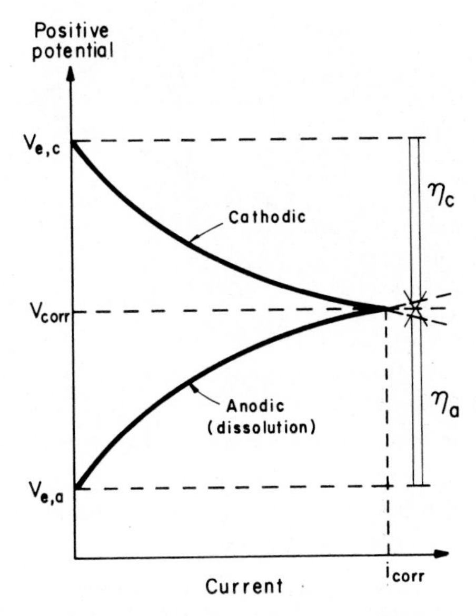

Fig. 9.3. A corrosion diagram in V–i coordinates. On the corroding metal the rates of the anodic and cathodic reactions are equal.

Our thought experiment relate to an imaginary homogeneous metal surface, or to a micro-heterogeneous surface, as with steel, where we cannot physically separate the parts of the surfaces on which the cathodic and anodic reaction occur. In some corrosion systems (corrosion macro-cells) this is feasible and corrosion diagrams of the types shown in figs. 9.3 and 9.4 can be measured. For example, if we want to see what would be the corrosion effect of a brass propeller on the steel hull of a ship, and what kind of corrosion protection should be applied, we could make a real cell and draw the real corrosion diagram.

The situation of having two or even more simultaneous electrochemical reactions occurring at the same surface (and making a net chemical reaction) is by no means limited to corrosion processes. Many chemical reactions in solutions catalysed by metals (various hydrogenation or oxidation reactions, involving organic or inorganic substances) are electrochemical in nature, and the analysis developed here can be used in these situations, as well (see also p. 109 and fig. 3.23).

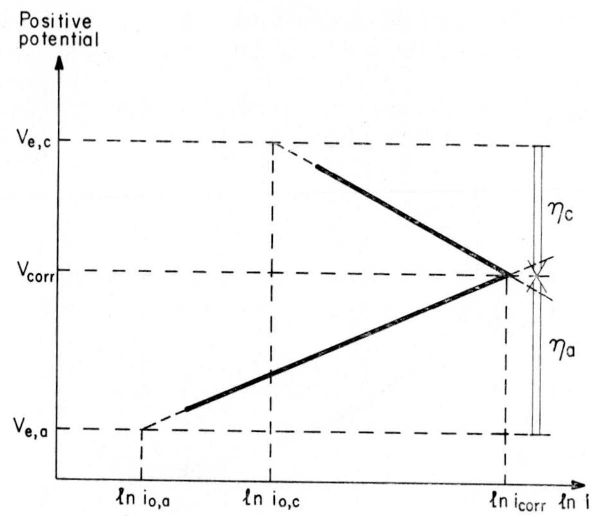

Fig. 9.4. Corrosion diagram in V–ln i coordinates.

A calculation of the rate of corrosion and corrosion potential

To calculate the rate of corrosion we start from the fact that a corrosion system can be considered as a self-driving cell, and equation (4.14) for the cell voltage can be used

$$V_i = V_{e,\text{cell}} - \eta_a - |\eta_c| - IR_{\text{sol}} \tag{9.1}$$

where

$$V_{e,\text{cell}} = V_{e,c} - V_{e,a} \tag{9.2}$$

i.e., the difference of the equilibrium potential $V_{e,c}$ for the cathodic process (e.g., H_2 evolution) and the equilibrium potential $V_{e,a}$ for the anodically dissolving metal.

We shall assume also, that both processes are charge-transfer controlled. Then, we can apply equations (3.25) and (3.26) in a slightly modified form:†

$$\eta_a = \frac{RT}{\alpha_a F} \ln \frac{i_a}{i_{0,a}} \tag{9.3}$$

† Instead of using β and $(1-\beta)$ for complex reactions, the experimentally measurable transfer coefficients α_a and α_c for anodic and cathodic reactions should be used. For simple reactions $\alpha = \beta$, but depending on the mechanism of the complex reaction could have different value.

and

$$\eta_c = \frac{RT}{\alpha_c F} \ln \frac{i_{0,c}}{i_c} \tag{9.4}$$

in which $i_{0,a}$ and $i_{0,c}$ are the exchange current densities for the anodic and cathodic process and α_a and α_c the effective transfer coefficients for these two processes. For the corrosion of a piece of metal we can assume that the solution resistance between the two sites at the metal surface where anodic and cathodic reactions occur is zero† ($R_{\mathrm{sol}} = 0$).

Now, since the corrosion system is a short-circuited self-driving cell, the cell voltage must be zero, i.e.,

$$V_i = 0 \tag{9.5}$$

and

$$i_a = i_c = i_{\mathrm{corr}}. \tag{9.6}$$

When we apply the general equation (9.1) to the corrosion system, we obtain the following expression:

$$0 = V_{\mathrm{e,cell}} - \frac{RT}{\alpha_a F} \ln \frac{i_{\mathrm{corr}}}{i_{0,a}} - \frac{RT}{\alpha_c F} \ln \frac{i_{\mathrm{corr}}}{i_{0,c}}. \tag{9.7}$$

We can rearrange this equation to:

$$\frac{1}{\alpha_a} \ln \frac{i_{\mathrm{corr}}}{i_{0,a}} + \frac{1}{\alpha_c} \ln \frac{i_{\mathrm{corr}}}{i_{0,c}} = \frac{FV_{\mathrm{e'cell}}}{RT}. \tag{9.8}$$

Then, we can rearrange the logarithmic terms:

$$\ln \frac{i_{\mathrm{corr}}^{(1/\alpha_a + 1/\alpha_c)}}{i_{0,a}^{1/\alpha_a} \times i_{0,c}^{1/\alpha_c}} = \frac{FV_{\mathrm{e,cell}}}{RT}, \tag{9.9}$$

and take the antilogarithm

$$\frac{i_{\mathrm{corr}}^{(\alpha_a + \alpha_c)/\alpha_a \alpha_c}}{i_{0,a}^{1/\alpha_a} \times i_{0,c}^{1/\alpha_c}} = \exp\,(FV_{\mathrm{e,cell}}/RT). \tag{9.10}$$

Finally, we can find the rate of corrosion, i_{corr}:

$$i_{\mathrm{corr}} = i_{0,a}^{\alpha_c/\alpha_c+\alpha_a} i_{0,c}^{\alpha_a/\alpha_c+\alpha_a} \exp \frac{\alpha_a \alpha_c}{\alpha_a + \alpha_c} \frac{F}{RT} V_{\mathrm{e,cell}}. \tag{9.11}$$

It is easy to see which factors determine the rate of corrosion and to what extent. Besides the thermodynamic equilibrium cell voltage $V_{\mathrm{e,cell}}$, the mechanism of the electrochemical reactions have an effect through the α terms. But, the most important effect is that of the exchange current densities, the i_0 values, the purely kinetic parameters, which are not determined by thermodynamics.

† In some corrosion systems this might not be true, as in the example of large macro-systems of the ship hull and propeller. If necessary, it can be taken into account.

A simple calculation can show numerically what can be the effects of $V_{e,cell}$, and i_0.

Let us take the example of zinc corrosion, and assume that $\alpha_a = \alpha_c = 0{\cdot}5$. The largest practical value of $V_{e,cell}$, can be about 1·5 V, if one changes to oxygen reduction as the cathodic reaction instead of hydrogen evolution. The change of the rate of corrosion, if all the other parameters are constant, can be calculated by using equation (9.11):

$$\Delta i_{corr} = \exp \Delta V_{e,cell}\,(F/RT)(\alpha_a \alpha_c/(\alpha_a + \alpha_c)) = \exp \frac{1{\cdot}5}{0{\cdot}06} \cdot \frac{1}{4}$$

Thus, change of 1·5 V increases the rate of corrosion about one thousand times.

Now, let us try to see the effect of a change of kinetic factors. The exchange current density for H_2 evolution, $i_{0,c}$, on impure zinc (as the technical product often is) can be as high as $1\ \mathrm{A\,m^{-2}}$, while on an amalgamated (i.e., mixed with mercury) zinc surface it can be very low, 10^{-6}–$10^{-8}\ \mathrm{A\,m^{-2}}$. If we use again equation (9.11), to see the effect of a change in the cathodic exchange current density, $i_{0,c}$, from 10^{-8} to $1\ \mathrm{A\,m^{-2}}$, i.e., an increase of 10^8 times, then:

$$\frac{i_{corr,\ impure}}{i_{corr,\ amalg}} = (10^8)^{\frac{1}{2}/\frac{1}{2}+\frac{1}{2}} = 10^4$$

The rate of corrosion of impure zinc can be 10 000 times larger than that of amalgamated zinc. In battery production, the zinc container for primary batteries and zinc electrodes for silver–zinc and other batteries are hence usually amalgamated to keep the corrosion of metallic zinc at a very low rate. There is no better way of destroying a zinc battery than to put into the battery electrolyte some salt containing ions of a metal with high i_0 for H_2 evolution. The zinc electrodes will corrode away in half a day.

The influences of the various parameters in equation (9.11) are illustrated in figs. 9.5 *a*, *b* and *c*.

From the kinetic equations for the anodic and cathodic processes (eqns. (3.25) and (3.26)) we can predict the value of the corrosion potential as well.

At the corrosion potential, both anodic and cathodic current densities are equal. Therefore, using equations (3.25) and (3.26), and instead of η_a, $V_{corr} - V_{e,a}$ (see fig. 9.4); and instead of η_c, $V_{corr} - V_{e,c}$, we can write the equation

$$i_{0,a} \exp\,(\alpha_a F/RT)(V_{corr} - V_{e,a}) = i_{0,c} \exp\,(-\alpha_c F/RT)(V_{corr} - V_{e,c}). \tag{9.12}$$

By rearrangement, we can obtain an approximate value for V_{corr} as:

$$V_{corr} = \frac{RT}{(\alpha_a + \alpha_c)F} \ln \frac{i_{0,c}}{i_{0,a}} + \frac{\alpha_a}{\alpha_a + \alpha_c} V_{e,a} + \frac{\alpha_c}{\alpha_a + \alpha_c} V_{e,c}. \tag{9.13}$$

The exchange current densities have a determining role in deciding the real value of the corrosion potential. By a less approximate development of the equation for V_{corr}, it can be shown that if $i_{0,c} \gg i_{0,a}$ the corrosion potential is very close to the equilibrium cathodic potential, $V_{\text{e},c}$, while when $i_{0,c} \ll i_{0,a}$ the corrosion potential is very close to the

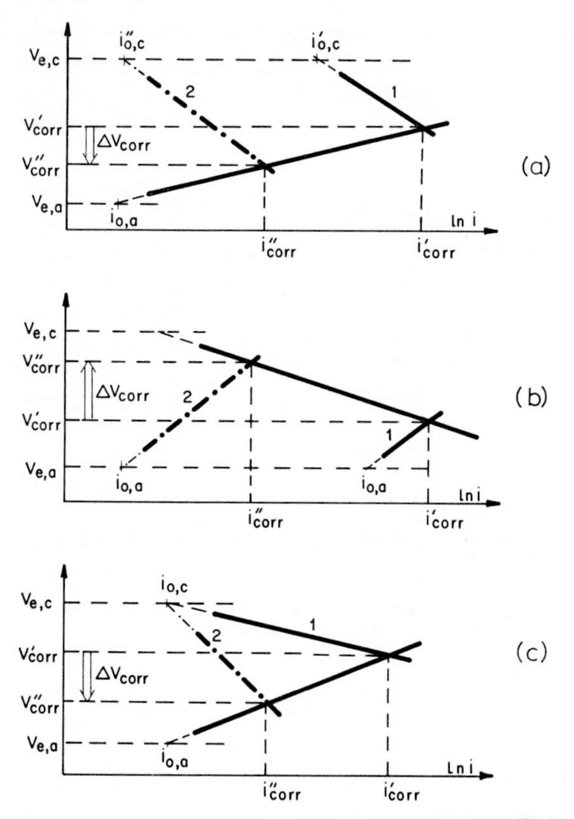

Fig. 9.5. Effects of changes from conditions (1) to conditions (2) in three cases: (*a*) If the exchange current density, i_0, for the cathodic reaction is decreased, the rate of corrosion is decreased, and V_{corr} becomes more negative. (*b*) If i_0 for the anodic reaction is decreased the rate of corrosion is decreased, but V_{cor} becomes more positive. (*c*) If the mechanism of the cathodic reaction is changed, and the gradient ($= RT/\alpha_c F$) increased, the rate of corrosion will decreased, and V_{corr} will become more negative.

equilibrium anodic potential, $V_{\text{e},a}$. This is the reason why we can measure approximately the 'equilibrium' potential of a zinc electrode in zinc sulphate solution, and why it changes with zinc sulphate concentration according to Nernst's equation, although corrosion is slowly occurring.

For zinc, $i_{0,\mathrm{Zn}} = 10\ \mathrm{A\,m^{-2}}$ while the corresponding value of $i_{0,c}$ for H_2 evolution in neutral (pH = 7) zinc sulphate solution is probably less than $10^{-2}\ \mathrm{A\,m^{-2}}$. If $\alpha_a = \alpha_c = 0{\cdot}5$, T = 25°C,

$$V_{\mathrm{corr}} = \frac{2{\cdot}3RT}{F} \log \frac{10^{-2}}{10} + 0{\cdot}5(-0{\cdot}780) + 0{\cdot}5(-0{\cdot}420)$$

$$= -0{\cdot}180 - 0{\cdot}390 - 0{\cdot}210 \approx -0{\cdot}780\ \mathrm{V}.$$

Thus, the zinc electrode potential observed during corrosion is not the equilibrium, thermodynamic value, but a corrosion potential close to the equilibrium potential, i.e., $V_{\mathrm{Zn}} \approx V_{\mathrm{e,Zn}}$. Conversely, if $(i_0)_c \simeq (i_0)_a$, the steady state corrosion potential will be in between $V_{\mathrm{e},a}$ and $V_{\mathrm{e},c}$.

Consideration of the calculation

In the above calculation, it must be stressed that we have taken every simplifying option possible, and we would have to force real circumstances into something which obeyed those we have assumed.

(1) We have assumed that, for the circumstances chosen, the corrosion potential occurs at more than 20 mV away from the equilibrium region for either of the two electrode processes making up a corrosion process—both the electrode process in which electrons leave the metal, and the one which is the actual dissolution (corrosion) step, in which atoms give electrons back to the metal. This is a mathematically simplifying step, if it is not made, 9.11 is not true.

(2) We have assumed that there are no oxide films upon the metal, because such films complicate the theoretical equations, even though they can be taken into account. This is sometimes the case, more often in alkaline solutions than in acid solutions.

(3) We have assumed that only one cathodic reaction (e.g., hydrogen evolution) takes place. In fact, oxygen reduction in a corroding situation often takes place simultaneously or exclusively (fig. 9.6).

There is no mystery about the calculation which we did above; only simplification due to the taking of a series of specially easy cases.

The place of thermodynamic calculations in corrosion: that they are always right, but often fruitless

In place of the kinetic theory of corrosion currents, and an ability to account for corrosion in terms of particles and solid state physics, the published doctrine of corrosion theory is very largely thermodynamic. A 'solid thermodynamic basis', it is called. Let us see what this means.

If we are going to have a reaction occurring spontaneously, it is a well known rule from chemical thermodynamics that the free energy of the overall reaction must be negative, or $V_{\mathrm{e,cell}}$ positive ($-\Delta G = nFV_{\mathrm{e}}$).

The Nernst equation (eqn. (3.36 *a*)) applied to the overall corrosion reaction of nickel, for example

$$Ni + 2H^+ \rightarrow Ni^{2+} + H_2 \tag{9.14}$$

is

$$V_{e,cell} = V^\circ_{e,cell} + \frac{RT}{2F} \ln \frac{c_{H^+}}{c_{Ni^{2+}}}, \tag{9.15}$$

or,†

$$V_{e,cell} = V^\circ_{e,cell} - \frac{2{\cdot}3RT}{F}\,pH - \frac{2{\cdot}3RT}{2F} \log c_{Ni^{2+}}. \tag{9.16}$$

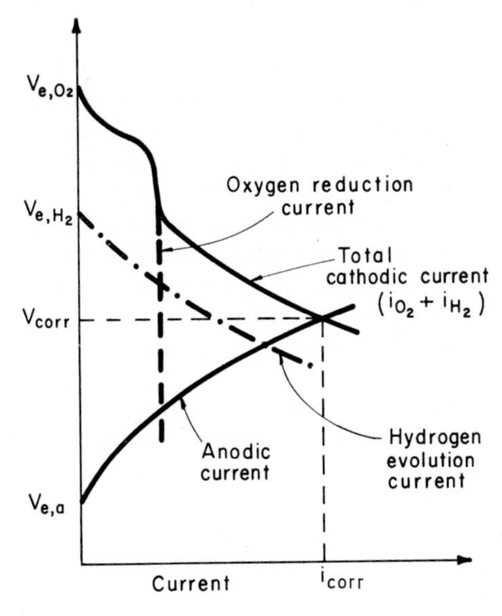

Fig. 9.6. Corrosion diagram when oxygen reduction and hydrogen evolution reactions occur together as often happens in acid solutions.

Hence, one can calculate the necessary conditions (concentration of Ni^{2+} and H^+ or pH) for $V_{e,cell}$ to be positive. For example, if $C_{Ni^{2+}} = 1$ M, corrosion is possible if $V_{e,cell} > 0$. We shall calculate the critical pH for the beginning of corrosion using equation (9.16) by putting $V_{e,cell} = 0$, and taking into account that for $C_{Ni^{2+}} = 1$ M, $\log C_{Ni^{2+}} = 0$.

Thus,

$$\frac{2{\cdot}3RT}{F}\,pH = V^\circ_{e,cell} = V^\circ_{e,H_2} - V^\circ_{e,Ni}. \tag{9.17}$$

From the Table of standard equilibrium potentials (see Table 5.3), (equilibrium potentials in 1 M solutions), one finds that

† To remind the reader, $pH = -\log c_{H^+}$.

$V^{\circ}{}_{e,Ni} = -0{\cdot}25$ V, and $V^{\circ}{}_{e,H_2} = 0$. Hence, since $2{\cdot}3RT/F = 0{\cdot}06$ V at 298 K, we can calculate the largest pH in which hydrogen corrosion is possible.

$$\text{pH} = (V^{\circ}{}_{e,H} - V^{\circ}{}_{e,Ni}) \frac{F}{2{\cdot}3RT} = \frac{0{\cdot}25}{0{\cdot}06} = 4{\cdot}11. \qquad (9.18)$$

Therefore, thermodynamically, if the pH is higher than 4·11, nickel cannot corrode, if it is below 4·11, it can corrode.

Thus, the suggestion is that one should firstly find out at what pH corrosion should begin to occur from the thermodynamic approach by plotting the reversible potential of hydrogen as a function of pH and finding where the free energy of the reaction for the dissolution of nickel, iron, etc., with evolution of hydrogen, becomes negative (or the corrosion cell voltage, $V_{e,cell}$, positive, as in the above example). A good analogy, which shows the limitation of treating corrosion thermodynamically, would be the situation in which one lined up a series of gasoline fuels, to determine their relative values as fuels. If one followed the guidance of thermodynamics, one would choose those with the largest free energy change as the ones which would burn most quickly with O_2. A surprise would await one if one did this, for the free energy of combustion of benzene with oxygen at room temperature is already negative, so that, on these grounds, benzene should take off, in flame, directly it is exposed to air.

For one cannot judge the velocity of a happening from its thermodynamics. Velocity, or the current which is its equivalent, is what counts in corrosion. Even the most academic technologist isn't interested in a case of corrosion that is indicated thermodynamically, but which will only take place significantly in a million years. It is the old story of electrochemistry before about 1950, the stress on Nernstian thermodynamics. Part of the treatment of corrosion in practice is still in the grip of it. The New Electrochemistry tells one, it is time to change.

Some qualitative conclusions from the kinetic theory of corrosion

Let us go back to equation (9.11) for the corrosion rate under the simplified conditions.†

$$i_{corr} = i_{0,a}{}^{\alpha_c/\alpha_a+\alpha_c} i_{0,c}{}^{\alpha_a/\alpha_c+\alpha_a} \exp \frac{\alpha_a \alpha_c}{\alpha_a+\alpha_c} \frac{F}{RT} V_{e,cell}. \qquad (9.11)$$

and try to see, at least qualitatively, what are the practical consequences for the real corrosion processes.‡

† More general equations for complex situations can be derived, the qualitative conclusions remain the same.

‡ One of the approximations used in the deduction of (9.11) was a neglect of the cathodic contribution to the anodic current (i.e., redeposition of metal) and the anodic contribution to the cathodic current, (e.g., evolution of oxygen). It is for this reason that i_{corr} is not zero for V_{corr} − ve from (9.11), which only applies well (apart from the effect of other simplifications) if $(i_0)_a$ and $(i_0)_c$ are not so very greatly different that the corrosion potential is almost the same as the reversible potential.

The pH of the solution can have a considerable role in determining the real value of $V_{e,cell}$, and through it whether the corrosion is possible or not. The larger $V_{e,cell}$, the higher will be i_{corr}. But this is not the only effect of pH on the corrosion rate. It has been established by kinetic experiments that exchange current densities, i_0, for hydrogen evolution, and also for some metals, like iron, cobalt, nickel, zinc, etc., are pH dependent. For hydrogen evolution on iron it is:

$$i_{0,H} = i^{\circ}_{0,H} \cdot c_{H}^{+0\cdot5};$$

and for iron dissolution; $i_{0,Fe} = i^{\circ}_{0,Fe} \cdot c_{Fe^{2+}} \cdot c_{OH^-}$ (i°_0) is the standard exchange current density at concentrations equal to unity). pH has an effect on both the thermodynamic (V_e) and kinetic (i_0) factors in 9.11.

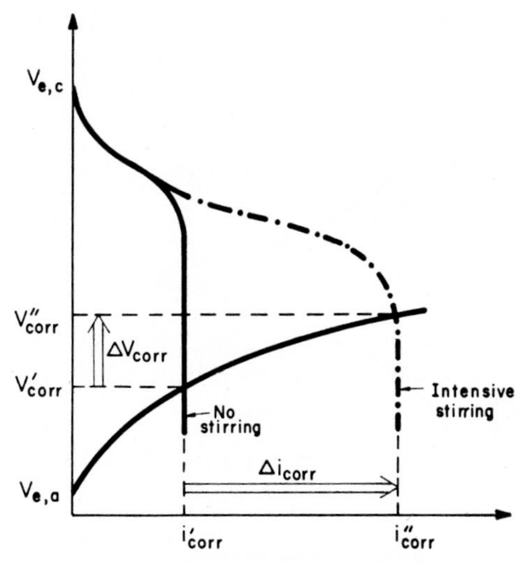

Fig. 9.7. If the concentration of cathodically reducing species in the solution is low, the rate of corrosion equals the limiting diffusion current. Stirring may increase the rate of corrosion considerably.

For pH values higher than +3, an additional complication can arise, particularly if i_0 values are large. If the rate of corrosion, as calculated using equation (9.11), is larger than the rate of diffusion of H^+ ions to the metal surface, it is obvious that the rate of corrosion will become controlled by the rate of supply of H^+ ions to the metal (fig. 9.7). The corrosion current is equal to the limiting current for the hydrogen evolution reaction (eqn. (4.8))

$$i_{corr} = i_c = \frac{F \cdot D \cdot c_{H^+}}{\delta} \qquad (9.18)$$

c_{H^+}, being the hydrogen ion concentration.

In this case, the rate of corrosion will depend on the mass-transport conditions in the solution (see Chapter 4), and intensive stirring can increase the rate of corrosion substantially. This situation often occurs when the reduction of oxygen (from air) dissolved in water is the cathodic step of the two electrochemical corrosion couple (solubility of O_2 in water is about 10^{-4} mol^{-1}).

The presence of redox ions in the solution, like iron (II) and iron (III) ions, may have a considerable influence on the increase of the oxygen corrosion reaction rate. A low exchange current density, i_{0,O_2}, for the oxygen reduction reaction and a low concentration of oxygen, keeps the corrosion induced by oxygen reduction at a relatively low rate. However, oxygen can easily oxidize iron (II) ions homogeneously in the

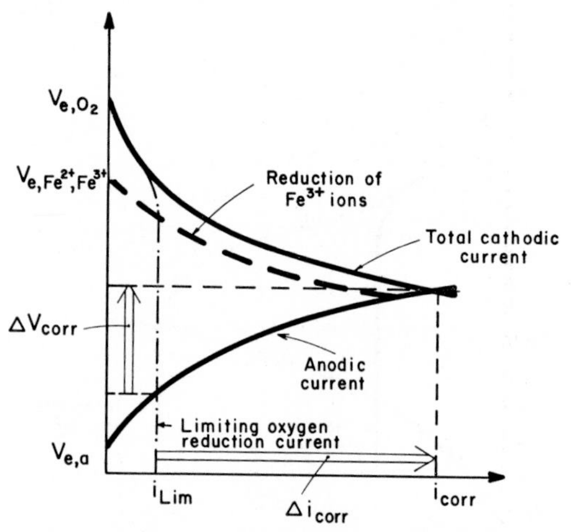

Fig. 9.8. Fe^{3+} ions in the bulk of the solution may increase the rate of corrosion far above that corresponding to the limiting oxygen reduction current.

solution. Even though the reversible potential for $Fe^{3+} \rightarrow Fe^{2+}$ reduction is more negative ($V_{e,Fe^{3+},Fe^{2+}} = +0{\cdot}77$ V) than for oxygen ($V_{e,O_2} = +1{\cdot}23$ V) and consequently $V_{e,cell}$ in equation (9.11) smaller, the effective rate of corrosion, using $Fe^{3+} + e \rightarrow Fe^{2+}$ as the cathodic reaction, can be much larger since $i_{0,Fe^{3+},Fe^{2+}}$ is very large (about 10^1 A m^{-2}) and the concentration of Fe^{3+} ions much larger than that of oxygen (so that, there are no mass-transport limitations). Figure 9.8 illustrates the possible situation.

Of great practical importance is the dependence of $i_{0,a}$ and $i_{0,c}$ on the composition of the solution in which a metal corrodes. Many groups of organic substances, including various amines, pyridine, quinoline, thiourea and similar compounds, are *adsorbed* at the metal surface (see p. 74) and decrease considerably the value of i_0 for the anodic or cathodic reaction, or both. These substances are known as corrosion inhibitors since, as shown in figs. 9.9 *a* and *b*, they decrease the rate of corrosion. Some inorganic compounds have a similar inhibiting effect (phosphates, chromates) and are important additives for corrosion protection. For example liquids, used in cars as coolants, must contain inhibitors, otherwise corrosion will be very rapid.†

Some metals can become passive, i.e, the rate of dissolution, or effective equivalent $i_{0,a}$, becomes so low that the overall rate of corrosion can be 10^4–10^5 times lower in the passive state than it would be, if the passivation did not occur. Passivation will be discussed on p. 259.

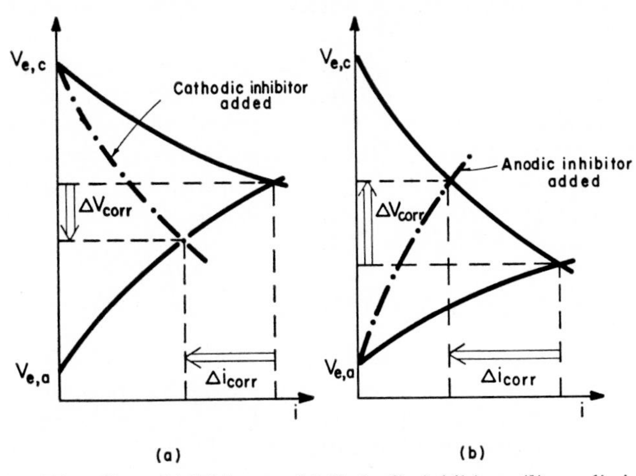

Fig. 9.9. The effect of inhibitors. (*a*) Cathodic inhibitor, (*b*) anodic inhibitor.

The reason for many corrosion processes is differential aeration, a different rate of supply of oxygen to different parts of a single piece of corroding metal; for example, a long iron pile immersed vertically in deep water. An explanation often used is that, deep down in water, there is less oxygen dissolved than there is near the surface, producing a kind of oxygen concentration cell between the upper and lower part of the pile, with potential difference, according to the Nernst equation,

$$V_{e,\text{cell}} = \frac{RT}{4F} \ln \frac{c'_{O_2}}{c''_{O_2}}. \tag{9.19}$$

c'_{O_2} and c''_{O_2} are the corresponding concentrations of O_2 near the surface and deep in water, respectively. Since $c''_{O_2} < c'_{O_2}$, the lower part is

† In the cooling system of a car, parts made of different materials are connected together: cylinders (steel), engine-block (cast iron or aluminium alloy), water-pump (aluminium alloy), radiator (copper), etc. Such a series of metals, in contact with a liquid, make up a series of corrosion cells (cathodic and anodic couples) independently of the presence of cathodic reactions due to H^+ discharge or O_2 reduction.

more negative and therefore is the anode of the corroding cell, and the conclusion was that it should corrode faster than the upper part. In fact this actually happens, but for quite different reasons. Because, qualitatively, the thermodynamic prediction seems to be correct, the concentration cell argument is still being used, even though the argument is not correct, and the real reasons are ignored.

Let us see what the real cause of differential aeration is. If we take a piece of iron and put it in a beaker, as shown in fig. 9.1, containing a solution with a small concentration of oxygen (we can bubble air at low rate through the solution), iron will corrode and have some corrosion potential V'_{corr}. If we do the same with another piece of iron of the same size and composition, but bubble more air through the solution, the corrosion potential will be more positive, V''_{corr}, and the rate of corrosion larger ($i''_{corr} > i'_{corr}$). However, if we connect these two iron pieces by a wire with negligible electric resistance, as shown in fig. 9.2, a new corrosion cell will be formed and current will flow through the external wire. The corrosion potential of each piece of iron is changed, and a new corrosion potential, V_{corr}, equal for both iron pieces, will be established. Since the anodic dissolution rate can be expressed in the form (eqn. (9.12))

$$i_a = i_{corr} = i_{0,a} \exp [(V_{corr} - V_{e,a})\alpha_a F/RT] \qquad (9.19)$$

it is obvious that since V_{corr} is the same at both iron pieces, then both pieces must corrode at the same rate per cm^2, but not with a higher rate at the less aerated sample, as claimed before. If the resistance in the circuit is increased, in other words, the *IR* drop is no longer negligible, the less aerated sample will dissolve at a lesser rate than the one with better aeration.

What causes the current we observe when the two samples are connected together? By connecting them together, the corrosion potential of the less aerated sample has become more positive than before ($V'_{corr} < V_{corr}$), and therefore the corrosion rate is increased from i'_{corr} to i_{corr}. Simultaneously, the corrosion potential of the more aerated sample has become more negative ($V''_{corr} > V_{corr}$), and therefore its corrosion rate is decreased from i''_{corr} to i_{corr}. It is this equalizing action which produces the current flow, the external current being equal to the *increase* of corrosion rate of the less aerated sample, or *decrease* of corrosion rate or more aerated sample. The electrons liberated at the more positive V_{corr} cannot be consumed in full quantity because of lack of oxygen at the less aerated sample, and therefore they go through the wire to the piece where there is plenty of oxygen to react with. Thus, the connection of two separate pieces of metal into one redistributes the rates of corrosion, making previously unequal rates equal over the surface, no matter what the local concentration of oxygen. Only if oxygen affects the metal surface so that the dissolution properties are changed ($i_{0,a}$ decreased), is it possible to have a larger rate of corrosion at less aerated parts. We can finish this discussion by concluding that differential aeration is not a general phenomenon creating larger corrosion of the less aerated part of the metal as the 'thermodynamic' concentration cell argument predicts, but rather one which makes the rates of corrosion of both parts of the metal equal, by increasing the rate of corrosion of one part and decreasing the rate of corrosion of the other part. Only if oxygen produces some inhibiting (or even passivating) effect on the dissolution rate ($i_{0,a}$) at more aerated parts, will the less aerated part corrode faster, as is sometimes† observed.

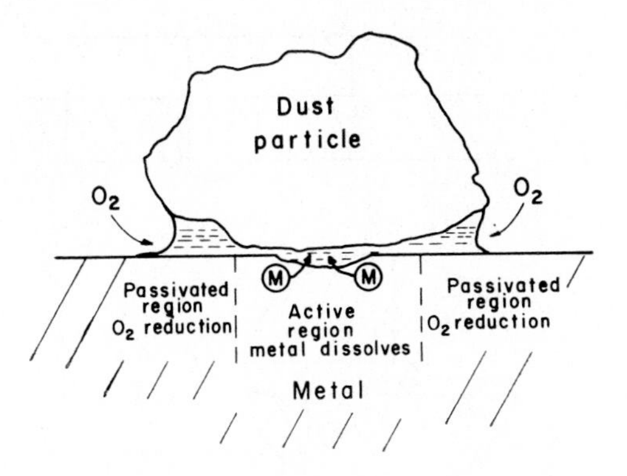

Fig. 9.10. Corrosion under a dust particle or water droplet is often faster in the central area due to the passivating effect of an oxygen-rich solution near the edge.

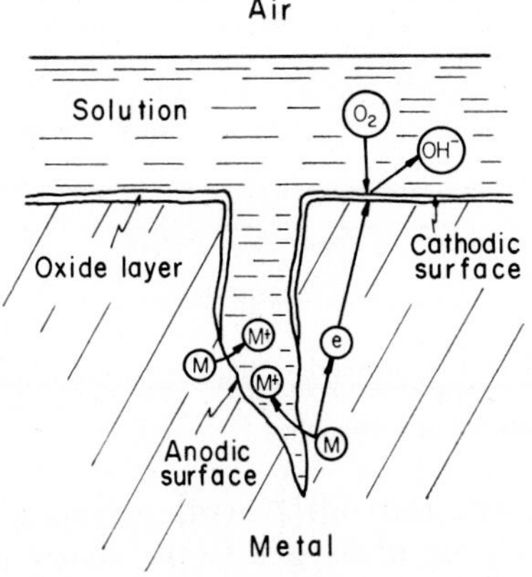

Fig. 9.11. Schematic representation of corrosion inside a crevice. A thin oxide layer provides a cathodic surface for oxygen reduction by electrons liberated by the dissolution of metal inside the crevice.

† The accelerating effect of differential aeration on the corrosion of less aerated parts is not a general phenomenon. For example, it can be observed in river and lake waters, but not in sea water (Cl^- ions prevent passivation!).

Practical Cases of Corrosion

Corrosion of metals develops in different ways, depending on the environment.

A common case is when a particle of dust falls onto iron. By capillary condensation, water vapour from air forms a thin water layer under the particle, and since polluted air contains SO_2, and CO_2, the water absorbs the gases and becomes an electrolyte. The same situation arises if water droplets find themselves on the metal surface. The metal part, covered with electrolyte containing oxygen or, if the NO

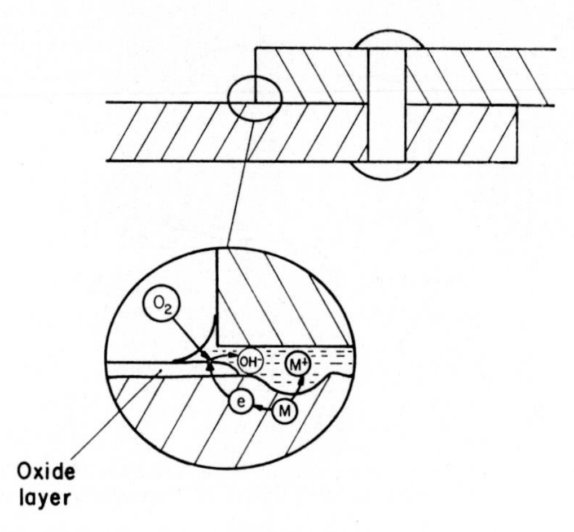

Fig. 9.12. Corrosion at the joint of two metal plates is often localized inside the crevice.

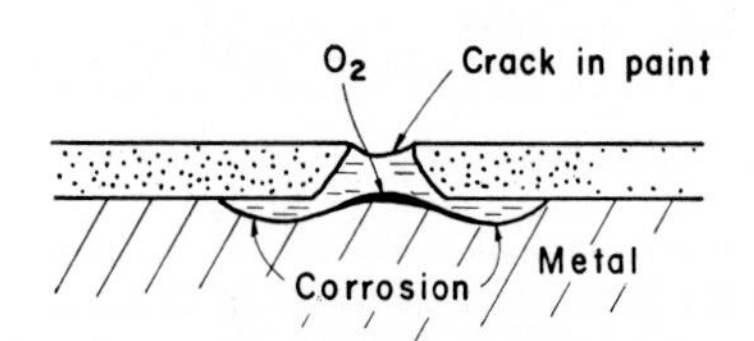

Fig. 9.13. At a crack in the protective paint, corrosion usually develops under the paint, where there is a lack of oxygen. It is the (invisible) part under the paint that becomes anodic and dissolves.

concentration is high, the nitric acid, corrodes under the particle. Due to the lesser supply of oxygen to the centre portion of corroding surface, and the greater amount of oxygen at the edge of the droplet, the dissolution of the metal occurs in the middle part of the drop, not at the edge. The result is accelerated corrosion in the centre of the wet surface (fig. 9.10). Similar situations arise in cases of corrosion shown in figs. 9.11 and 9.12, for the accelerated corrosion in crevices when the outer part, in better contact with air, is covered with a thin oxide layer, electronically conducting, on which the cathodic reduction of oxygen occurs, while the inner, unprotected part corrodes.

One more example is the scratch or hole in protective paint (see fig. 9.13) on a metallic construction (e.g., a car body, bridge, etc.), when most of the corrosion happens not at the exposed metallic surface but under the paint.

An often-quoted example of the effect of differential aeration (differences in supply of oxygen to different parts of a metal surface) is the corrosion of underground pipe-lines going through various kinds of soil, for example a dense clay and porous sand as shown in fig. 9.14. The part buried in clay corrodes faster than the part in sand because of the formation of a macro-corrosion cell with corrosion currents of up to 5 A going through the pipe. However, it is not the oxygen concentration cell effect, as often claimed, which accelerates the corrosion of a pipe in clay, but a different anodic dissolution rate (i.e., different $i_{0,a}$) for iron in the wet (and perhaps more acidic) clay, from that in porous,

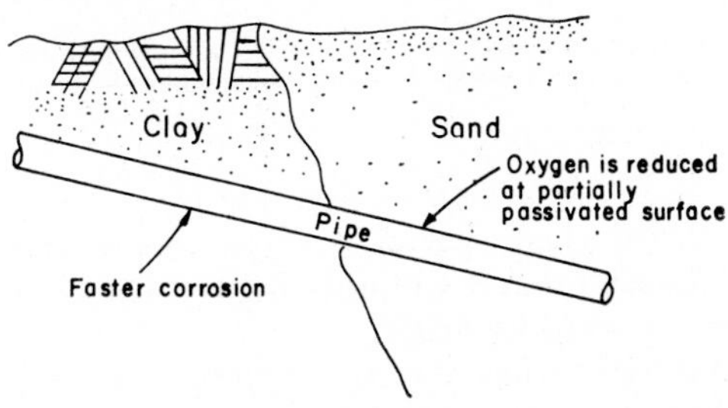

Fig. 9.14. An underground pipe-line can corrode faster in wet and dense clay than in porous, sandy, soil, since oxygen has better access through the sand.

often more dry, sand soil. This effect produces the corrosion cell, and if the supply of oxygen through porous sand is sufficient, the pipe surface will partially or completely passivate, serving as a more or less inert cathode in the electrochemical cell, pipe in sand–pipe in clay, thus accelerating the corrosion of that part of the pipe in clay.

Two more common examples of corrosion systems are shown in fig. 9.15. One occurs in the canning industry when tin-covered iron sheets are used for can production. If for any reason, by corrosion or mechanically, a hole develops in the tin layer, a corrosion cell is formed between the tin layer and iron at the bottom of the hole. Since the iron corrosion potential is more negative than the potential of tin, the iron behaves as the anode of the corrosion cell, dissolves, and a hole in the sheet may appear. In another case, with galvanized iron sheets, when the outer layer is zinc with a more negative corrosion potential than that for iron, the hole in the zinc layer is not so dangerous as that in the previous case. In the corrosion cell formed, the zinc is the anode, and iron the cathode, so that most of the corrosion is localized at the zinc surface, i.e., zinc corrodes instead of iron. Zinc has a protective effect. The iron can be saved by sacrificing zinc. This principle is used for protection of some underwater constructions and for the protection of ships. The parts to be protected are connected with pieces of zinc or other metals or alloys having a more negative corrosion potential than the metal to be protected. The cheap zinc corrodes, and the ship, etc., remains relatively cathodic, and hence protected against corrosion.

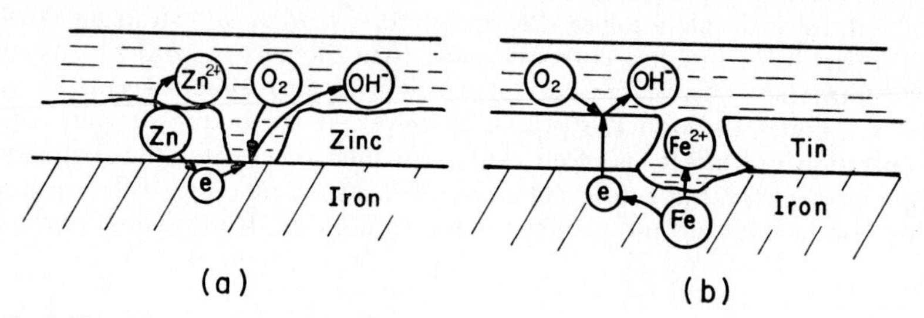

Fig. 9.15. (*a*) Iron is protected from corrosion by a layer of zinc, even if this is not homogeneous. (*b*) However, iron corrodes wherever a crack in a tin layer develops.

Passivation

Passivation occurs when a metal, without visible change, changes its surface properties such that it will not dissolve when placed in solution, and is no longer attacked by acids.

This is natural passivation, the sort of thing that happens if one puts a piece of iron into rather concentrated, nitric acid. Suddenly the iron is 'in a different condition' and it will no longer dissolve in another acid, say, sulphuric acid.

Now, we can induce the same kind of behaviour and, therefore presumably the same kind of state of the metal's surface—at will—with a potentiostat. We can control the potential of the electrode in such a way that its potential is more positive, the extent being chosen at will. If we do, and record the corresponding values of the anodic current as a function of the potential we apply, we get a curve of the type shown in fig. 9.16.

Some of this curve can immediately be described. In the first part, A–B, of fig. 9.16, there is just anodic dissolution of iron. That this dissolution does not continue unimpeded for much of an anodic potential change arises from the fact that the i–V relation does not continue (see fig. 9.16) in the same exponential shape which one would expect for the dissolution of metals, which is that of fig. 9.3. Some dramatic happening must occur at the peak (at B) of the current–potential relation of fig. 9.16 when, with the help of our potentiostat, we push the potential past a critical amount, called the passivation potential. We find that now, instead of increasing, the current violently decreases, as shown in fig. 9.16. It dies, or almost dies, after the current has got down to C; it changes little as we increase the potential further. Indeed, we may go on increasing the potential for perhaps one-half of one volt until we reach the thermodynamic value of the evolution potential for oxygen (1·23 V more positive than the hydrogen equilibrium potential), when oxygen evolution will begin, due to the fact that water is being oxidized, i.e., $2H_2O \rightarrow O_2+4H^++4e$.

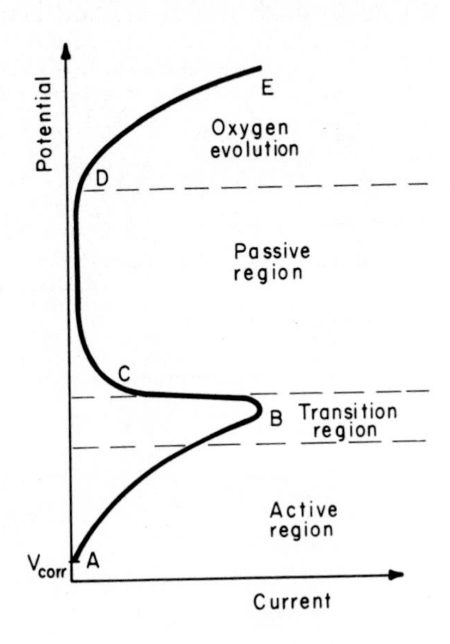

Fig. 9.16. Passivation.

The mechanism of passivation

Views on this have varied between two extremes. At the one extreme, it is considered that the blockage of individual kink sites upon the metal by oncoming hydroxyl ions or some other oxygen-containing particle (OH^- or even O^{2-}, (fig. 9.17), encouraged to adsorb on the metal by the increasingly positive potential) stops the metal ions from breaking free from the surface of the metal, diffusing across the surface of the metal, and going into solution. That alone is enough to cause passivation. But there are difficulties for this view, because the concentration of ions necessary to block the kink sites in the metal would be about 0·01–0·1% of that necessary for full coverage. It would be difficult to determine any oxide on the metal at the point of passivation. But it is known that there is oxide, at least a monolayer, at the current peak on fig. 9.16.

Another extreme view is that the metal dissolves in the solution and the concentration of its ions increases until the solubility product of one of the metal's hydroxides is exceeded. This precipitates (as shown in fig. 9.18), forming a jelly-like layer on the metal, in which (and as the potentiostat makes the potential of the electrode more positive) some change—for example the introduction of non-stoichiometry—occurs at the actual potential of passivation, the peak of the current–potential curve in fig. 9.16. Thereafter, the current decreases; for the non-stoichiometry introduces the possibility of electronic conduction. The metal ions no longer go through the oxide, and hence no metal ions

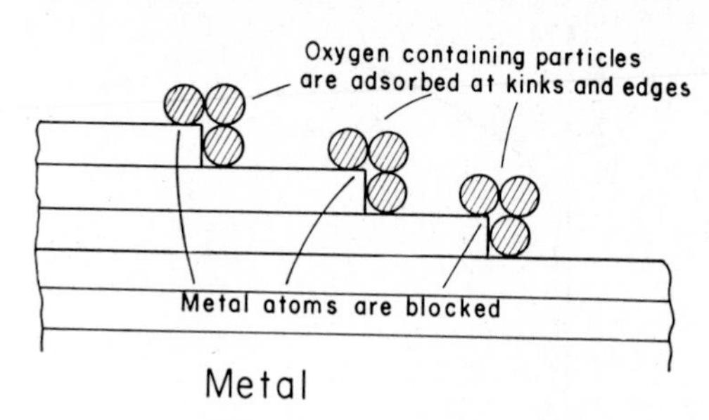

Fig. 9.17. Illustrating the adsorption–passivation theory.

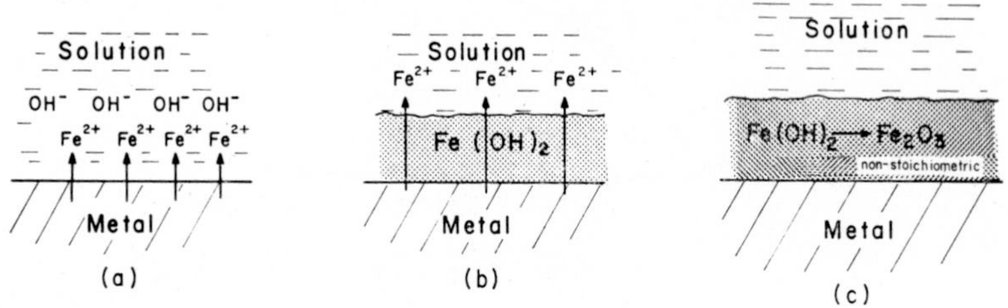

Fig. 9.18. Illustrating the precipitation-and-passive-layer-formation theory, when the local concentration of Fe^{2+} ions near the dissolving metal (*a*) exceeds the solubility product of $Fe(OH)_2$, a layer of hydroxide forms (*b*), but since it is porous, the metal still dissolves. The passivation occurs when the hydroxide is transformed to the higher valent, probably non-stoichiometric, oxide (*c*).

dissolve. They stop leaving their electrons in the metal behind the oxide and the current falls.

These two theories have been examined by work with a machine called an 'ellipsometer'. This is a device which shines polarized light on to the metal while it is being passivated. At first one looks at the light reflected off the electrode surface at a potential where no oxide film forms. One notes, for example, the characteristics of the light; what change in phase, Δ, it undergoes when it reflects off the surface of the metal, and how the amplitude of one of its phases, ψ, varies due to absorption of some of the light by the metal.

The oxide is then induced to form, and the changes in the amplitude of the light, and its change of phase, are again measured.

At the same time, a cathodic current is passed across the surface of the passivated oxide and one can find out (cf. the example given earlier with hydrogen on platinum, p. 124) how many Fe^{2+} and Fe^{3+} ions in the oxide per m^2 are on the electrode.

From this information, it is possible to determine (i) the thickness of the film as a function of potential; (ii) what the refractive index of the film is, thus identifying the oxide present; and (iii) something about the absorption of light in the film—its spectroscopy.

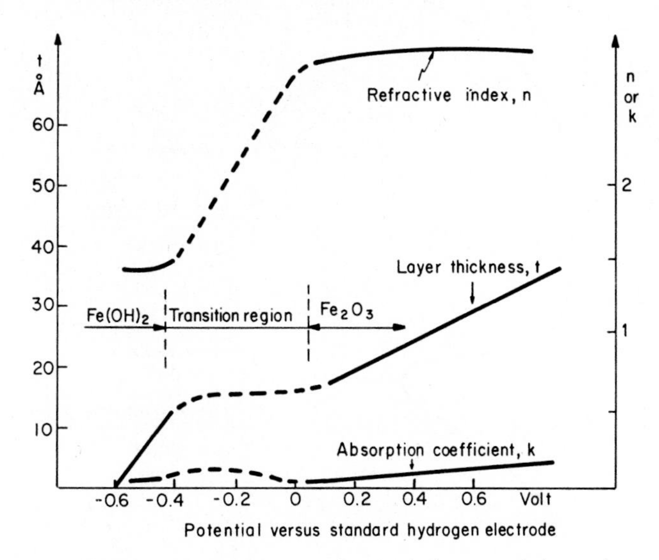

Fig. 9.19. Variation of layer thickness, t, refractive index, n, and absorption coefficient, k, with electrode potential, as determined ellipsometrically. Iron in borate buffer solution of pH = 8·4.

What does this information tell us? The results are shown in fig. 9.19.

At first a film forms on the surface of the metal in the region A–B (cf. fig. 9.20); but it is a thin one, probably patches or clumps of oxide, because there is still some dissolution of the iron along with the formation of a film. At the peak, the monolayer oxide covers nearly all the surface. But at the peak of the current–potential relation (fig. 9.20) something else begins to happen, a change in structure of the oxide; the formation of a new kind of oxide begins. Whether this new oxide forms on top of the old monolayer, or whether it is a transformation of it, is as yet a moot point.

What is the actual cause of passivation? For iron, the simple answer seems essentially to be: 'blocking of the pure iron surface by a monolayer of oxide'. Is there nothing more to it than that? We really don't know whether this formation of the higher oxide which forms after the peak is an essential in forcing the current down, or not; at the present time, it seems not.

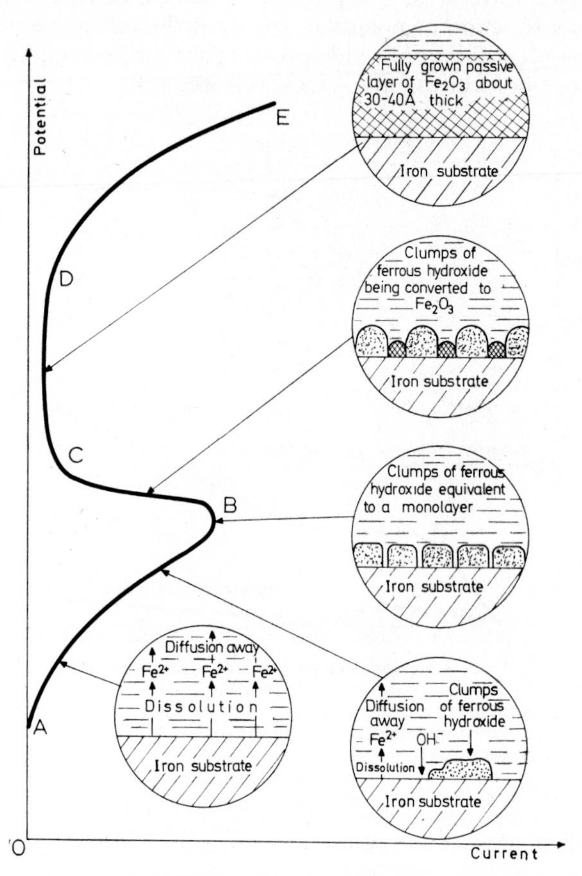

Fig. 9.20. Genshaw–Brusic–Bockris model of formation of passive layer on iron

Self-passivation

We have described, on the basis of ellipsometric calculations, the situation with respect to a passivation stimulated in the laboratory, where the potentiostat controls the potential and we can take a look at what is happening at any time. What we are now interested in is self-passivation, which occurs by means of the natural action of materials in contact with solution.

It is easy to see how this may happen. Iron dissolves anodically with a rather unusual shape of potential–current dependence (fig. 9.16), with passivation occurring at a certain characteristic potential depending on the metal and surrounding solution. So the only necessary condition for passivation is that somehow the potential of the metal be adjusted to be more positive than that of the peak potential on the passivation curve. In the potentiostatic experiment an outside instrument drained electrons from the iron, but we might use other means. Why not form a cell in which iron is the anode, and a piece of platinum (supplied with oxygen) is the cathode? The reduction of oxygen on platinum will consume electrons from the metal and the cell will behave as a self-driving corrosion cell. The cell should correspond to the usual corrosion cell, and if short-circuited, the common corrosion

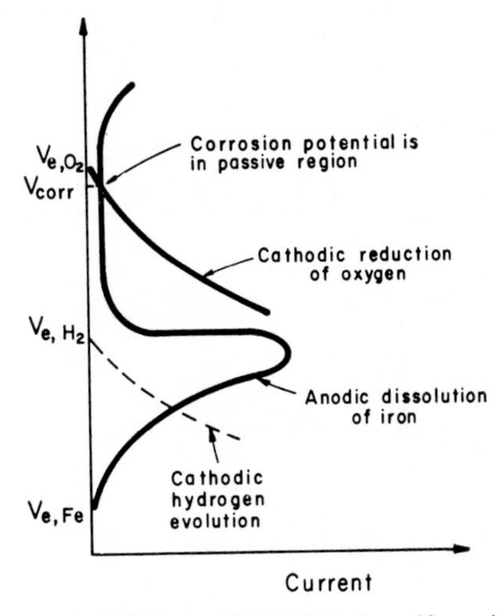

Fig. 9.21. Corrosion diagram illustrating the self-passivation of iron.

potential should be established at both electrodes. Figure 9.21 differs from fig. 9.3 only in the shape of the anodic dissolution curve for iron. In this case it is a typical passivation curve. The intersection of the cathodic current–potential line for oxygen dissolution and the anodic current–potential line for iron dissolution, determines the corrosion potential. If it is in the potential region of passivity for iron, the necessary conditions for ferrous oxide film formation and passivity exist, the iron will spontaneously passivate. The iron can be easily depassivated by replacing oxygen at the platinum electrode with hydrogen (the equilibrium potential of which is more negative by about 1·2 V), when the intersection point of the anodic dissolution line and the cathodic, hydrogen evolution line is more negative than the potential peak; in other words, in the region of active metal dissolution.

The passive film on iron and other metals is not a complete insulator, but an electronic conductor. Therefore, at the passive surface oxygen reduction can proceed, but with a different rate than on bare metal. Consequently, the electrochemical reaction of the cathodic reduction of oxygen can proceed on a passivated surface as well. Hence, the self-passivated iron can be regarded as any other piece of corroding iron with corrosion potential and corrosion current determined by the intersection point of the cathodic reduction curve for oxygen and the anodic dissolution curve for iron (cf. fig. 9.3). If it happens that the curves intersect in the passive region of the iron dissolution curve, iron will become passive, and thereafter it will corrode at a far slower rate than active iron. The self-passivation of iron is enforced by the oxygen reduction reaction, which brings the corrosion potential into the passive region (fig. 9.20).

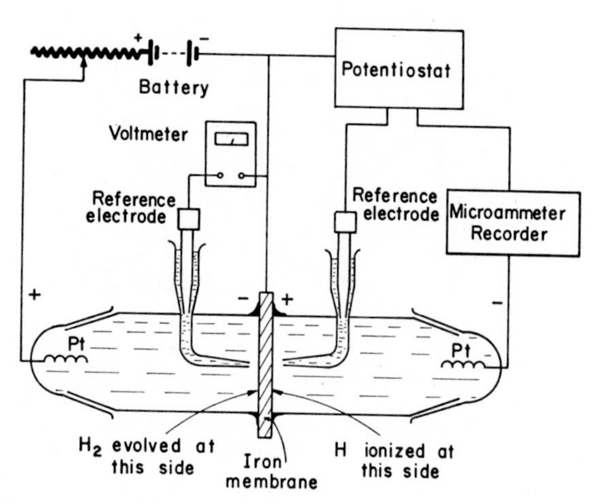

Fig. 9.22. Measurement of hydrogen permeation rate through an iron membrane.

The Electrical Criterion of Hydrogen Damage in Metals

So far we have dealt with damaged metals as though damage always occurred by anodic dissolution, in an isolated state. Our case has been that corrosion occurs by means of local action—by iron atoms sending electrons back to the metal, and these electrons finding partners with protons at other parts of the surface.

There are two other methods by which metals decay, and one of them has no electrochemistry in it. This is erosion, the wearing away of matter by the impact of other matter, as rain on rocks. But there is a third way in which metals decay, which has an important electrochemical aspect—hydrogen damage.

What is the essence of hydrogen damage? It is damage which occurs when a metal, particularly iron, comes into contact with either hydrogen produced electrolytically in a plating bath, or during corrosion, or even just direct hydrogen gas in contact with iron. Then, when the conditions are right, the metal loses its strength, it tends to fall in pieces, and one can tear it apart like paper. It is said to have become 'embrittled' in the sense that it no longer acts as a metal.

It is clear that, from an engineering point of view, the occurrence of hydrogen embrittlement of a metal in a practical device could mean disaster to a structure in which weight or stress rested on the metal. It must be admitted that some aspects of hydrogen embrittlement are still not entirely clear. However, we begin to get closer to a knowledge of it. We present here the essentials of the viewpoint of the 1970's.

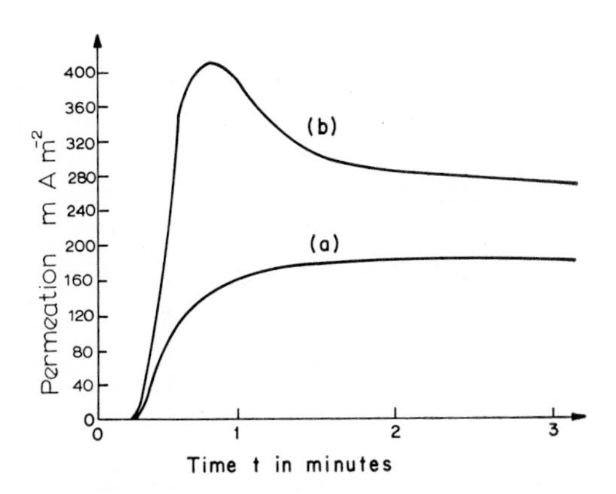

Fig. 9.23. Typical hydrogen permeation curves. (*a*) A normal type obtained when overpotential on the cathodic side is below the critical value. (*b*) An abnormal type showing the decrease in permeation with time, obtained when the overpotential is above a certain critical value, at which internal damage to the metal occurs.

The hydrogen permeation–time curve

Let us suppose that we take a metal and put it in contact with an aqueous electrolytic solution, and subject it to a controlled potential (see fig. 9.22). Hydrogen evolves upon the metal, and a small fraction of the hydrogen goes through it. We measure this hydrogen by some means, for example, a mass spectrometer, or by ionizing it on the other side of the metal and counting the current as it goes through, and we watch the permeation of hydrogen as a function of time. A typical result, so long as the potential is held below a critical overpotential, η_{crit}, is shown in fig. 9.23, curve (a). If we turn the current off, we can let the H atoms dissolve out of the metal and begin all over again:

then nothing has changed. If we increase the overpotential, making the hydrogen come off faster, according to equation (3.26), we again repeat the figure, and again get a permeation–time line of the same shape as before; turn off the current; start again. We could go on and on repeating the permeation–time line.

We go on, indeed, so long as the overpotential for the evolution of H_2 remains below a certain overpotential, η_{crit}. At this point, we find that the permeation–time line can no longer be reproduced. It now becomes as in fig. 9.23, curve (b).

It seems reasonable, therefore, to assert the following: When an overpotential, η_{crit}, has been applied to the metal, the interaction of the hydrogen with the metal is such that something new happens to the structure inside the metal. The new happening must be inside, because we are watching the rate of permeation through the metal.

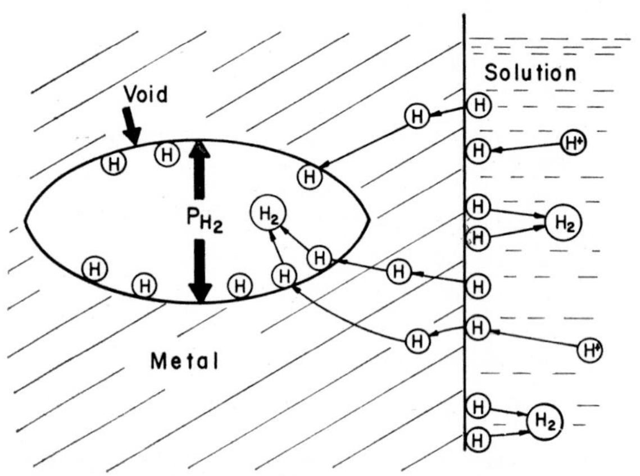

Fig. 9.24. Adsorbed atomic hydrogen can permeate into iron, building up the pressure inside a void. When the pressure exceeds a certain critical value, the void spreads and becomes a 'crack'.

It seems reasonable to say that the metal has at this point—at this η_{crit}—'become embrittled'. Now, 'embrittled' has up to now been just a phrase in this presentation, and we should say what it means. It means that the metal inside is damaged. We know all too little about the inside of metal polycrystals; but one of the things that we have to assume to explain the phenomena which we observe is that they do contain small voids, and these small voids often form near centres of extra stress. It is easy to show that hydrogen is attracted to and diffuses to regions of stress.

It would seem, therefore, quite acceptable to say that the hydrogen may diffuse through to these voids, adsorb on the inside of their walls, and then create a high pressure of molecular hydrogen in the void itself.

One of the things we could do, therefore, would be to find out what would be the equivalent pressure of the hydrogen inside a void, corresponding to the electrical overpotential which we have to put on the outside of the metal specimen to make hydrogen evolve on it at a certain rate. Also we could find the pressure needed to spread a crack, and finally relate these two pressures to find out what would be the overpotential necessary to spread a crack.

What would be the overpotential necessary to spread a crack?

Let us assume that the mechanism of the H_2 evolution reaction is the fast-discharge–slow-combination mechanism

$$H^+ + e \rightleftarrows H_{ads}$$

$$H_{ads} + H_{ads} \rightarrow H_2$$

which has been discussed previously on p. 115.

With the second step as rate-determining, the surface coverage, θ_H, is dependent on overpotential, according to the relation (cf. eqn. (3.53))

$$\theta_H = \theta_{0,H} \exp(-F\eta/RT) \qquad (9.20)$$

where $\theta_{0,H}$ is the coverage at the equilibrium potential at atmospheric pressure (i.e., $\eta = 0$). Therefore, as the overpotential† increases, the larger is the surface coverage θ_H, and more hydrogen will penetrate into iron, eventually reaching the voids. It will accumulate inside the void, and build up the pressure, until it reaches equilibrium with the adsorbed hydrogen at the surface, θ_H.

If we assume that the adsorption is of the Langmuir type (cf. p. 65), pressure and coverage will be related (for $\theta \ll 1$) according to the equation

$$\theta_H = k p_{H_2}^{1/2} \qquad (9.21)$$

where k is a constant ($p_{H_2}^{1/2}$ comes from the fact that each molecule splits into two atoms). From equations 9.20 and 9.21 we get the final equation†

$$p_{H_2} = p_{0,H_2} \exp(-2F\eta/RT), \qquad (9.22)$$

relating the pressure of H_2 inside the void, p_{H_2}, outside pressure of H_2 at the equilibrium potential (most often it is atmospheric pressure, i.e., equals 1), p_{0,H_2}, and the overpotential, η.

Thus, for any value of overpotential, η, there is a pressure, p_{H_2}, developed in the void, which is given by the above equation. We must mention here that what we have said is correct only if the second step in the hydrogen evolution mechanism is rate-determining, i.e., if the surface coverage increases with the overpotential according to the

† In visualising the changes of pressure from (9.22), note that η is negative during hydrogen evolution.

equation (3.53). If proton-discharge is the rate-determining step, there would not be accumulation of surface hydrogen, and therefore no penetration inside the metal.

If the void is of the shape of a double convex lens it is possible, by mechanical considerations, to relate the properties of the metal: γ—surface energy, Y—Young's modulus, and the size of the void defined by the length of its longer axis, l; to the critical internal pressure p_{crit}, needed to break the material and enlarge the void. It comes out that this relation has the following form

$$p_{crit} = \left(\frac{16Y\gamma}{3l}\right)^{1/2}. \tag{9.23}$$

By combining this equation with the previous one for pressure inside the void (eqn. (9.22)) one can evaluate the critical overpotential which will cause increase of pressure inside the void above the safe value, i.e., cause damage. If we assume that the outside pressure p_{0,H_2} is equal to atmospheric pressure,

$$\exp(-2F\eta/RT) = \left(\frac{16Y\gamma}{3l}\right)^{1/2} \tag{9.24}$$

or, after the proper rearrangement

$$\eta_{crit} = -\frac{RT}{4F}\ln\left(\frac{16Y\gamma}{3l}\right). \tag{9.25}$$

Thus, we have got the electrical criterion for the overpotential at which hydrogen damage in a metal commences. If the overpotential of hydrogen becomes more negative than the value η_{crit}—given by equation (9.25)—the metal will start to undergo damage.

There is a direct application of this equation. If we are electro-depositing a metal on another metal, and evolving hydrogen on it at the same time, we have a precise designation of how negative the potential may go. A higher value will cause internal damage to the metal: embrittlement, and possible disaster to a structure supported by the metal concerned, will follow.

Significance of the electrical condition for damage to metals

It may be thought that the deduction given applies mainly to some academic controlled experiment—polarize the metal to a certain critical overpotential, and find out if there is a change in the ductility of the metal. But this would not be a sufficient picture. The electrical condition which is deduced above applies to any piece of corroding metal, for example, the stanchion on a pier, the tail of a plane.† We have

† Structures such as parts of aircraft are also subject to damage by embrittlement and corrosion. When an aircraft is on the ground, parts of it are covered by a thin film of moisture. Such parts may corrode. When the corrosion occurs, e.g. under dust particles where moist vapour has condensed, H may cover part of the surface, and commence to diffuse inside the metal to voids, from which embrittlement may occur ((cf. fig. 9.24).

talked about the value of the potential which is needed for spreading cracks, and what has to be worked out by a corrosion engineer is the mixed potential of the metal in terms of the corresponding hydrogen overpotential. However, if we have a diagram of the corrosion potential as the one shown in figs. 9.3 or 9.4, representing the cathodic and anodic current for the corroding iron, we can find out what the hydrogen overpotential is for that particular pH, and so make up the i–V diagram for the corrosion. If V_{corr} is negative to η_{crit}, embrittlement may occur. Hence, all we need to do, to find whether the metal is damaged or not, is measure its potential, and then apply the electrochemical theory of the hydrogen breakdown of metals derived here.

Corrosion and Electrochemistry

After reading this chapter the reader probably realizes the basically electrochemical nature of processes involved in corrosion, passivity and hydrogen embrittlement, and the necessity to control the electrochemical parameters of systems, if the stability and long life of metal constructions is required. Metal stability and processes having influence on it must be of concern to everybody using metals in practical applications. It is not, however, the general more or less uniform corrosion slowly eating the metal construction which matters so much (though this is of interest too), but in a great number of cases, corrosion occurs at particular, critical, spots of the metal structure. These types of corrosion often destroy equipment of far greater value than the value of the corroded part itself. For example, pitting corrosion might cause gas pipeline or boiler explosions. Stress corrosion cracking might cause breakdown of an aircraft or the steering system of a bus. The first step in a rational way to increase the avoidance of these occurrences is fully to understand the reasons for their happening.

The present knowledge of electrochemistry offers answers to a number of corrosion problems, but it is not being used widely. Since corrosion is an interdisciplinary activity involving modern (solid state oriented) electrochemistry, metallurgy, materials science, and engineering, the proper solution of specific corrosion problems will arise only through a thoroughly serious synthesis of all of these fields.

CHAPTER 10

electrobiophysics

THE area of electrobiophysics is considerably vaguer than the other areas that we have talked about. This is not only because of the complexity of the phenomena themselves, common to all molecular biophysics. It is because the hold of traditional thermodynamic electrochemistry has been even stronger here than in other areas. The result has been that a large number of 'explanations' of phenomena have been given in vague terms, in terms of 'tendencies', but with a minimum of modern electrochemical arguments in terms of kinetics and mechanism. *A central error—of tremendous significance for the understanding of biological phenomena—is the assumption that thermodynamic reversibility is present in the processes which give rise to the omnipresent potentials in biological symptoms.*

All that is generally agreed upon by electrochemists at this time is that there are many aspects of biological phenomena which involve potentials and currents, and the explanation of these must be, in some way, *electrochemical* in nature (for there are no electromagnetic sources of potential generation in the body).

Several outstanding examples can be quoted here. For example, if as shown in fig. 10.1, a large nerve axon, or alternatively, muscle tissue, is put in a saline solution of about the same composition as those found in the body, it is possible to measure the existing potential difference between the interior of the cell and the external solution.† For that purpose, two identical reference electrodes (e.g., calomel electrodes) are used. One, with the Luggin capillary (see page 95) of about 10 μm (or even smaller), at the tip, is connected to the interior part of the cell, and the other is connected to an external solution. The calomel electrodes themselves have the same potential (with respect to the KCl solution inside them), and if there were no potential differences across the cell membrane, the potential difference across the meter would be zero (the two liquid junction potentials between KCl and the two solutions each side of the membrane can be neglected if the concentration of KCl is great, e.g., more than 3 M) This potential difference, often called the *cell membrane*, or *cellular*, *potential*, usually has a value of some 60–110 mV, the exterior being more positive. This relatively stable potential difference, often called the 'resting potential', can be disturbed by the application of some external means. For

† The axon is a lengthy part of the nerve cell and in certain crustaceans might be 1 mm in diameter, and up to 1 m in length.

example, if two small metal electrodes are put at each side of the cell membrane and a short current pulse is applied across the membrane, a sudden change of potential, the (so-called 'action potential') is observed, as shown in fig. 10.2. This potential change can be produced also by other means, e.g., by the chemical action of some drugs. Some types of nerve cell are sensitive to light, pressure, temperature, etc. When an arrangement with several measuring electrodes distributed

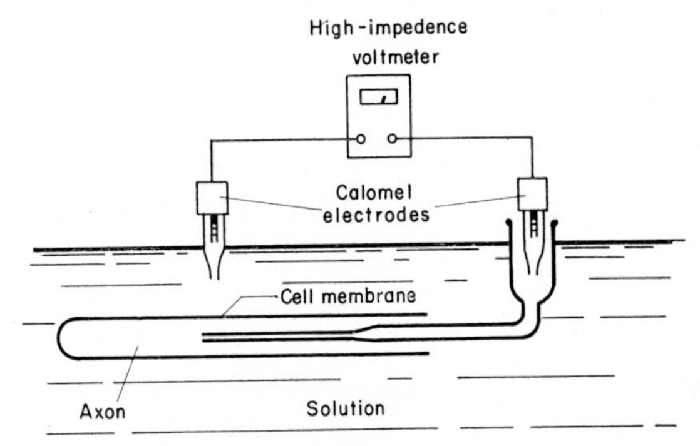

Fig. 10.1. Measurement of the electrochemical potential across a biological cell by means of two reference electrodes placed at each side of the cell membrane.

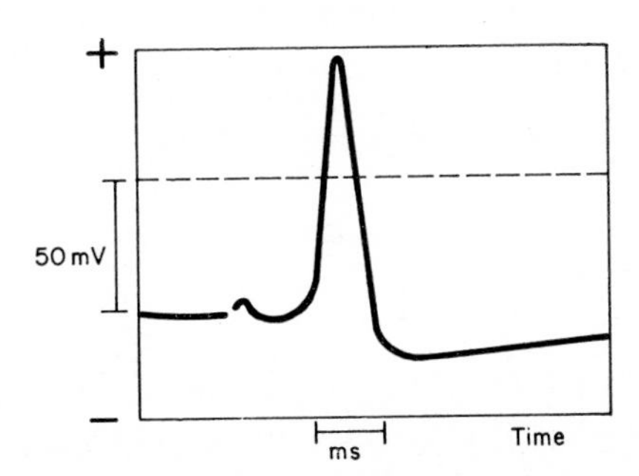

Fig. 10.2. Changes of the cellular potential of a squid's giant axon as recorded on an oscillographic screen, when a short square electric pulse is applied at one end of the axon. The break on the line indicates the moment the pulse was applied. The horizontal broken line is the zero line.

along the nerve axon is used, and a change of potential (action potential) is induced at one end of the axon, a movement of the 'action potential' spike along the axon can be detected, and it has been found that its speed is some 10–100 m s^{-1}, depending on the axon. The difference in potential between the part of the membrane where the potential is disturbed (being negative) and the rest of the membrane at the normal 'rest potential' produces electrochemical local cell action and consequently, the appearance of current passing through the cell (see fig. 10.3). This *conduction of current through nerves* is the basic mechanism of transfer of information from the receptory nerve cells in the body to the brain. It is electrochemical in nature.

The *clotting of blood*, as was mentioned in Chapter 1, also depends on electrochemical processes; its occurrence is sharply dependent upon whether the substrate on which the clotting occurs has a potential more positive than about 0 V versus the standard hydrogen electrode (see fig. 1.4). Interaction of blood particles is greatly dependent on double layer structure and charge. Induced changes of double layer structure and charge, as carried out in these experiments with platinum electrodes, make the clotting possible. Other materials used in surgery for implants (teflon, gold, stainless steel) have different potentials of zero charge (see p. 43). Hence, if they are kept at the same potential on the conventional scale, there will be a different excess charge on

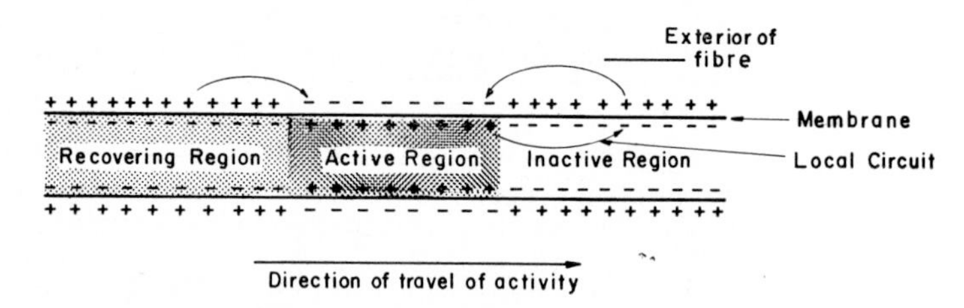

Fig. 10.3. Diagram of the events during the propagation of the 'action potential' spike, and creation of the current in the nerve axon, according to the model of Hodgkin and Huxley. The reversal of the membrane potential during the spike produces the local circuit current between active, and as yet inactive, regions and excitation of the new spike along the axon, with its propagation into a more distant, as yet inactive, region.

each of these metals, and hence a different degree of electrical interaction with the colloidal particles (erythrocytes and leucocytes) which make up blood. Those having a sufficiently intense charge of the same sign as the blood particles will repel the latter, i.e., no clotting. But if the charge is insufficiently repulsive, or even attractive, the colloid particles tend to *discharge* onto the metal, hence become unstable.

Encephalographic waves are the oscillations in potential difference between properly positioned electrodes in the skull which have potential amplitudes of 5–200 μV and frequencies from 0·5 to 30 Hz (see fig. 10.13). They contain numerous forms which are indicative of the state of the brain, and vary with states of waking, sleep, thinking, emotional arousal, etc. Similarly, the electrical activity of the heart is used in electrocardiology for diagnostic purposes. The failure of the heart to operate in a regular periodic manner can be restored by pacemakers, devices supplying regular current pulses to the heart muscle. The existence of these periodic electrical phenomena in a biological system, *where there is no possibility of an electromagnetic origin*, would indicate an electrochemical cause.

The Cell and its Potential

In the sense of rough experimental data, bioelectrochemistry is an old, traditional field, particularly in respect to the investigation of the cellular potential. A typical biological cell, in a simplified version, is presented in fig. 10.4. Many difficulties exist in the way of a satisfactory measurement of cellular potential, due to the small dimensions of the experimental object, and the fact that the introduction of any micro-electrode or Luggin capillary tip inside the cell destroys to some extent the original, natural, structure of the interior of the cell, if it does not kill it completely.

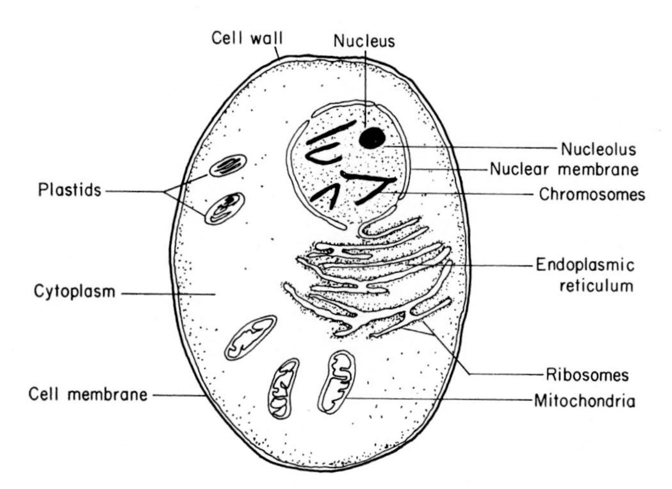

Fig. 10.4. Simplified diagram of a biological cell. Most of the components named are found in all living cells.

One of the peculiarities of biological cell systems is the large difference in alkali metal ion concentrations in the interior of the cell and the exterior liquid. The concentration of K^+ ions inside many cells is some 40 times *larger* than outside, while the concentration of Na^+ ions is about 25 times *smaller* inside the cell than outside. Most of the theories proposed for explaining cellular potentials start from this fact.

The Donnan potential approach

As early as 1900 MacDonald proposed the idea that the cellular potential arises as the consequence of the semi-permeability of the cell membrane. It was thought that the membrane was not permeable to anions but was permeable to cations, particularly K^+. The idea was thermodynamically treated for the ideal case by Donnan in 1911; the potential difference across the boundary layer is called the Donnan potential.

How does the Donnan potential arise? Let us consider the situation when the membrane separates two solutions, one, on the left-hand side in fig. 10.5, containing negatively charged protein molecules, R^-, and *high* concentrations of K^+ ions (e.g., the interior of the biological cell),

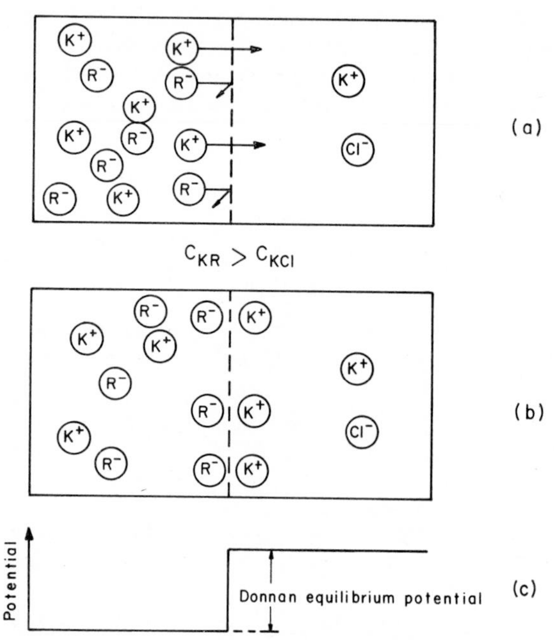

Fig. 10.5. If the initial concentration of KR is larger on one side of a membrane impermeable for R^- ions, than the concentration of potassium salt on the other (*a*), some K^+ ions cross the membrane. A Donnan equilibrium potential difference across the membrane will be established (*b*). Further diffusion of K^+ ions will be stopped by the resultant potential field across the membrane. Oriented towards the left-hand side of the boundary.

and on the right-hand side the second solution containing KCl in *smaller* concentration than that present inside the cell. If both anions, the R^- and the Cl^-, cannot permeate through the membrane, only K^+ ions can pass through, and the normal tendency for equalizing concentration will push K^+ ions from left to right in fig. 10.5. However, since K^+ ions passing through carry positive charges, which cannot be compensated by negative anionic charges, the movement of K^+ ions will be stopped by the potential field which will develop across the membrane. The state of equilibrium will be established with an increased concentration of K^+ ions on the right-hand side of the boundary, outside the cell.

Donnan treated this equilibrium thermodynamically and for the simple ideal situation (complete impermeability for R^- and Cl^- ions) obtained the equation for Donnan potential, V_D:

$$V_D = \frac{RT}{F} \ln \frac{(c_{K^+})_{ex}}{(c_{K^+})_{in}} \tag{10.1}$$

$(c_{K^+})_{in}$ and $(c_{K^+})_{ex}$ indicating K^+ ion concentrations in the interior and exterior of the cell, respectively. This is a Nernst type of equation (see eqn. (3.36)) for an electrochemical potassium ion concentration cell, and it has been used extensively in attempts to analyse the variations of the cellular potential since then, with various changes in the ambients around the membrane.

However, the application of the Donnan potential concept for explaining the origin of the cellular potential has been criticized very seriously in recent times. A Donnan equilibrium, producing a potential difference at a boundary, is a typical thermodynamic equilibrium, with zero electrochemical free energy difference between the interior and exterior of the cell. What is then the driving force for the dynamic processes taking place inside our body? The establishment of equilibrium could surely by expected after death. The other serious difficulty with the Donnan potential is that Na^+ ions, having the same charge as K^+ ions, should cause a similar effect and therefore influence the cellular potential. The problem was 'solved' by another *ad hoc* assumption—that the membrane is impermeable to Na^+ ions as well as to anions.

However, in 1940, Heppel showed that Na^+ ions do penetrate, and therefore redistribute themselves, through the membrane. If this is correct, the Donnan potential equation should be written in the form:

$$V_D = \frac{RT}{F} \ln \frac{(c_{K^+})_{ex} + (c_{Na^+})_{ex}}{(c_{K^+})_{in} + (c_{Na^+})_{in}}. \tag{10.2}$$

This is not a very helpful step, for, since the sums of concentrations of K^+ and Na^+ ions inside and outside the cell are nearly equal, the Donnan potential would be close to zero.

Most of the basic assumptions used for application of the Donnan potential concept to biological cells appear to be disproved and it seems that it should be abandoned.

The liquid junction potential approach

The second approach for evaluating the cellular potential is to consider the cell membrane as the permeable separator between two solutions having different concentrations of ions, this difference being produced (in a manner not stated) by some other process, the metabolic processes of the cell. In that case, one can treat this situation as the one producing the so-called *liquid junction* or *diffusion potential.*

What is the liquid junction potential, and when does it appear? The liquid junction potential† appears at the boundary of any two liquid phases (e.g., two solutions) if they have different concentrations of the same ions, or even when the solutions contain different kinds of ions. Let us take the simplest case of the liquid junction between two solutions containing different concentrations of HCl with no membrane between them, as shown in fig. 10.6. Following the normal tendency

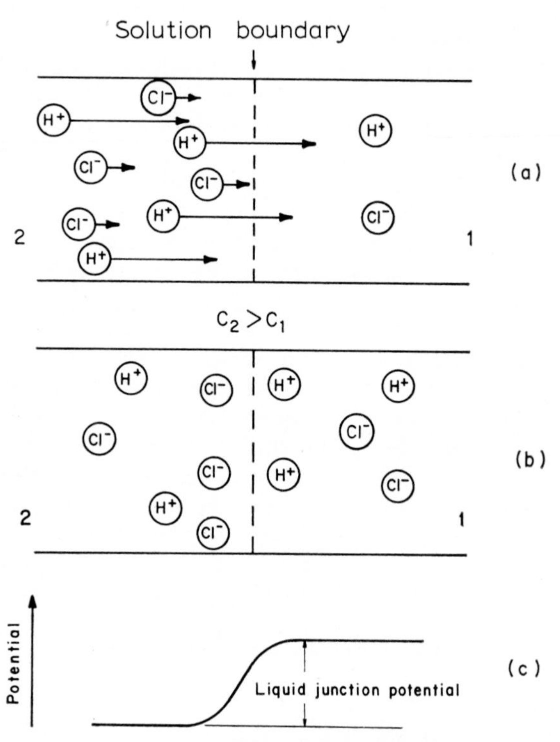

Fig. 10.6. When two solutions of different concentration of the same or different ions are brought into contact (*a*), the different velocities of ions crossing the boundary produce a charge separation across the boundary layer (*b*) and liquid junction potential (*c*). When the concentrations are equalized the liquid junction potential vanishes.

for equilibration of concentrations, both H^+ and Cl^- ions will start diffusing from the solution having higher concentration into the solution having smaller concentration. However, the different ions have different properties, even when they have identical charges. For example, they differ in dimensions, in the number of water molecules

† This is actually a potential difference, just as an electrode potential is a potential difference, but the word 'difference' is often dropped for practical reasons.

in the hydration shell, etc. These differences produce differences in the rates of diffusion of different kinds of ions into otherwise identical conditions for diffusion. In fact, H^+ ions move six times faster than Cl^- ions. These differences in the rates of moving of ions can be experimentally measured if an external electric field is applied to the solution by means of two platinum electrodes and the velocities of individual ions in the field observed. One way to compare the different mobilities of ions is to use their absolute mobilities μ_+ for cations, and μ_- for anions, defined as the rates of movement of ions (in m s^{-1}) under unit electric field (i.e., 1 V m^{-1}).

Now, the velocity of H^+ diffusing across the boundary (fig. 10.6) is larger than that of Cl^- ions, so that an increasingly large number of H^+ ions will find themselves on the other side of the boundary, not accompanied by an equivalent number of Cl^- ions, which are left behind. The result will be a separation of charge, the more dilute solution becoming positive and more concentrated solution negative, with the potential gradient across the boundary. The potential gradient, acting against the movement of H^+ ions, slows down the rate of movement of H^+ ions to that of the Cl^- ions (the velocity of which is *increased* by the potential gradient). This potential difference is called a liquid junction potential. One should note, however, that diffusion of H^+ and Cl^- ions across the boundary takes place all the time until the two concentrations in the two solutions become equal. This is a non-equilibrium process, and the liquid-junction potential is *not* a thermodynamic potential. The liquid-junction potential disappears when the two concentrations become equal. However, it might exist for long periods of time if the volumes of the solutions are large enough, or it might maintain itself at a stable value if the concentrations of the ions is kept different on the two sides of the membrane by some external means.

The subject of liquid-junction potentials was considered by Henderson in 1907. For the simplest case of two solutions having different concentrations of the same solute, c_1 and c_2 ($c_1 < c_2$), the liquid junction potential can be calculated according to the approximate Henderson equation:

$$V_{LJ} = \frac{u_+ - u_-}{u_+ + u_-} \frac{RT}{nF} \ln \frac{c_1}{c_2}. \tag{10.3}$$

If we apply the liquid junction potential concept to a biological cell having a membrane permeable for K^+ ions but not permeable for Cl^- ions (i.e., $u_{Cl^-} \ll u_{K^+}$, or $u_{K^+} - u_{Cl^-} \approx u_{K^+}$), the Henderson equation for the liquid junction potential difference between the internal and external parts of the cell can be written in the approximate form

$$V_{LJ} \approx \frac{RT}{F} \ln \frac{(c_{K^+})_{ex}}{(c_{K^+})_{in}} \tag{10.4}$$

which again looks like a Nernst equation (see eqn. (3.36)) applied to a concentration cell. However, one has to be careful in distinguishing between similarity and identity. The ionic mobility of Cl^- ions through the membrane is never zero, and might vary from membrane to membrane, which would mean that the approximation used in evaluating equation (10.4) cannot be generally accepted and equation (10.3) or a similar one should be used. There is also a basic difference between the liquid junction potential concept and the Donnan equilibrium concept. In the liquid junction potential concept discussed above, the system *is not in equilibrium*. Since the cellular potential is stable, there must be some other mechanism, the biochemical processes which compose the cells metabolism, which keeps the concentration difference between the interior and exterior of the cell in a *steady state condition*. Thus, the cellular potential might be understood as a *steady state liquid junction potential.*

The Hodgkin–Huxley theory

The steady state liquid junction potential idea has been elaborated in more detail by Hodgkin and Huxley since 1949. They developed the following relation for the cellular potential

$$V_C = \frac{RT}{F} \ln \frac{P_{K^+}(c_{K^+})_{ex} + P_{Na^+}(c_{Na^+})_{ex} + P_{Cl^-}(c_{C^-})_{in}}{P_{K^+}(c_{K^+})_{in} + P_{Na^+}(c_{Na^+})_{in} + P_{Cl^-}(c_{Cl^-})_{ex}} \qquad (10.5)$$

where P_{K^+}, P_{Na^+}, and P_{Cl^-} represent the permeability of the corresponding ions through the cell membrane, the other symbols are the concentrations, as used before in equation (10.1)†.

It is assumed that, in the resting state (i.e., when there is no exterior stimulation of the membrane), the permeability of Na^+ ions is lower than that for K^+ ions ($P_{Na^+} \ll P_{K^+}$), and also P_{Cl^-} is small (an assumption proved later to have a very weak factual background), whereupon the Hodgkin equation becomes similar to the Henderson equation, for the liquid junction potential, but takes into account the real permeabilities of the ions. Hodgkin and Huxley proposed an explanation of the appearance of the 'action potential' (see fig. 10.2), which initiates the nerve current. According to their theory, the cellular potential changes when the permeability of Na^+ ions, P_{Na^+}, is changed by the action of an external stimulant (electric field, chemical action, light, etc.). But why the external stimulant should bring about such changes in P is unknown. The sudden inflow of Na^+ ions into the cell brings the cellular potential down to zero, or even reverses it in a short time, as shown in fig. 10.2. When the stimulant stops acting, the permeabilities become the same as before and the potential goes back to the resting value. However, there is one difficulty in this mechanism of action

† Properly, one should use activities instead of concentrations which might differ considerably inside the cell.

potential. It is not clear why the sodium ions brought inside the cell during the stimulation should go out, since the outer concentration of Na^+ ions is never lower than in the interior of the cell. In the resting state it is normally about 25 times higher outside than inside. To overcome this, a concept of a hypothetical 'sodium pump' action has been suggested without any serious explanation on the molecular level. It has no clearer meaning than that given by an indefinite reference to 'some process connected with the cell metabolism'.

More modern hypotheses for the cellular potential

The Hodgkin–Huxley theory is useful in explaining cellular 'resting potential', 'action potential', etc., and is sometimes in agreement with the findings. But there are serious problems with it, even if one puts aside the mysticism of the hypothetical 'sodium pump'. For example, Grundfest showed in 1954 that injection of large quantities of K^+ or Na^+ ions inside the cell changed the cellular potential only by a few millivolts, instead of the 38 mV expected according to the Hodgkin equation.

There have been some more attempts recently to introduce more modern thinking into the processes involved in the formation of the cellular potential. For instance, Ling developed a comprehensive theory of the living state based on what is called an association–induction hypothesis. His hypothesis is based on two well-known chemical facts. The first one is that the presence of fixed negative charges on large molecules (e.g., $-COO^-$ groups in cationic ion exchange resin) can lead to a selective association with cations from the solution, K^+ ion being held much more tightly than Na^+ ion. The second one is that atoms or an atomic group at one end of a molecule can induce change to another atomic group at the other end of the molecule. A typical example of the induction effect is the substitution of H atoms in acetic acid with chlorine; trichloracetic acid ($CCl_3.COOH$) is a much stronger acid than acetic acid. According to Ling, the biological cell should be regarded as a highly organized network of long protein molecules, their free carboxyl groups selectively associated with K^+ ions and consequently producing a high internal content of potassium and a low content of sodium. The cellular potential appears as a consequence of the existence of fixed negative free charges on the outside part of the protein membrane forming an electrical double layer with ions from the surrounding solution.

Another interesting attempt (and one that brings molecular biology and modern electrochemistry in sight of each other) is that of DelDuca and Fuscoe who, in 1965, connected the existence of the cellular potential with the metabolism of cells by considering the living cell as an elementary biological fuel cell, run by oxygen at the exterior part of the membrane (the cathode), and glucose as the fuel at the *interior* of the membrane (the anode) (see fig. 10.10). Then, the potential difference across the membrane, the cellular potential, should be dependent on the reaction rates at the surfaces, and the electrical conductivity of this membrane, as in any other fuel cell (see Chapter 7). We shall talk more about this approach (p. 282).

Some Aspects of Biochemical Energy Conversion

The food taken in by a human organism is equivalent, if all is converted to heat, to about 12×10^6 J every 24 hours. Were this energy spent at a constant rate with 100% efficiency of conversion to mechanical work, the power provided would correspond to about 140 watt. There are basically only two ways of converting the energy of chemical reactions to mechanical work. The first one is via some kind of heat engine with the Carnot efficiency of $(T_2 - T_1)/T_2$ and the second is via electrochemical processes providing potentials and fields to bring about mechanical work (see p. 211). It is clear that biochemical energy conversion cannot be associated with any kind of heat engine, for allowing 10 K for the temperature difference inside the body for such a hypothetical engine, the Carnot efficiency would be about 3% ($\varepsilon = 10/310$).† Therefore, the total available mechanical power would be about $1/31 \cdot 140 \simeq 5$ watt. It is known, however, that the circulatory system in the human organism operates under a roughly constant power of about 10 watt. As Bockris and Srinivasan pointed out in 1967, the fact that the observed efficiency of biological systems in the conversion of chemical to mechanical energy is so much greater than that expected thermally, implies that the overall mechanism of this energy conversion is likely to be electrochemical.‡

No matter what is the detailed mechanism of the conversion of chemical energy to biomechanical work, it is clear that the oxidation of food by oxygen is the basis of life. The food is 'digested', i.e., converted to simple organic molecules, e.g., glucose, and by means of the circulatory system, brought to the biological cells. Biochemists have been able to detect the large number of molecular species which represent the intermediate stages in the oxidation of glucose, or other basic molecules to the final oxidation stage, CO_2. This oxidation process occurs in a stepwise manner, each particular step being catalysed by a specific catalyst, usually a large organic molecule called an enzyme or co-enzyme. All these reactions are believed to be of the redox type, i.e., one molecule is being reduced and the other oxidized, the basic step being *electron or charge transfer*. One simple example of a metabolic reaction is the oxidation of glucose to gluconolactone by oxygen

† $T_2 = 37 + 273 = 310$ K.

‡ When the organism feels too cold it does not simply produce more heat by 'burning' more fuel, but starts shivering. It is the mechanical work which is converted to heat, not the heat into mechanical work.

in the presence of the co-enzyme flavinadenindinucleotide (FAD), often called glucose oxidase enzyme.

In the first step, two electrons are transferred to the co-enzyme, i.e., the enzyme is reduced

$$G + FAD + 2H^+ + 2e \rightarrow FAD\text{–}H_2 + Gl,$$

where G = Glucose and Gl = gluconolactone

In the second step, the reduced form of FAD exchanges two electrons with oxygen, forming hydrogen peroxide, and oxidizing itself to the initial form,

$$FAD\text{–}H_2 + O_2 \rightarrow FAD + H_2O_2.$$

Glucose and gluconolactone represent a redox system which can be characterized by its standard redox potential. The same applies to the two forms of FAD, and a whole number of oxidation products and enzymes which biochemists find in biological cells. A small number of such systems is shown in Table 10.1, with their standard redox potentials at pH = 7. It is the difference of the electrochemical redox potentials which provides the driving force for all these biological reactions. However, thermodynamic quantities do not tell us anything about the rate and mechanism of the reaction. We know the reactions are occurring, but how? What determines the rate? Can we somehow control the rate according to our wishes and needs?

Table 10.1. Potentials of biochemical oxidation–reduction reactions

Reactants	Products	$V°$ (volt)
Acetaldehyde + H_2O	acetate$^-$ + H^+	−0·581
Alanine + H_2O	pyruvate$^-$ + NH_4^+	−0·119
NH_4^+ + H_2O	NH_2OH	+0·562
Ascorbate	dehydroascorbic acid	+0·166
Aspartate	oxoloacetate^{2-} + NH_4^+	−0·097
NADH + H^+ (reduced form of Nicotine-amide Adenine Dinucleotide	NAD^+ + 2H	−0·320
Ethanol	acetaldehyde	−0·197
Glucose + H_2O	gluconate$^-$ + H^+	−0·47
Glucose	gluconolactone	−0·364
Glutamate$^-$ + H_2O	*a*-oxoglutarate^{2-} + NH_4^+	−0·121
Glyceraldehyde 3-Phosphate^{2-} + HPO_4^{2-}	glyceroylphosphate 3-phosphate^{4-}	−0·286
Glycerate$^-$	hydroxypyruvate$^-$	−0·158
H_2O_2	O_2 (gas)	+0·295
Lactate$^-$	pyruvate$^-$	−0·185
Malate^{2-} + H^+	pyruvate$^-$ + CO_2	−0·330
Pyruvate$^-$ + H_2O	acetate$^-$ + CO_2	−0·699
Sorbitol	fructose	−0·272
H_2O	O_2 (gas)	+0·820

In finding answers to these questions we may help to solve some of the major problems in biology, such as the causes of cancer, the nature of 'life', the mechanism of growth, the action of drugs, etc.

Electron mobility in large organic molecules

As we have seen, charge transfers between large molecules are one of the elementary steps in the overall redox processes in biological cells. Most of our common experience tells us that organic molecules behave like insulators, i.e., the mobility of electrons is almost zero. Assuming that this is correct, the transferred charges should be localized to an atom in the large macromolecules, and the only way that these charges could be transferred in a number of successive steps along a certain distance (e.g., across a membrane having O_2 outside the biological fuel, glucose for example, inside) is by the rotation of the molecules. It is very difficult to accept that large macromolecules like enzymes and

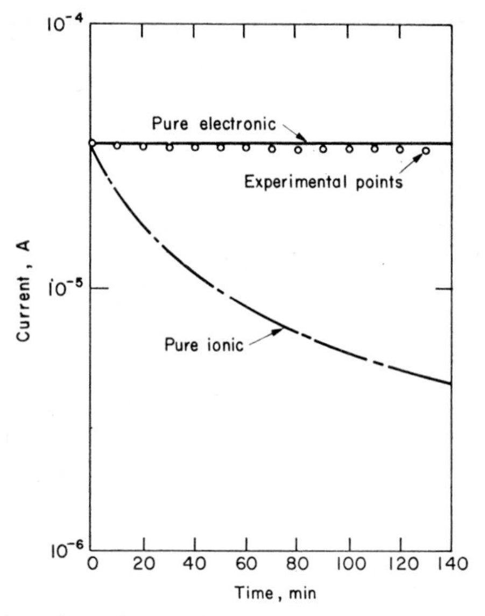

Fig. 10.7. The time dependence of the current passing through wet crystalline haemoglobin.

proteins can *rotate* at a sufficient rate in highly organized macromolecular systems—as biological cells indeed are—to provide the observed rate for the overall reactions.

There is ample evidence from recent work that, in fact, large protein and enzyme molecules have the properties of semiconductors, i.e., can carry electric currents along chains. For example, Barney Rosenberg showed in 1962 that the current passing through wet crystalline haemoglobin is practically independent of time. This would not be expected if the current was *ionic*, due to the increasing consumption of the water by electrolysis as time proceeds (see fig. 10.7). It must, therefore, be electronic. The existence of a rather significant electron mobility can be easily understood in the case of many enzymes having conjugated double bonds, (—C=C—C=C—). The resonance effect (cf. that for a benzene ring) produces huge π orbitals along the chain in which electrons can move freely. Protein molecules do not have long conjugated double bonds, but the protein molecule is crosslinked by peptide bonds (—C(=O)—N(H)—). A portion of the polypeptide chain can be represented in the following form:

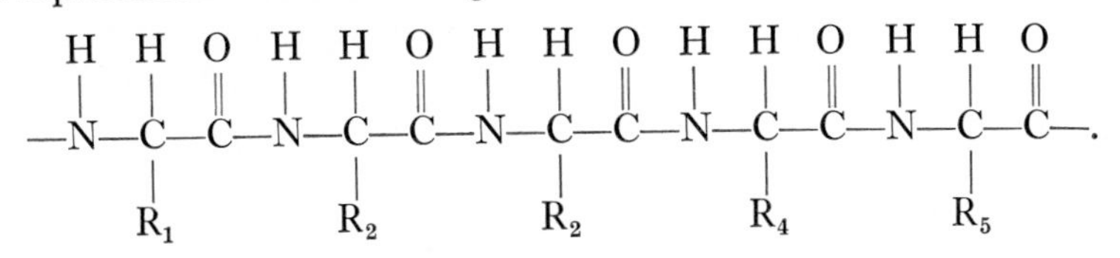

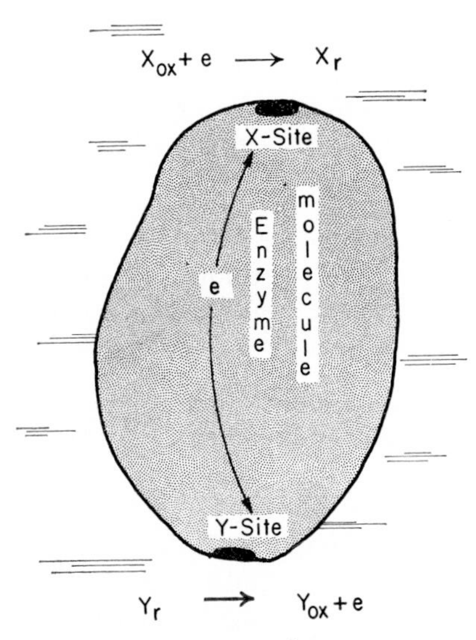

Fig. 10.8. Cope's model for a redox enzyme particle.

It has been suggested that the orderly repetition of the peptide bond can form an electronic conduction band, as in any normal semiconductor crystal; or even that the close conjunction of electron-donating > NH and electron accepting > CO groups can lead to the tunnelling of electrons along the chain. Following these arguments, Freeman Cope in 1964 proposed a model for redox reactions involving enzymes, and as is shown in fig. 10.8. The resemblance between this electrochemical model and the electrochemical processes involved in the metallurgical production of titanium shown in fig. 3.23 is obvious: the enzyme mechanism in biology, the apparently chemical synthesis of titanium metal in a molten salt, and the corrosion of metals in moist environments (see p. 82) all go by the same electrochemical mechanism. This is an example of the unification brought about by applications of the New Electrochemistry.

Biological systems as fuel cells

As we mentioned before, it is difficult to understand the origin of the cellular potential, and the factors which can affect it, without involving (though vaguely) the metabolic processes taking place in the biological cell. An attempt to treat both problems simultaneously is that of Del Duca and Fuscoe who originated the concept of biological cells as fuel cells (see p. 211). At one type of site on the biological cell (equivalent to the anode), the food metabolite is oxidized, while on the other type of site, the cathodes, oxygen is reduced. Ions pass through the solution (inside the membrane pores) carrying current between cathodic and anodic sites (just as they do in the ionic transport in solution occurring in any electrochemical cell), while electrons flow from anodes to cathodes through the macromolecules. These replace the wire joining the electrodes in normal fuel cells, and the evidence recently given by Rosenberg for semiconduction in some biological substances makes more acceptable this part of the model.

In fig. 10.9 the biochemical processes involved in oxidation of the metabolite are represented in the traditional, biochemical way. However, the same system can be visualized in a more modern way as a fuel cell system, for example, as shown in fig. 10.10. The existence of considerable resistance for electron transport through the macromolecules, and the overpotentials of the charge-transfer reactions involved, as in any other fuel cell system (see Chapter 7), controls the potential difference across the membrane, usually measured as the cellular potential.

A direct experimental argument in favour of this concept comes from measurements of the change of cellular potential under the influence of a current pushed through the living cell membrane by means of two microelectrodes, one being inside the cell and the other outside (p. 269). It has recently been shown that not linear, but rather *logarithmic* relations exist between the current and the measured displacement of the cellular potential. For instance, in fig. 10.11, results obtained by Lazarro Mandel in 1970 show the relation between potential and the logarithm of the current density, with slopes averaging close to 0·12 V. The relationship obtained resembles the basic electrochemical kinetic equation (see eqn. (3.26) and fig. 3.17)

$$i = i_0 \exp(-\beta F\ RT)\eta$$

and seem to provide strong evidence for a rate determining interphasial

Standard redox potential/V	−0·35	−0·32	−0·06	?	?	+0·26	?	+0·29	+0·82
	mH_2	NAD^+	$FADH_2$	oxidized coenzyme Q	reduced cytochrome b	oxidized cytochrome c_1	reduced cytochrome c	oxidized cytochrome a	H_2O
	m	NADH	FAD	reduced coenzyme Q	oxidized cytochrome b	reduced cytochrome c_1	oxidized cytochrome c	reduced cytochrome a	$\frac{1}{2}O_2$

electron flow →

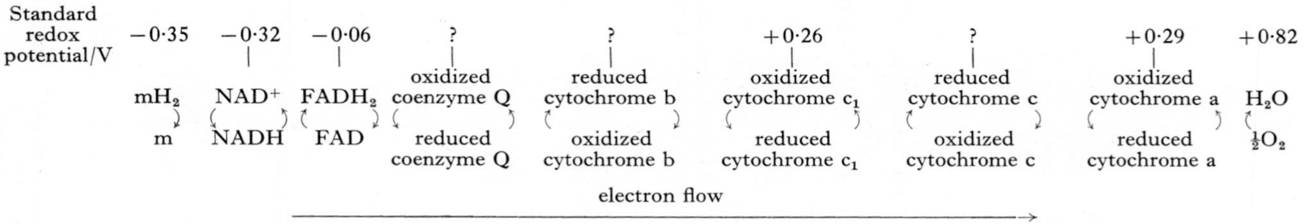

Fig. 10.9. Redox processes and an electron transport chain between metabolite mH_2 and oxygen, occurring in mammalian mitochondria, involving various specific enzymes. The standard redox potential of each part of the chain is indicated.

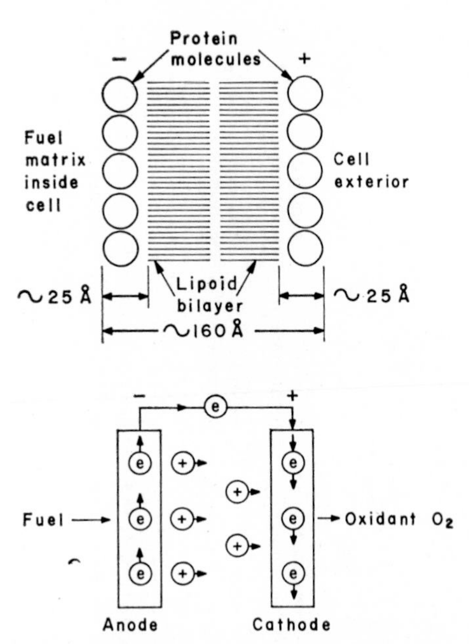

Fig. 10.10. Del Duca and Fuscoe's model showing the resemblance of the gross structure of a cellular membrane to an electrochemical fuel cell.

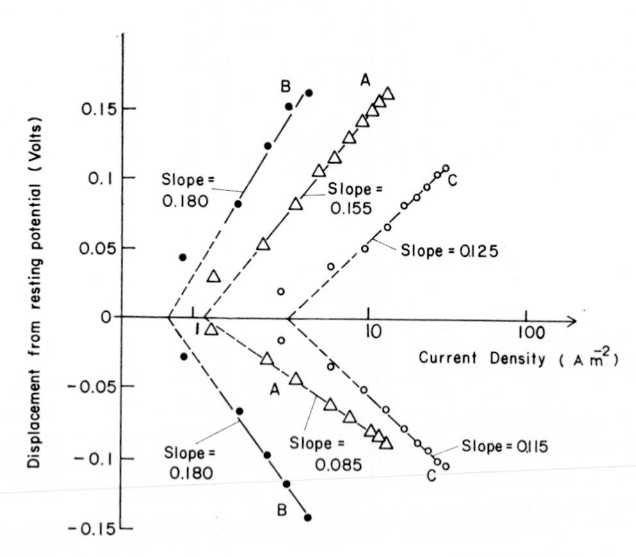

Fig. 10.11. Displacement from a resting potential versus the logarithm of the current density passed through membranes: (*a*) from gastric mucosa; (*b*) from the skin; (*c*) through a perch's swim bladder.

charge transfer reaction as the governing reaction at least in the biological processes examined by Mandel. The experimental slope of 0·12, corresponding to a transfer coefficient $\alpha = \beta = 0{\cdot}5$ indicates (see eqn. (3.48)) strongly that the rate determining step is an electron transfer between the reacting particle in solution and the membrane, i.e., charge transfer at the interface.

Taking Cope's model of enzyme reactions, and Del Duca and Fuscoe's fuel cell model approach, one can understand some basic events happening in living cells in terms approaching those of modern electrochemistry, without any need for mystical sodium pumps and improbable assumptions of thermodynamic equilibria existing in still living systems. The chemical chain of enzymatic redox reactions in fig. 10.9 can be taken as a complex electron conductor with overall resistance R_E, shown in fig. 10.10, electrons being transferred by charge-transfer processes between enzyme molecules. In such a way, the enzyme chain produces the electronic conductor linkage between oxygen reducing sites on one side of the system and metabolite oxidizing site on the other side of the system. Since the ions in the solution can carry the ionic current from one end of the chain to the other, the reaction can proceed as long as the internal electric resistance of the conducting molecules, is sufficiently low, and the rates of interface charge transfer reactions of metabolite and oxygen are sufficiently high. A potential difference develops between the two ends of the chain and, as in a fuel cell system (see eqn. (4.14)) depends on the external resistance of ionic conduction around the chain R_{ion}, the internal resistance of the chain to electron transport, and the rates of the charge-transfer reactions in which electrons are given to the cell, and the oxygen reduction reaction in which electrons are donated to O_2. A decrease of current, i.e., a slowing down of metabolism, can be understood in terms of adsorption of some organic molecule at either one or the other end of the chain, therefore inhibiting the interfacial charge transfer reactions (see p. 96), or by the action of some molecules (enzymes) somewhere along the chain, perhaps changing the electronic conductivity of enzymes involved in the chain.

This model is very elementary and crude, and as yet cannot give proper quantitative answers to some experimental facts observed by cellular potential measurements. But it suggests that cellular potentials (and the variations in them so often observed) cannot be treated independently of cell metabolism, and that the changes observed in the rate of metabolism may be related to the variation in interfacial potential differences. The energy needed to produce and sustain variations in overpotentials, as for example, in the 'action potential' transfer along the nerve axon, can come from the electrochemical metabolic processes directly, just as the energy of the overpotentials set up at the interfaces in fuel cells is taken from the total available energy, i.e., the free energy, of the chemical reaction of fuel cells.

We can conclude this Section by pointing out three major conclusions:

(1) Del Duca and Fuscoe, Cope, and Mandel have all suggested models for fundamental processes in living organisms which involve electrochemical interphasial charge transfer, rather than electron transfer within the solid phase, as rate determining steps in some biophysical processes.

(2) The time has come, therefore, to ask whether a rate controlling interfacial electron transfer step may not be a more general phenomenon in biochemical reactions than has been hitherto thought.

(3) Why is it that biochemical reactions occur with such marked differences to chemical reactions? For example, they tend to have low activation energies, as indeed do electrochemical reactions. Might it be that many biochemical reactions involve electrochemical mechanisms, i.e., consist of a series of cathodic and anodic reactions occurring at the same rate at different parts of the system? Are thermal collisional reactions the exception rather than the rule in biological systems?

Oscillatory Phenomena in Biological Systems

The existence of oscillatory phenomena in biological systems is a well-known fact. Our nervous system controls the frequency of the beating heart. If the information is sent to the heart that there is not enough oxygen in the cells, for example when we are running, the frequency will be increased, the blood recirculated thus faster, as well as more oxygen per unit time being taken in by panting. Information as to whether we are looking at a sheet of white or green paper is transferred by excitation of the sensory cells in the eyes by light of different frequencies. It is the different frequencies of the nerve impulses which transmit the differences to the brain. The brain itself produces electrical oscillations, part of which we can register as *encephalographic* waves of various frequencies and amplitudes. We do not know much about the oscillatory processes in the brain and their effects upon the other parts of the body, or even on the surroundings†, but it is well-known that the patterns of encephalographic waves (i.e., frequency and amplitude) of various parts of the brain vary with emotional, mental and bodily activity. How do these oscillations originate, what is their mechanism, can we control some of them when something starts going wrong–these are questions which presently have no answer. It is obvious that part of the answer concerning the *origin* of the electrical oscillations in the brain, and how they are affected by our moods, must be electrochemical at an atomic level. But we have no direct evidence as yet as to what the detailed mechanism is.

† For electrical oscillators *radiate*. The mechanism of such oscillations, and their reaction to external electric and magnetic fields, may lay the basis for a scientific understanding of borderline phenomena, e.g., telepathy.

There are, however, certain actual electrochemical systems, which in some aspects behave similarly to biological systems, for example, under specific conditions they may behave as permanent oscillatory systems. In 1968 Victor E. Shashua observed oscillations of potential difference across an ultra-thin ion exchange double membrane under a permanent flow of current. Since the thickness of the Shashua membrane approaches that of biological membranes, the two systems can be compared.

The polyelectrolyte double membrane (of Shashua) was prepared by a surface interaction of polyacrylic-polyacrylamide copolymer with the

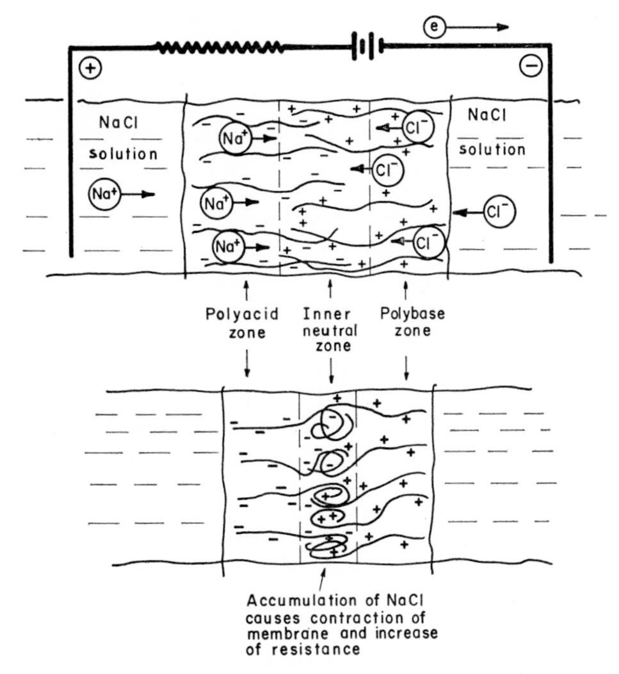

Fig. 10.12. The probable structure of Shashua's membrane in the process of oscillation.

polybase dimethylaminoethyl acrylate. The membrane obtained consisted of long polymer molecules, some of them having fixed negative groups ($-COO^-$) and therefore stipulating positive cations (Na^+) and the other having positive ($-NH_3$) groups, attracting negative anions (Cl^-). The probable structure is shown in fig. 10.12. After the membrane was placed between two identical solutions of 0·15 M NaCl, each containing an electrode to pass the current through the membrane, the variation of membrane potential was measured with two calomel electrodes at each side of the membrane.

If the current was larger than some critical value, undamped oscillations of potential which persisted for hours would be obtained. A remarkable aspect of the oscillations is their resemblance to certain neuronal processes: the duration of the spike (see p. 269) is about 1 millisecond and the frequency is some 20 Hz.

The mechanism of the oscillatory behaviour is produced by ionic transport of current, different ion selectivity of three portions of the membrane and certain properties of large macromolecules. Thus, the current is carried predominently by Na^+ ions in the acid zone and Cl^- ions in the base zone of the membrane, both kinds of ions moving inwards. This leads to an accumulation of NaCl in the inner zone, with a considerable increase of NaCl concentration inside the membrane. It is known, on the other hand, that an increase of salt concentration will induce contraction of these macromolecules, which are extended in low salt concentration and tightly coiled in high concentration. Contraction of molecules increases the resistance of the membrane and therefore increases the potential difference for the same current strength. Simultaneously, the higher concentration inside produces an osmotic inflow of water, and diffusion of NaCl out. As this happens, the coiled molecules start extending, their resistance to the passage of current becomes lower and the membrane potential starts decreasing. The oscillating process can go on indefinitely if the *current* is passing through all the time. A similar behaviour was observed by Torsten Teorell (1955), who used a ceramic membrane. However, one certainly cannot say that the mechanism of the oscillatory phenomena in actual biological systems is established because we have been able to create some electrochemical analogues.

Oscillatory phenomena have been observed in some more typical electrochemical systems as well. For example, the potential of a platinum fuel electrode in a fuel cell shows regular periodic oscillations, as shown in fig. 10.13, if the fuel is methanol, formaldehyde, or formic acid and if the current density is sufficiently high. The frequency of oscillations depend on the current density used. According to Herbert Hunger, the oscillations are produced by accumulation of adsorbed side products which block the surface and inhibit the main reaction. Since the current is constant, the potential becomes more positive until it reaches a value when the adsorbed inhibitor is oxidized and removed from the surface, the potential again becoming more negative. The process continues indefinitely.

One very interesting group of new electrochemical devices, relevant to biological systems, are called 'solions'. These devices have some functional similarity to vacuum tubes and transistors in that the internal flow of charged particles, in the case of solions in the solution, is controlled through various factors of design to yield a desired behaviour in an external electric circuit. Because the velocities of ion movement in solution are low in comparison to the electron velocities in vacuum

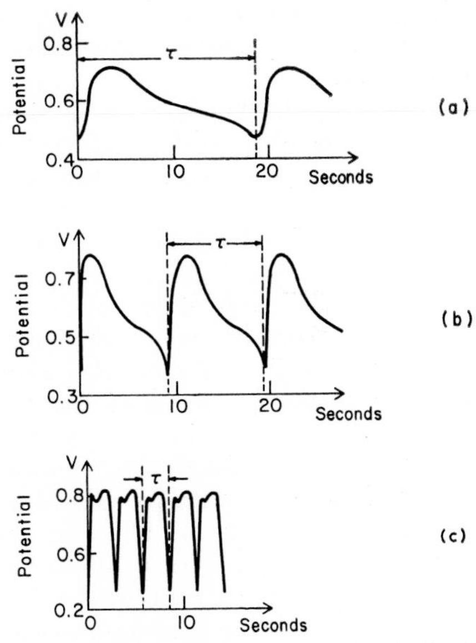

Fig. 10.13. Periodic potential variations of a platinized platinum electrode in 3·7 M $H_2SO_4 + 1$ M CH_2O, at constant current. (*a*) 20 mA; (*b*) 30 mA; (*c*) 400 mA.

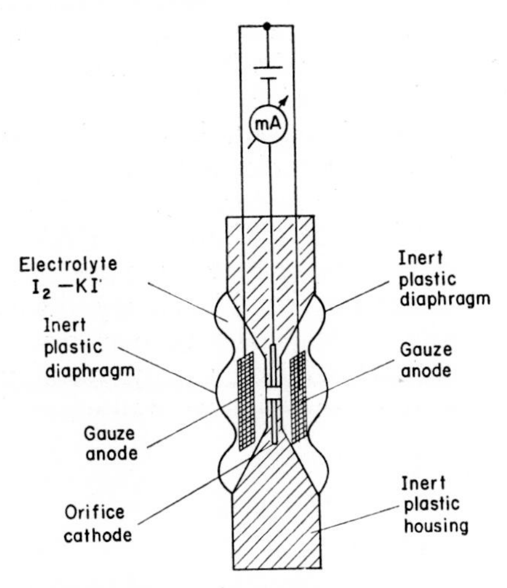

Fig. 10.14. Solion detector. Pressure variation on one membrane causes flow through an orifice and disturbs the diffusion layer at the small orifice cathode. Consequently a limiting diffusion current increases, and follows the variation of the pressure.

tubes and transistors, solions are low frequency devices (less than 1000 Hz) and in low frequency regions they have certain practical advantages over transistors.

A typical solion pressure change detector is shown in fig. 10.14. The system consists of a cathode with small orifice exposed to the solution and two anodes at both sides. The only possible electrochemical reactions are:

$$I_3^- + 2e \rightarrow 3I^-$$

at the cathode, and

$$3I^- \rightarrow I_3^- + 2e$$

at the anode. Therefore, there is no net change of composition of the solution with a permanent flow of current. However, as the area of the cathode is much smaller than that of the anode, the cathodic current density is larger than the anodic. For proper functioning of a solion, the area of the cathode of the device, should be small enough so that the cathodic reaction is controlled by a limiting diffusion current (cf. eqn. (4.8)). Therefore, any factor affecting the diffusion layer thickness, in this case the moving of a solution through the orifice caused by change of outside pressure on one membrane of the device, produces a change in current. If the pressure is oscillating, the current will oscillate in the same manner.

By using designs varying in detail, solion units can be made to perform as a transducer, integrator, differentiator, multiplier and amplifier. All that is needed is an electrochemical redox system with fast charge-transfer reactions, proper design of electrodes, membranes and current to pass through. Do not many biological systems possess just these features? It would be difficult to say no. Is this kind of electrochemical electronics the basis of some of the computer-like processes taking place in the brain?

As Szent-Györgyi† has pointed out, the biological system is essentially an electric device. The macromolecular structure is its framework, as the visible parts of an electric motor are the framework in which the transformation of electrical energy into mechanical work takes place. The fuel of life is the electron, or better, the energy it takes over from photons in plant photosynthesis; this energy the electrons give up gradually while flowing through the cellular machinery. It is the electrochemical mechanism of this energy transformation into the various manifestation of life to which we wanted to give some basis in this Chapter.

† A. Szent-Györgyi, Bioelectronics, Academic Press, New York, 1968, p. 79.

CHAPTER 11

looking back on this book—and forward to a better future

THE New Electrochemistry grew from the ideas of Volmer, Gurney, Butler and Frumkin, published in the 1930's. In the 1960's, electrodic electrochemistry powered space vehicles; and became recognized as the essential partner to electricity from Atomic Energy as the basis for a future, clean technology.

In our second chapter we investigated such things as inner and outer potentials, surface potentials, and the more conventional potentials of electrochemical cells. We delved into the *structure* of the interphase between metal and solution. There, the change in potential is about 1 V over about 5 Å. All electrochemical science, and hence many practical phenomena, depend upon this extremely powerful 10^9 V m^{-1} electric field across the interphase between metal and solution.

Then, in Chapter 3, we dealt with the actual electron transfer process at the interface. The equation which relates the *rate* of flow of electrons across the interface (i), to the displacement (η) in the Fermi level of electrons in the metal from which the electrons are coming, is:

$$i = Bc_i \exp(-\alpha\eta F/RT)$$

where B, α and F are constants, and C_i is the concentration of ions in solution.

When we change the overpotential of the metal we are putting more electrons into it, changing the excess surface charge, changing the energy levels of the electrons in the metal. The molecules in the double layer want them but only in their *empty* energy states which the quantum theory shows are the ones which may accept electrons. So the Fermi level has to be raised—more *over*potential—until the energy of some of the electrons in it is high enough to be equal to, and hence transfer to, states in the ions of the solution.

In Chapter 4 we wanted to know about the way in which the ions in a solution were transported up to the electrode. Here we invoked established ideas about diffusion, and touched on electroanalytical chemistry, and the relation between the limiting current through a solution and the concentration of ions in it.

In Chapter 5, we began to show the *relevance* of electrochemistry to many aspects of technology and practical life, starting by considering some organic reactions. We could take a molecule and make it undergo a path chosen by the energy of the Fermi level in the metal, and which we can choose by adjusting the potential applied from our outside circuit.

How many volts we have to use to do this, and therefore, how many joules per kilogram a compound is going to cost us by the electrochemical route, are factors as vital for practical realization as those of whether the electron can transfer through the energy-barrier of the interface. This is where electrocatalysis (which reduces the voltage needed) becomes important. The electronic properties of the metal of the electrode are related to electrocatalysis through the adsorbed atom bonds formed with reaction intermediates.

In Chapter 6, electrodeposition and electroseparation showed how one could turn back used metals into usable new products: the mines of the future are the scrap heaps of today.

In Chapter 7 we saw how electrochemistry may hold the key for the future of clean transportation. *Electrochemical* energy conversion is not limited by the Carnot efficiency expression.

Abundant electrical energy at perhaps a quarter of the present price, should be as little as two decades away. Electrochemical energy *storage* is then the role electrochemistry would play. We shall never be able to have atomic reactors in cars, they would always (with their shielding) be too heavy. (Chapter 8.)

Electrochemical science also gives the basis for the protection of metallic structures against corrosion (Chapter 9). Electrochemically caused corrosion does not merely give us breakdown of metals due to anodic dissolution. Hydrogen atoms, adsorbed on the surface from the electron accepting reaction in corrosion, go into the lattice, and produce hydrogen molecules *at great pressures* in tiny holes which exist *within* metal lattices. Such pressures gradually make internal areas in the metal strain and part, the voids grow to cracks, the cracks spread and join up: the metal weakens.

The last chapter, Chapter 10, concerns the electric double layer within the human body and discusses the role played by electrochemistry in the functioning of biological cells and many other phenomena, including in the views of some, some basic aspects of cell division.

This book is small, but the message it is written to convey is large: an environment unpolluted by power generation, in which men can live in the future, is possible through an electrically based technology.

INDEX